Best Books  70

Freezing Point

Freezing Point

Cold As a Matter of Life and Death

Lucy Kavaler

The John Day Company

New York

Book Design and Drawings by Carl Smith
Library of Congress Catalogue Card Number: 78–107206
Printed in the United States of America
Second Impression

MAY 12 '71

In Memoriam

Tilla Sproge-Dippel

It Is a Noble Subject

That any of my friends should wonder at my having been induc'd to write of such a Theme, I freely confess that I have sometimes been tempted to wonder at it myself; and therefore I think myself obliged to give my Readers an account . . . Why I thought fit to write of Cold at All? . . .

The subject I have chosen is very noble.

Robert Boyle,
New Experiments and Observations Touching Cold
1683

✳ Acknowledgments

In this book it has been my aim to show how living things adapt to cold, how cold kills, how it cures, and how mankind can use it for his benefit. The subject is so broad and basic that my research over the course of years has led me into many seemingly unrelated areas. These have ranged from studies of hibernating animals to interplanetary travel, from blood banks to TV dinners, from heart transplants to mass death, from artificial insemination to immortality, from the Antarctic ice cap to the red soil of Mars, from prehistory to speculations about the future.

In all of this research I have been aided by a great many people. Whenever possible I have spoken at length with men preeminent in each of the many fields covered, and have communicated by telephone and letter with those whom I could not visit. A number of scientists have furnished me with unpublished data which I could not have obtained in any other way.

I should like to express my thanks to the doctors—in practice and in research—who helped with the medical chapters dealing with cryosurgery, transplants, hypothermia, and other procedures involving cold: Irving S. Cooper, St. Barnabas Hospital; ophthalmologist Charles D. Kelman; Vojin P. Popovic, Emory University Medical School; Juan Negrin, Jr., Lenox Hill Hospital; Robert J. White, Western Reserve University; Richard J. Ablin, Millard Fillmore Hospital; Manuel Riklan, St. Barnabas Hospital; Richard R. Lower, Medical College of Virginia; dentist Fred G. Emmings; neurologist Roger Duvoisin; John E. Coe, University of Texas, Medical Branch; Ian MacLean Smith, University of Iowa; C.R. Stephen, University of Texas, Southwest Medical School; Adrian Kantrowitz, Maimonides Hospital; Denton Cooley; Linde Division, Union Carbide Corp.; and the American Parkinson Disease Association.

Assistance for the chapters concerning freezing of living cells was given by Arthur Rowe, New York Community Blood Center; Harold T. Meryman, Blood Program, American National Red Cross; Marion T. Alexander, American Type Culture Collection; Irvin C. Mohler, American Type Culture Collection; M.T. Coleman, Influenza Laboratory, National Communicable Disease Center; J.K. Sherman, University of Arkansas School of Medicine; Michael E. Glasscock III, Otologic Medical Group of Los Angeles; the Eye Bank for Sight Restoration; Thoroughbred Racing Association of the United States; and the American Kennel Club.

Freezing as a way to immortality was described to me by Robert C.W. Ettinger; Saul Kent, Cryonics Society of New York; Ev Cooper, Life Extension Society; and E. Francis Hope, Cryo-Care Equipment Corp.

Thanks must also go to those who aided me in the research on the chapters dealing with the effects of cold on man: Colonel Elmer F. Clark, ret., U.S. Army; David M. Knize, University of California; David E. Bass, U.S. Army Research Institute of Environmental Medicine; Donald C. Hilton, polar specialist, U.S. Army.

My investigations into adaptations and habits of animals of polar regions were assisted by Carleton Ray, Johns Hopkins University; I.D. Cocioba, Beth Israel Hospital; Jacob M. Hiller, Beth Israel Hospital; G. Edgar Folk, Jr., University of Iowa; David A. Mullen, University of San Francisco; and John McNeill Sieburth, Rhode Island State University.

Information about the plant life of cold regions was provided by William C. Steere, Director, New York Botanical Gardens; Lucien J. La-Croix, University of Manitoba; Allan H. Mick, Director, Alaska Agricultural Experiment Station; J. Levitt, University of Missouri; and Agricultural Research Service, U.S. Department of Agriculture.

Kurt G. Sandved, National Science Foundation; Robert C. Faylor, Director, Arctic Institute of North America; and Chester C. Langway, Jr., United States Cold Regions Research & Engineering Laboratory, United States Army, were of help in offering material on the Antarctic and Arctic.

Weather control was discussed with me by Archie Goodman, Bureau of Reclamation; and Peter H. Wycoff, National Science Foundation.

The chapters on food and ice cream received assistance from Joseph H. Colquitt, National Association of Refrigerated Warehouses; Leonard S. Fenn, National Association of Frozen Food Packers; Paul E. Roman, Association of Home Appliance Manufacturers; Dean Stambaugh, Breyer

Ice Cream; R. Thévenot, Director, International Institute of Refrigeration; International Association of Ice Cream Manufacturers; General Dynamics Corp.; General Foods; the Manned Spacecraft Center, Houston, NASA; and the Economic Research Service, United States Department of Agriculture.

Help on the hibernation sections was furnished by Raymond Hock, Northrop Space Laboratories; Robert G. Lindberg, Northrop Space Laboratories; and the Hibernation Information Exchange.

My research for the chapters on space was aided by Sanford M. Siegel, University of Hawaii; Willard F. Libby, University of California; Robert L. Wildey, Center of Astrogeology; R. Smoluchowski, Princeton University; and NASA.

And I should like to add a final word of thanks to my husband and to my agent, Marie Rodell, for their help and encouragement.

*

Contents   *Page*

1

Introduction: The Strange Ways of Cold

The first snow had fallen in October and by November the ground was white as far as the eye could see. The German army had battled its way to the outskirts of Moscow and Leningrad. It had by then destroyed thousands of Soviet aircraft, wiped out entire divisions of the army, and taken more than a million prisoners. The days were clear and cold and quite beautiful. Then in December, just as the Japanese in another part of the globe were attacking Pearl Harbor, the temperature dropped abruptly from slightly above zero to -32° Fahrenheit. The Russians making a desperate counterattack suddenly found themselves with an ally—cold. The German soldiers shivered in their smartly fitted uniforms; their feet in stiff jackboots were frozen, and their fingers were frostbitten. They fell back to winter positions. This was the first interruption of the German takeover of Europe, and the first hint of the defeat that lay ahead.

History was repeating itself. More than a century earlier Napoleon lost an army and an empire in the Russian snows. The suffering of his men in that bitter winter might have served as a warning to the Nazi invaders.

Even today in less frigid regions cold brings death every year. During a single winter in Wisconsin between 22,000 and 30,000 deer perished of a freeze. In Tennessee a fifty-seven-year-old woman went into the backyard during an unprecedented cold snap; her frozen corpse was found the following day. And in Europe the director of the Zurich Medical Institute took a stroll in the mountains near his home one day, was overcome by the cold, and died.

Cold is usually considered to be hostile to mankind. Most people hate cold, and with reason. Unlike the beast's, man's ability to adapt to cold is slight at best. The brown bat, the Arctic squirrel, the marmot can retire into hibernation and let the chilling winter winds and storms pass them by, but man cannot. The butterfly can hide in a cocoon, the plant survive without its fragile leaves, the fungus and bacterium become dormant when it is too cold to feed and reproduce. Birds escape from winter by means of physiological drives that propel them over continents and oceans. But man has not evolved in ways that help him to endure the cold. Needing all his cunning to survive, he has been battling cold as if it were an enemy for all his history.

But gradually there has come a change. Long viewed as lethal, cold is emerging as a great hope of man's future. A new science known as cryogenics, after the Greek word *kryos* for cold, has come into being and within a generation has made invaluable contributions to such diverse fields as medicine, food processing, rocketry, and animal husbandry.

The cold that can kill can also cure and is today a major weapon in the battle against disease. On a December day in 1967 a South African doctor chilled a patient before giving him a new heart. The cataract that would cause blindness is lifted off the eye with cold; the formerly inoperable brain tumor is excised in an operation made possible only by cold.

Five people in the entire world, one an Australian aborigine, are known to possess the rare blood type Rh Null. A baby was born to one of them a year or so ago. The antibodies in his mother's blood would have killed him had he not been able to receive transfusions of the same rare type. The blood that saved his life had been frozen months earlier in foreknowledge of the coming event.

A prize bull impregnates hundreds of cows he has never mounted. And so the breed is improved. Man, too, could control his heredity by means of frozen reproductive cells. The brilliant scientist, the musical genius, the great artist could beget countless children long after death.

Some people have become so infatuated with cold that they believe it will conquer death altogether and offer a form of immortality to the body as well as the soul. They would rise, like Lazarus, from their frigid tombs and thaw out in an era when age, ugliness, deformity, and disease are no more.

The exceptional breadth and scope of cryogenics means that no single description of cold can be applied to all its aspects. Cold is properly defined as the slowing of molecular movement, and absolute cold is the moment at which all activity stops. But this is a laboratory definition. In biological terms, cold is purely relative. Fish swim in below-freezing Arctic waters, in perfect comfort, while a naked inactive man may be chilly after but two hours at a temperature of 80° or 82°F. Cold can also be explained as an aspect of metabolism. A cold body performs all its functions more slowly. The actual temperature that accompanies low metabolism, however, varies among the species. As life on this planet is based on water, cold is often popularly defined as any temperature below the freezing point of that liquid. As water freezes at different temperatures depending on atmospheric pressure and salt content, it can be seen that this is a relative definition, too.

The response of nonliving matter to cold, like that of living things, varies according to kind. Most liquids shrink and grow heavier when frozen into a solid. Water, however, expands and becomes lighter when it turns to ice. This exceptional quality makes the earth particularly hospitable to life. If ice were heavy and sank to the bottom, most rivers, lakes, and much of the ocean would remain frozen solid all year around. The rays of sun in summer could not reach far enough to melt all the ice laid down in winter. Marine life could not flourish and vast regions of the earth would, like the Antarctic today, be locked in ice.

There is another world of cold, more frigid by far than ice, where the range goes from -200°F. on down to nearly absolute zero (-459.69°F.). Such cold is a characteristic of the universe. The stars themselves are hot, but the vast spaces that lie between are but three degrees above absolute zero. Man creates comparable temperatures artificially on earth. A new technology has evolved based on gases frozen until they become liquid. In this world of supercold the rules that apply to molecular behavior elsewhere are overthrown. Liquid helium runs uphill, instead of down, climbing over the sides of a container and out. Electrical current flows endlessly through metals that offer no resistance to its passage. Computers become unbelievably small, magnets incredibly efficient, and atom smashers more powerful than any in the past. The thrust of liquid hydrogen and liquid oxygen lifts rockets off the ground and sends spacecraft on journeys to the moon and beyond. The liquid gases interact in the fuel cells on spaceships, producing electricity and making water as a by-product.

Practical applications of more moderate cold add to man's comfort and pleasure. Cold has freed the diet from the limitations of time, place, season, and cooking skill. The strawberry that was plucked last June can bring enjoyment in January, and king crab appears on dinner tables thousands of miles away from the Alaska waters where it was caught. Meals are served months or years after they were first cooked. Ice cream was once a luxury reserved for royalty alone; today the average American consumes one and a half quarts a month. Billions of ice cubes are pried out of refrigerator trays to cool water, highballs, and soft drinks.

By means of cold, it is possible to escape the heat. A simple cooling system was included in the space suits worn by astronauts exploring the surface of the moon. Those who inhabit warm climates on earth may live in air-conditioned homes, travel in air-conditioned cars, work in air-conditioned offices. Wherever they go—to a restaurant, a movie, to school, church, the sports stadium—refrigerated air surrounds them. In the shopping center they stroll down air-conditioned sidewalks, passing from one cooled store or refreshment stand to the next, returning perhaps to an air-conditioned parking lot. Sows in air-conditioned piggeries bear more and bigger piglets in each litter; hens lay more eggs in refrigerated chicken houses, and chinchillas in cooled pens are furrier. In Texas the best dogs have air-conditioned kennels. And in Saudi Arabia pilgrims on their way to Mecca can stop for rest and prayer in an air-conditioned shelter.

Prayer was once thought to be the only way to induce the rain to fall. Today seeds of silver iodide force rain out of clouds according to the will of man. Thus a plane flies along releasing the chemical spray and moments afterward rain or snow drops on barren ground. The seeds make an ice crystal form in the cloud and it gets heavier until it must fall and water the parched land. Sometimes a cold fog hangs over airports, making landings dangerous and preventing takeoffs. Let a plane fly into that fog and place seeds of silver iodide, dry ice, or liquid propane into it, and all at once the fog dissipates and the ceiling lifts. During a hailstorm antiaircraft shells shoot silver iodide into rain clouds or seed-bearing rockets are launched from planes. The huge hailstones that would destroy the crops are disintegrated into tiny, harmless ice pebbles. Scientists are already working on ways to take the dread power out of the hurricane and hold the lightning in the thundercloud. Weather control will ultimately make it possible for the desert to bloom and produce crops to feed the huge populations of the future. More of the globe will become habitable.

The breeding of plants better able to endure the punishing cold of Arctic winters, medical advances, and improvements in clothing, building materials, and transport have already expanded the world for man. Much of the Arctic is being thrown open to industrialists as well as pioneers.

The attitude to Antarctica is changing, too. "Great God, this is an awful place!" wrote explorer Robert Falcon Scott in 1912 before struggling on to a slow death on the ice plateau. Today that region is described most enticingly in travel folders.

*

Part One

Cold As an Environment

2

Man—A Tropical Creature in a Cold World

"Man has a strange, almost psychopathic, unwarranted fear of cold. It is a leftover from the last ice age," declares Colonel (ret.) Elmer F. Clark of the U. S. Army Materiel Command, an expert on cold climates.

We are essentially tropical creatures in a world curiously unsuited to our bodies' needs. As warm-blooded animals, the hottest parts of earth should be our natural habitat. A naked man resting quietly is really comfortable only when the temperature around him is 85° to 88°F. He can remain in this warmth for hours or days on end without becoming either overheated or chilled. Let him lie around in a room heated to 80°F., and he will eventually become chilled. Because 80°F. is too far below all human body temperatures.

Although the oral thermometer reading, 98.6°F. on the average, is traditionally given as the temperature, it is actually only one of many body temperatures—and of itself varies by as much as three degrees from morning to night as a result of food intake and activity. Rectal temperature may be one degree higher. But this, too, does not exhaust the variations among the internal organs. The liver is one to two degrees warmer than the kidneys. As for the rest of the body, the farther from the center, the cooler the temperature. The skin is coolest of all, measuring about eight to ten degrees lower than the interior. On a freezing day even those who like the winter may find that hands and feet become painfully cold. This is not surprising, because the extremities can drop more than thirty degrees while the rectal temperature remains in the normal range.

Cold As an Environment

Out of doors on a cold day the breath freezes and little swirls of mist form around the nose and mouth. This mist serves as a personal weather report, proof that the thermometer registers below the freezing point of water. When the temperature is far below zero, the breath freezes with a loud, crackling noise. Whatever the weather, though, some body heat passes out with each exhalation of air and water vapor. A mining engineer in northern Alaska had to travel on a day when the cold was -40°F. He needed to get an address out of his wallet and as his huge mittens made him clumsy, he took them off for a few seconds. Glancing down, he observed a strange phenomenon. An eerie fog was rising from his exposed hands. The cold had been great enough to freeze the water vapor rising from his skin. Even though it cannot be seen in warmer climates, about a quart of water in vapor form passes out through the unbroken skin every day. This insensible water loss is of great value in hot weather, as, along with perspiration, it cools the body. Sweat is secreted in large quantity in the heat, and is virtually absent in the cold. But the amount of water and thus of heat lost through the skin does not decrease in frigid weather. This is but another indication of man's tropical orientation.

Because water is lost through skin and breath all year around, the need for fluids in winter is far greater than most people think. In fact, dehydration has been found to be a major problem for people working in the far north or south. Newcomers to logging camps in the Arctic, for example, often complain of exhaustion and can hardly believe their more experienced companions who say that dehydration is the cause. Wearied by cold and wind, they feel too little desire for water to bother taking a drink.

Everyone feels much colder on a windy day than on a comparable one that is still. The moving air carries heat from the body more rapidly than still air. It has proven very difficult to set down in scientific terms exactly what the wind means. As recently as 1961, an Army Medical Research Laboratory report described a fall day with a temperature of

50°F. and a breeze of ten miles per hour as equivalent in effect to a winter's day with a temperature of -12°F. and no wind. But common sense would indicate that this is not so. A windy fall day is raw and uncomfortable, but most certainly it does not feel subzero. The error of that report and many others, according to the Arctic Aeromedical Laboratory in Alaska, is that the comparison is based on the assumption that no wind at all blows on a still day. But there is always some movement in the air, and each person adds some of his own. Even on a so-called windless day, these movements produce the equivalent of a wind of four miles per hour. And so the 50° day with the ten-mile-per-hour wind is properly equated with a still day at 40°F. The wind can make the difference between safety and great danger of freezing. A temperature of -22°F. is not pleasant, but it is not dangerous on a still day. Should the winds reach twenty-five miles per hour, anyone out of doors must be completely protected by Arctic-type clothing, or he is very likely to be injured.

Acclimated to solid earth, man can endure cold even less well in water. He must swim vigorously and so keep up his body heat if he is to stay for long in water that is below 80°F. For lazy floating or the dog paddle, water temperature should be well up in the 90's. Most people like to have their bath water somewhat warmer than that. Members of polar bear clubs may prove their vitality by quick dips in icy seas, but they are in and out in a hurry. They are wise not to dally, as their light swimming trunks afford them little protection against the chill. Four British volunteers, good swimmers all, plunged into water that was 40.5°F. One collapsed with extreme difficulty in breathing after one and a half minutes, and none of the others was able to stay afloat for long. Sometimes a prolonged exposure is forced upon people when a boat capsizes or a plane crashes over water. Once overboard, man's survival depends on a speedy rescue. It is the opinion of the Office of Naval Research that a naked man can survive in water of 32°F. for less than an hour. Normal clothing is not designed to keep water out and prolongs the safety period only a little. Experiments on survival in cold water have been made in the Antarctic. They are not reassuring. Although wearing a neoprene suit while diving in 29.6°F. south polar waters, Navy Lieutenant David Lavallee reported feeling extreme discomfort after only twenty minutes. At one point he pulled his hood away from his face. Although his mouth and jaw tolerated the chilling fairly well, pain was intense on his chin and temples.

Despite the wide swings of temperature in the water and air around us, our body temperature changes surprisingly little. A human being can endure small deviation from the norm and functions really well only when his temperature remains within the narrow range of 97°F. to 102°F. This temperature is maintained as long as there is a balance between the heat produced by metabolism, sunshine, and hot air and that lost by evaporation, cold air, and wind. The body's thermostat breaks down only under extraordinary pressure—prolonged exposure to extreme cold or heat. Let the outdoor thermometer register 101°F., and the cold-blooded animal's temperature will quickly equal it. In the wintertime that same creature is healthy and happy with a body temperature of 41°F. But man's internal environment does not match his external world so easily. If a naked man sits in 42.8°F. water for one-half to three-quarters of an hour —and this has been done in a research project—his temperature will fall only to 96.8°F.

In terms of life and death, warm-blooded creatures though we are, we can endure far less heat than cold. Let the temperature rise a mere 6.4 degrees above normal—106°F. on a rectal thermometer—and there is danger of heat stroke and death. And survival is all but impossible for anyone whose temperature reaches 110° to 112°F. On the other hand, the body can recover from chilling to temperatures many times farther removed from the norm. Even without medical help, the victim of accidental chilling may not die until his body temperature has dropped twenty degrees or more below normal.

Man—A Tropical Creature in a Cold World

On March 23, 1756, a Swedish peasant staggered out of doors after a drinking party and fell asleep in the snow. The next day his friends sobered up and went out to find him. As he was frozen solid, they decided that he was dead. He was carried home and a coffin was hurriedly obtained for him. As the afternoon waned, a doctor friend among the mourners decided that the "dead" man had not been examined properly. Although he could detect no breath or heartbeat, the doctor noticed that the pit of the stomach was still a little warm. And so he ordered that the arms and legs be rubbed while he applied heat to the chest. The man recovered, and the doctor reported on this case to the Swedish Academy of Sciences.

Unfortunately for the modern doctors studying the report, he gave no information about the actual body temperature. Many years later the Nazis, using medical research as an excuse for methodical cruelty, provided some documentation. Giving as a pretext the scientific goal of discovering LT_{50} (mean lethal temperature), they selected eight inmates of the infamous Dachau concentration camp and immersed them in cold water that had been chilled to exactly 39.2°F. There the prisoners stayed until they died; their temperatures were taken at regular intervals. The average time required for death was sixty-five minutes in the icy water. And the lethal body temperature varied from 75.6°F. to 84.2°F., with LT_{50} at 80.6°F. The eighth man threw off the calculations by surviving a body temperature of 77.4°F. and immersion for just under three hours. The validity of the experiments can be questioned in any event, as Dachau inmates were for the most part so close to death from starvation and mistreatment that their reaction could not be considered typical. What is surprising is that they surpassed the Navy's estimated survival time for only slightly colder water.

In 1951 a Chicago woman lay in the street all night in a drunken stupor. The temperature outside was between 0.4°F. and -11°F. By the time she was found and taken to a hospital, her heart was beating only twelve to twenty times a minute, and she was breathing three to five times. Her temperature was 64.4°F. and doctors believed that it must have risen about four degrees before it was measured. If so, she set a record for achieving the lowest temperature endured by anyone surviving accidental freezing.

It is possible that the true record-holder is a little boy of three who was lost for twenty hours in a forest near Karlskoga, Sweden. When taken to the hospital, he appeared dead and his rectal temperature was 62.6°F. The child recovered completely.

These people, to be sure, are exceptional, as death usually results from exposure to far less rigorous cold. On the average, women resist freezing better than men do because of an extra layer of advantageously distributed subcutaneous fat.

As quite a number of survivors of accidental freezing like the Chicago woman and the Swedish peasant have been drunk, the question naturally arises whether the alcohol level in the blood plays a role in improving resistance to cold. Alcoholic rats were put into a state of profound hypothermia by researchers at the University of Texas Southwestern Medical School in Dallas. Their hearts continued to function at temperatures which had stopped the hearts of a control group of nonalcoholic rats. When rewarmed, the hearts of the drunken rats resumed beating before those of the sober animals. Experiments performed on dogs indicate that alcohol consumption cuts down the risk of irregular heart action. Much more research in this area is needed, however. The fact that many drunken people survive freezing may simply be due to the fact that drunks are more likely than sober people to be accidentally frozen in the first place. Lying down on an icy street is hardly a considered action.

The exposure to cold is one of the greatest challenges to be faced by the body. It is comparable, say scientists, to the effect of fear, rage, pain, asphyxia, or extremely heavy physical labor. All call forth a coordinated life-saving response, which was named by W. B. Cannon, one of the pioneers in temperature research, "the fight or flight reaction." The body fights to retain its warm-blooded state, and the metabolism rises to meet the challenge and produce more heat.

The fight reaction is ruled by the hypothalamus, a tiny bit of brain tissue that lies beneath the thalamus at the base of the midbrain and that also controls appetite, water balance, and sympathetic nervous system activities. This is the body's thermostat. The posterior portion of the hypothalamus controls cold and the anterior heat.

When a person goes outside on a cold day or plunges into an icy sea, his skin, which is in contact with the air or water, is naturally the first place to feel the cold and respond to it. Discomfort is registered in specific spots or receptors that react either to cold or to heat. The cold receptors are more numerous and closer to the surface than are those for heat. Sudden extreme cold stimulates these spots to frenzied activity and they send out a whole burst of warning impulses before adapting to the change. The sensation of cold is, therefore, rapidly lost when one goes swimming in chill ocean or lake waters, but the message has by then been passed along anyway.

The first physiological response to the stimulus of cold takes place in the blood vessels in the skin. They constrict, so that less blood can flow to the surface and be chilled. The skin thus acts almost like an outer garment, insulating the inner portions of the body. The warm blood is concentrated in the internal organs and their temperature may even rise slightly.

The hypothalamus, which has received the nerve impulses set off by the skin receptors, activates the sympathetic nervous system. And just as in the comparable situations of terror or fury, the heart pumps faster and the glands secrete additional quantities of adrenalin and other stimulating hormones. The expression "hot with rage" is literally true; the metabolism rises. And heat is the main by-product of metabolism.

When the stimulation reaches the skeletal muscles, the most effective of man's defenses against cold is activated: the muscles begin an involuntary, uncoordinated shivering that varies in intensity with the cold. This is remarkably effective in raising the body's metabolic rate. When a person is slightly chilled, the shivering is only a tremor and increases the amount of warmth being produced in the body by twenty to twenty-five percent. In severe cold it consists of violent spasms and the results in terms of internal heat production are startling. The increase is 400 percent.

Yet shivering is not enough. It is perfectly apparent to anyone who has ever remained out in bitter weather for any length of time that shivering does not really make him feel warm. Guides on mountain-climbing expeditions advise novices not to wait to feel cold before putting on protective clothing. They have observed at first hand that the body heat is not restored. Shivering will prevent any further heat loss and will save one from freezing to death—provided, of course, that the exposure is not too prolonged or extreme. But the most violent spasms the body can produce will not replace one iota of the warmth already lost. And particularly if the chilling is gradual, warmth is lost before shivering starts. In one test, naked men remained in a room at 60°F. for an hour or more before beginning to shiver, although they had all become very cold long before then.

Sometimes, when the chilling is rapid, the shivering may come even before it is really needed. Healthy people have been known to start shivering from cold with a rectal temperature of 100.6°F. Their skin temperature had dropped, and this was stimulus enough. On the other hand, shivering often ends long before the chilled person warms up. He finally returns to his snug house and throws off his coat. His shivering stops, even though body heat is still far below normal. Nonetheless, he continues to get warmer without any further spasms.

The suggestion that there is a nonshivering source of heat production was first made in 1872 by the French physiologist Claude Bernard, but no one listened to him then. The theory was not fully accepted until scientists came to understand the role played by the hypothalamus. In an experiment this area of the brain was stimulated in chilled animals that were shivering in uncontrollable spasms. Although no warmth was applied, the shivering stopped.

The onset of shivering can be hastened or postponed; it is an example of mind over matter. A woman who hates the cold goes out on a January day bundled up in a fur coat, fur hat, lined boots, and cashmere knitted gloves. Her husband, a winter sports enthusiast, wears only a heavy jacket. Yet it is the wife who begins to shiver the moment they are outside; the man is perfectly comfortable. As women are physiologically better adapted to endure cold, the reverse reaction would seem more logical. But shivering can be brought on by the mere fear of being too cold. Even stranger is the fact that mild shivering can be held off for a time by sheer willpower, by a determined "I will not be cold; I like the cold."

The U. S. Weather Bureau recently announced job openings for twenty-eight men. The specifications were unusual in one particular: only men who thought they could endure temperatures of -80°F. need apply. The job involved manning weather stations in the Arctic. In framing the job specifications, personnel officers recalled an often-told war story: the Army tried a variety of tests designed to tell which men should be sent to a tropical zone and which to a northern sector. It soon became obvious that test results were no guide to the rapidity of a soldier's adjustment. A far better way turned out to be asking each man: "Do you like cold better than heat?"

There is no doubt that some individuals stand cold better than others do. Fat people, to take the most obvious example, are more comfortable in winter than are thin ones. Their cold endurance is increased by the insulating capacities of subcutaneous fat. The need for this is such that men at polar bases gain a small amount of weight during the winter. This could be explained away by the decrease in exercise and the longer hours spent in sleeping, along with a larger amount of food consumed. But no such relationship has been found. Regardless of food intake or degree of activity, the men reveal an increase in the quantity of insulating subcutaneous fat, as well as a greater skinfold thickness. Then in the summer both weight and the extra fat beneath the skin are lost. Some scientists question the evidence, though, on the ground that there are no valid comparisons with people who live in temperate zones.

Support for the theory has been presented by physiologists who have studied long-distance swimmers. Before entering cold water, such as the English Channel, their bodies are coated with a heavy layer of grease as protection against the freezing water. But experienced swimmers have additional physiological protection. After years of swimming, they develop a thicker layer of subcutaneous fat.

In the course of a normal life most people, even thin ones, are adequately protected from the cold by the body's temperature-regulating mechanism. It fails, however, in emergencies. Some deaths from freezing, therefore, still occur each year. They are rare only because recovery is possible until almost the very end. On a hiking trip in Greenland recently one young man wandered away from his party and collapsed from exposure to cold. Fortunately his companions found him and carried him back to a shelter, where they placed him on a bed, covered him with a single blanket, and waited to see if he would begin to shiver, as they had seen enough of cold exposure to know that shivering is a sign that the chilled person is still capable of rewarming himself. Should shivering not take place, the rescuers must increase the amount of heat by any means at hand—hot-water bottles, electric lights, and robes or blankets. If the breath has all but stopped—and this is likely to happen only in polar regions when the temperature drops to below -82°F.—artificial respiration should be applied. Anyone who has been chilled to that extent is really best off in a hospital where there is equipment for coping with all the side effects produced by cold. The gastrointestinal tract, for example, is virtually paralyzed with no peristalsis taking place, and treatment is needed to prevent damage.

Even when the patient begins to recover he should not be fed by mouth until peristalsis resumes. Intravenous injections of glucose may be needed, too, particularly if the freezing person is drunk.

Another rescue technique consists of placing the victim in a hot tub with a water temperature of 110°F. if he is conscious and 115° to 120°F. if he is in a coma. Then oxygen is administered. In the Antarctic a few years ago Commander George J. Dufek fell into the icy ocean while being transferred from one ship to another in a chairlift. Upon being rescued, he was given the hot-water treatment and he recovered without any injury.

Survival depends upon rescue. Had the Swedish child and the drunk in Chicago not been found in time and rewarmed by others, they would have died. The heart endures cold more poorly than any of the other internal organs and it would soon have failed. A man exposed to extreme heat can function despite elevated body temperature until almost the moment of his death from heat stroke. Not so with cold. The mountain climber becomes exhausted and stops to rest for a moment, falls asleep in the snow, and freezes to death. He is a stock figure in tales of adventure. Yet the stories do not exaggerate; they express a simple, hard fact: the victim of cold quickly loses his ability to help himself.

"Man becomes incapable of conscious, life-saving decisions when deep body temperature is lowered by only 7°F.," reports Dr. David E. Bass of the U.S. Army Research Institute of Environmental Medicine. "Furthermore, long before this point is reached, he has become subjectively so uncomfortable that he must spend 100 percent of his effort toward mere survival."

Normal function is impossible. The hiker cannot walk on to reach the shelter; the scientist cannot make weather observations; the driver cannot repair his truck. Virtually all man's defenses against cold come to immobilize him. The constriction in the blood vessels in the skin that is the body's first response to chilling is most marked in the extremities. A drop in hand temperature to only 59°F. is accompanied by acute pain. In severe cold the fingers and toes can become virtually bloodless appendages because shunts in the circulatory system send blood away from them. The blood flow is reduced to one-fortieth or sometimes one-fiftieth of the normal amount. The advantage of this mechanism is that it conserves the heat of the body within, but the drawbacks are considerable. The fingers are all too likely to become frostbitten, and even before this, all dexterity is lost. A scientist measured the degree of the loss of sensitivity by dropping a light ball on his fingers and noting his reaction. Then he chilled them to 68°F. with ice bags and tried again. He felt absolutely nothing until the impact was six times as great. This loss of sensitivity can be critical when skillful use of the hands is needed for life-saving actions.

Shivering, the body's major reflex effort against cold, is so unpleasant that it lowers the morale almost immediately. The normal reaction is to huddle miserably and do nothing. In addition, violent shivering in heavy spasms makes coordinated activity all but impossible. This is particularly unfortunate because the freezing person's salvation lies in exercise. It is five times as effective as shivering alone and can actually restore the heat previously lost. The heat produced by strenuous exercise warms the blood flowing through the muscles. This blood travels deep within the body, heating the internal organs before returning to the extremities. This is why hands and feet are the last parts of the body to warm up.

The violence of man's psychological and physiological reactions to cold might lead one to assume that man neither would nor could live in frigid climates. Yet he has done so. A good many people inhabit areas of Alaska, Canada, the U. S. S. R., and Scandinavia that are relatively near the North Pole; the Australian aborigine sleeps naked in night temperatures that are close to freezing, and the primitive Indians of Tierra del Fuego, uncomfortably close to the South Pole, wore no clothes to protect them from sleet-filled air and icy water until civilization intruded.

Man—A Tropical Creature in a Cold World

In explaining such phenomena, Dr. Per F. Scholander, one of the world's leading experts in cold physiology, declares: "As to the notion that man does not acclimate to cold—this is for the birds."

An attempt to prove this definitively was made twenty-five years ago by Sir Stanton Hicks of the University of Adelaide, who led a party armed with thermometers into the bush in arid central Australia. The natives there slept out of doors in night temperatures that averaged 39.2°F. They seemed perfectly comfortable. Sir Stanton tried to find out how much their temperatures dropped during the night hours. It proved difficult to make exact measurements, however, because the young warriors refused to submit to a rectal thermometer.

By the late 1950's, when Scholander and a group of scientists went back to repeat the experiments, the natives had become much more cooperative. Six Australian aborigines and four white men spent a cold night together. As they lay on their canvas cots attempting to rest, the body temperatures of the white men began to drop. Almost at once they started to shiver and increased the metabolic rate by about thirty percent. Their internal temperatures thus were held close to normal levels.

The natives' reaction was markedly different. Although experiencing the same degree of cold, they did not shiver and their metabolism remained unchanged. As a result both their body and skin temperatures fell to levels far below those of the white men. They experienced no discomfort and slept soundly, while the scientists were tossing and turning miserably. The natives' adaptation to cold had taken an unusual form. The change had been in the shell of their bodies. This is the area that lies between the core and the skin surface. The insulation had become greater than normal as a result of constant cold exposure. Although naked, they were wearing an extra coat of flesh. It kept some of the cold away from the internal organs. The body shell of the Australians conducts thirty percent less cold to the core than that of white men.

Cold As an Environment

The same experiment was then repeated with other aborigines living in a hotter area of the Australian continent around Darwin. The natives there experienced cold only in the winter nights. Even so, they proved better able to endure chilling than the white scientists. Although their cold adaptation did not equal that of the aborigines in the colder sections, the body shell provided them with extra insulation. Their metabolism was higher than that of the other natives, but lower than that of the white men. Because the tropical natives were as a rule exposed to less cold than white men, scientists concluded that this adaptation to cold had become a racial characteristic, varying in degree according to the amount of cold experienced.

Physiologists then went on to study indigenous people in other frigid areas of the globe and they made a surprising discovery: the improved insulating capacity that aided the Australian aborigines was strangely lacking in natives of other cold regions. Yet these people were able to withstand as great or greater amounts of cold in comfort. Environment and evolution had produced other modes of acclimatization.

The climate of the islands of Tierra del Fuego is one of the very worst in the world. Rain mixed with sleet or snow falls winter and summer and a heavy cloud cover conceals the sun. Winds sweep constantly over the barren, rocky islands. The Ona, Yahgan, and Alacaluf Indians who were the original natives are all but extinct. Scientists succeeded in finding a few of the Alacaluf and nine of them participated in the research project. They went to bed with a metabolic rate that was 160 percent higher than that of the white men. As the hours passed it fell only gradually, maintained at a fairly high level by occasional fits of shivering. The Indians did not wake up, despite the spasms. Unlike the Australians, their rectal temperatures fell very little—never going below 97°F. The skin temperature, on the other hand, dropped nearly as much as that of the Australians, to 82.4°F. This was only two degrees lower than that of the white men. The feet, however, remained warmer than those of the scientists, a result of better conduction of heat from the body core to the extremities.

The acclimatization of the Tierra del Fuego Indians is metabolic, while that of the Australians is insulative.

A slightly different form of adaptation has occurred among inhabitants of the northern hemisphere—the Pangnirtung Eskimo hunters of Cumberland Sound and the Old Crow Indians of the Yukon Territory. Their acclimatization is akin to that of the southern hemisphere Tierra del Fuegans, but by no means identical. The metabolic rate at the start of the night is higher than that of the white man, but lower than that of the Alacaluf. A key difference appears as the night progresses. Unlike the Australian with his unchanged metabolic rate and the Tierra del Fuegan with his slight decline, the metabolic rate of the Eskimo or Arctic Indian actually increases while he sleeps. Other distinctive traits are that the rectal temperature falls slightly below that of Alacaluf and white man, while the skin temperature, particularly of the Eskimo, is higher than the white man's. The feet, as with the Alacaluf, remain comparatively warm.

This does not exhaust the number of adaptations to cold. Lapp nomads who live within the Arctic Circle of Scandinavia have adjusted to cold in a manner that is a variant of the acclimatization of the southern hemisphere Australian. Their metabolism, no higher than that of the white man at the start of an experiment, rises only slightly during the night. The rectal temperature, therefore, falls in response. Not all Lapps are nomads; some have settled in farms and villages and live in heated houses. By now they have lost their adaptation to cold and respond in much the same way as do citizens of temperate zones.

Just how far can modern civilized man go in adapting to extreme conditions? Eight young Norwegian students took part in a six-week endurance test in that cold region in the mountains that lies above the tree line. During the day they hiked, fished, and hunted reindeer; at night they took their rest lying naked on cots covered only with light sleeping bags each made out of a single military blanket. The temperature around them was 37°F. During the first week they were so uncomfortable that they slept very little. Gradually a change took place. They slept while shivering. As people can get used to almost any kind of discomfort, this was less surprising than the discovery that they were literally no longer as cold. Skin temperature did not drop as far as it had in the beginning. Cold feet had been particularly troublesome in the first nights, with temperatures down to 56°F., close to the threshold of intense pain. After the men had become acclimated to cold, their feet remained at a comfortable 81°F. This adaptation of these city-bred men was related to that of the Eskimo, Arctic Indian, and Tierra del Fuegan. The metabolic rate of the Norwegians, like that of the northern hemisphere natives, rose during the night, increasing the amount of heat their bodies were capable of producing. When the students returned home at the end of the experiment, they were unable to sleep in their warm beds covered with blankets. Their altered bodies yearned for the cold night and the light sleeping bag.

The rise in metabolism was the most significant of their adaptations to cold, but it was not the only one. Small but useful vascular changes took place in hands and feet. This adjustment occurs whenever people are subjected to cold regularly. Fishermen and butchers, for example, who keep their hands in icy water or on icy meat for long periods, are still able to use their fingers skillfully. The winters are bitter at Fort Churchill in Canada. The hands of men who work out of doors become inured to the intense cold, while those who have indoor jobs never gain manual dexterity in the freezing temperatures. When men stay for more than a few weeks in polar regions they change to lighter boots and mittens than they needed at first. These general observations were given a formal test at Cambridge University in England recently. Subjects sat in a cold room for two hours daily. At the end of two weeks their hands had accommodated to the cold. They were more comfortable and also less vulnerable to frostbite than when they started the test.

Adjustment to cold is a highly individual matter. Thousands of soldiers suffered frostbite during the Korean War as they fought their way northward along the Yalu River. But thousands of others, exposed to exactly the same temperatures and dressed in exactly the same type of clothing, did not. Army physiologists observed that cold injury was six times as common among men from warm climates or with a tropical heritage as among men from the northern states.

"There appears to be inherent susceptibility which present knowledge of temperature-regulating mechanisms is insufficient to explain," reports Lieutenant Colonel William H. Hall, Commanding Officer of the U. S. Army Research Institute of Environmental Medicine.

This might be in some way related to the circulatory system. When the fingers or toes become chilled, certain of the constricted blood vessels periodically open and allow a flush of warming blood to enter and prevent freezing. This mechanism is much better developed in some persons than in others. Those soldiers who were frostbitten in Korea, then, may well have possessed relatively poor circulation. Scientists suggest that civilians considering work in our northern states or answering the Weather Bureau's advertisement for polar service might have the circulation of their hands tested. The frostbite-prone could thus be identified in advance.

While frostbite can occur anywhere—a single hospital in Denver each year admits seven people who have been frostbitten in the Rocky Mountains—it has been a particular hazard of military operations in the cold, claiming more than 115,000 victims in World War I. Four centuries before the birth of Christ, Xenophon led a Spartan army in retreat across the Carduchian mountains. The soldiers suffered from the piercing winds and biting cold. Some historians believe that Xenophon's leadership was all that saved his men from giving up and perishing in the cold. As Xenophon wrote in his account of the campaign, "Toes dropped off from frostbite."

Dreadful though this sounds and was, frostbite was not an unmitigated evil in Xenophon's day, nor is it now. In the final analysis, for the person lost in a snowstorm or wandering alone through a frigid landscape, frostbite may be all that stands between him and death. The warm blood that is directed away from fingers and toes is concentrated around the internal organs and protects them from harm. Frostbite can thus be the price of survival in the cold.

But most people who become frostbitten are not in any danger of death. Their bodies may well be warm; only the hands, feet, and face are cold. Sometimes frostbite is the end product of extreme carelessness, as when a drunken person lies down in the gutter on a winter's night. Most often, frostbite is due to absentmindedness. On a terribly cold day a man takes off his gloves to light a cigarette or brush sleet out of his eyes. He tries to fix the motor on a stalled automobile with his bare hands, forgetful or ignorant of the fact that heat loss is speeded by contact with metal.

Exercise is the best way of avoiding frostbite and other cold injury, but because hands and feet are slow to warm up, the chilled person becomes overtired and too soon stops stamping up and down and waving his arms about. Just to compound the damage, fatigue of itself has been found to lower resistance to cold injury.

Perhaps someday, Army doctors speculate, better ways of conditioning people to cold will be found or drugs will be developed that can safely stimulate the body's temperature-regulating mechanism to work more efficiently. At present, however, they are conceding the impossibility of producing "a superman as effectively immunized against cold as he can be against smallpox or yellow fever."

Lacking immunization procedures, there is no substitute for care. By the winter of 1965 the U. S. Eighth Army in Korea was able to boast of only six cold-connected injuries. Experts maintain that there is no real excuse for any to occur. Even at McMurdo Sound, the main U.S. station in Antarctica, there were only three cases of frostbite during a recent season, and all were minor.

"A man can stay out for hours in cold that is far below zero if he observes sensible rules," states Army cold regions expert Colonel Clark. "He should never face into the wind. Each man should keep checking the fingers and noses of his companions to spot frostbite at its first appearance. This is heralded by a patch of white."

Much of the research into physiological reactions to cold has been done by the Army in the interests of military preparedness. The late Air Force General Henry "Hap" Arnold once predicted that the North Pole would be of great strategic importance should there ever be another world war. Such planning seems a waste of time, to say the least, when another world war would very likely end life in polar as well as temperate and tropical zones. Still, whatever the reason for gathering the information, it is proving valuable to anyone who must live in a cold climate.

The Army has worked out a detailed table explaining the risk of freezing, according to the speed of the wind and the outdoor temperature. It rates weather conditions as bringing little danger, increasing danger, and great danger of frostbite for exposed flesh. Should the wind blow at twenty miles per hour, for example, and the temperature be between 5° and -22°F., any part of the body that is not covered by warm clothing is likely to freeze within a few minutes. When the wind is at thirty miles per hour and the temperature between -22° and -58°F., frostbite can occur in less than half a minute.

The greatest danger of frostbite comes not when the weather is at its coldest, but when low temperatures are followed by a thaw or by rain. This situation was first described by Napoleon's surgeon, Baron Dominique J. Larrey, and has been reaffirmed by countless other physicians since. Heat is lost rapidly from a wet hand or foot.

Dr. David N. Knize and a group of scientists at the University of Colorado Medical Center recently calculated exact correlations between the degree and duration of cold exposure and the amount of tissue lost in subsequent amputations. The critical temperature, they noted, was 20°F. After studying 163 case records they reported that not one person escaped losing some tissue if exposed to temperatures lower than this for an hour or more. The time spent in the cold can make all the difference between serious injury and minor discomfort. Three men, out of doors for less than half an hour when temperatures were below -10°F., were uninjured, while two others who spent more than twenty-four hours at temperatures slightly above the freezing point required below-the-knee amputation.

This information is not of purely theoretical interest, declares Knize; it can help to determine which course of treatment should be initiated. Knize has already conducted experiments in which animals were protected by surface medication from suffering the full extent of a predictable cold injury.

Unfortunately, frostbite most often occurs in places where medical care is not immediately available. Frostbite can be helped by the right first-aid treatment and made infinitely worse by the wrong one.

"Rub them well with snow and escape unharmed," wrote Robert Boyle in 1683. "If those whose hands or feet, or faces are frozen, approach them too near or hastily to the fire; they are in danger of losing, or at least much prejudicing the overhastily thawed parts."

This unsound advice has had extraordinary longevity. Even today one hears of frostbitten mountain climbers rubbing their frigid feet with snow. It would be hard to select a more harmful treatment. Both cold and massage add to the likelihood of permanent injury.

Boyle's warning against approaching "too near" the fire is nearly as unwise as the rest of his counsel. Rapid rewarming is the very best way to save fingers or toes. Thawing in water warmed to a temperature between 104° and 113°F. is the most efficient method. The frozen hand or foot, which is hard and white, should be left in the water only until it looks flushed. In the polar wastes, the winter battlefield, or icy mountain peak, heated water may be sadly lacking. In that case, body heat can serve as substitute, with the hand placed under the armpit, the foot cradled in the arms of a warm companion, the nose covered with a warm hand. Care must be taken not to rub the injured area. If it is essential for the mountain climber, hiker, forest ranger, soldier, or member of a polar expedition to walk in order to reach a place of safety, the foot should be left frozen until then. Once it is thawed, walking will hurt it.

After thawing, the frostbitten area can be covered with dry gauze. No ointments or tight bandages should be applied and the blisters should not be opened. All of this can be done by the companions of the injured person, and in cases of mild frostbite this is often enough. A quick return of sensitivity indicates that the thawing has been successful.

More serious cases need medical treatment, with the administration of tetanus toxoid and antibiotics to prevent infection. This may be followed by whirlpool baths in a mild disinfectant and special exercises.

Anyone who has been frostbitten once is in particular danger of a repetition. And a person with a circulatory disease, such as arteriosclerosis, is exceedingly frostbite-prone.

The constriction of blood vessels, which is the body's first response to cold, can produce some untoward side effects. On an Antarctic expedition a man cut his hand on a sledge. Days later the wound was still raw. This experience has been shared by many in frigid parts of the globe. The closing off of the blood vessels may in some manner retard the healing process, but no one knows how or why. As most people tend to think of cold as being clean and healing, this unwholesome reaction is quite unexpected.

Ask a group of people selected at random if cold weather is healthy. Almost all of them will say that it is. Does getting chilled bring on the common cold? But of course. These mutually exclusive views are held by a vast majority. For of all beliefs about cold, none is more persistent than that it brings on the common cold. Now a group of doctors at Baylor University College of Medicine, Houston, have performed a study that stands as a denial of this faith. Volunteers who had been inoculated with an actual cold virus and wearing only light cotton shorts were sent to a room cooled to 40°F. By the time they came out they were chilled, shivering, and miserable. By all odds, they should have been down with colds by morning. The expected failed to happen. A few of them did catch cold, to be sure, but so did some of a second group of inoculated volunteers who had stayed warm to serve as controls. In fact, the number was just about the same.

Everybody knows that cold, wet feet today mean a scratchy throat and clogged nose tomorrow. But this belief, too, is not standing up to scientific scrutiny. The obliging group of human guinea pigs got wet as well as cold, and again, no more colds resulted than among the people who kept their socks dry. Despite the widespread publicity given this study, mothers have not become lenient about letting children go out in the rain without their rubbers and mufflers.

But what about the undeniable fact that there are many more colds in winter than in summer? The Baylor physicians explain that people are indoors far more in winter than in summer, and are in close proximity to one another. If any person in a room has a cold, his sneezes and coughs fill the air with viruses that are breathed in by someone else. The astronauts in the 1968 space mission in Apollo 7 were neither chilled nor wet, but they were certainly close together. Captain Walter M. Schirra, Jr., had a cold and quickly passed it on to his crew members, Major Donn F. Eisele and Walter Cunningham.

The temperature in the Philippine Islands changes rather little from one season to the next, but most colds are caught between June and September. That is the rainy season there. One might think that this supports the wet feet theory, but the doctors who documented the seasonal fluctuation refuse to believe it. As with the winter in the north, they contend that the rain drives people indoors, where they cluster together and exchange viruses.

While agreeing that cold will not give a healthy person a cold, scientists do not absolve cold of blame for aggravating other physical illnesses. The reduction of blood flow in the peripheral vessels makes cold particularly hazardous for people suffering with the heart condition angina pectoris. A man who is able to climb stairs easily in the summer may suffer a mild attack when doing the same thing in winter. According to a study recently completed by the National Heart Institute, moderate exercise begins to be troublesome for angina patients when the temperature reaches a barely cool 59°F. The colder the weather, the likelier the onset of the clenching chest pain that characterizes the disease. Cold cuts down on the flow of blood, while exercise raises the blood pressure and increases the demand for oxygenated blood. The heart muscle of the person with angina simply cannot fill the need.

If the cold is intense enough, it may of itself cause a rise in blood pressure. Prisoners in Siberian labor camps have been found to suffer from hypertension, particularly on bitter days.

The effect of cold upon the emotions has not yet been fully assessed. It has been observed that mentally unstable individuals adjust poorly to cold and have more than their share of cold injuries, such as frostbite. There is no question also that fits of depression seize usually equable people under conditions of great cold. This has been a recurring problem among personnel on polar expeditions. "A gloomy melancholy air lowered on the brows of our shipmates, and a dreadful silence reigned among us ... the hour of dinner was hateful," wrote a sailor traveling through frigid Antarctic waters in the eighteenth century.

Depression like this, however, could be due to the extraordinary sense of isolation rather than to cold alone. In areas, however cold, where people have a normal social life, emotional reactions are more moderate. The evidence is mounting, nonetheless, that irritability at least can be a side effect of cold exposure. When the cold is severe, the amount of adrenalin produced by the body increases. This occurs even without a full-blown "fight or flight" reaction.

While moderate cold is exhilarating to those who like it,

extreme cold is exhausting. The person who started out cheerfully on a mountain climb or hike suddenly finds himself unable to take another step. The pack becomes a burden too heavy to manage. In areas where below-zero temperatures are frequent—such as Siberia, northern Greenland, the Antarctic—newcomers are incapable of doing any but the lightest tasks. Their breathing is labored and panting. Perfectly healthy men may spit blood, and pains similar to those of rheumatism develop in the joints. The body must be given time to adjust. The same men who are tired within minutes of starting a task on their first day in the Antarctic eventually become able to work for as long as four hours in temperatures of -45°F. or lower, moving hundred-pound fuel drums and performing other hard physical labor. As with all cold acclimatization, some individuals improve more than others.

Remove the average man from his heated office, his warm home, electric blanket, and car, and what happens? "Most people can become acclimatized to cold in two weeks of intensive effort," the leader of a recent polar expedition observes. "In the Arctic we begin by taking men out for only an hour at a time. When we see them shivering, we go in again. The next day they find that they can stay out a little longer. They will not adapt, however, if they rush indoors at the first sensation of chilling. A man must endure a little discomfort if he is to become acclimated."

The person living in modern America or Europe seldom needs to become physiologically adjusted to cold, as he has succeeded in shielding himself from it most of the time. "His success has been almost solely technological," comments Ralph F. Goldman of the Army Research Institute of Environmental Medicine. "Modern man is probably less well adapted biologically for living in the cold than his cave-dwelling ancestors, who were inured and acclimated to a degree of cold exposure which modern man has been clever enough to avoid."

3

Conquering Cold with Cunning

On a late winter's day in 1967 a sick Eskimo woman and her husband left their home at Agapa above the Arctic Circle in Siberia to go to a hospital 150 miles away. Traveling on dogsled, they were caught in a snowstorm and became lost. The dogs died and the food ran out. At last the husband decided to leave his wife and go for help. He succeeded in reaching a town and a search party set off. But the Arctic storms were so severe that the hunt dragged on for two weeks. During that time the temperature had dropped to -50°F. When the rescuers finally came upon the Eskimo woman, she was virtually buried in the snow. Nonetheless, she survived this experience. The blanket of snow plus her inherited metabolic adaptation to cold may have saved her.

The fact that snow or ice can provide warmth, paradoxical though it sounds, has long been known to the Eskimos. In the winter when no other building materials are found, they have employed the ice as a protection against itself. In the days when igloos were commonly used, an able-bodied man possessed of nothing but a knife with a long blade was expected to cut the necessary blocks of ice and build an igloo large enough for his family and himself in one hour. The igloo was formed of an ascending spiral of the blocks of snow. To provide light when there was no glass, the Eskimo cut a thin piece of fresh-water ice and used it as a skylight. The family slept on a platform of snow covered with twigs and furs. In regions where driftwood or stone was available the Eskimo would build a cabin, knowing that the snow would drift over it during the winter storms and keep it snug.

The Eskimos have been particularly adept at dealing with their hostile environment. Snow-blindness is a problem peculiar to polar regions where there are large unbroken stretches of white snow gleaming in brilliant sunshine. In other areas the eyes are adequately protected from the sun's ultraviolet rays by the eyebrows and eyelashes and the position of the eyes in the head. In the days before sunglasses were imported, the Eskimos cut two tiny slits in a piece of leather, wood, or cloth, and tied this over their eyes.

The acclimatization of natives of frigid climates has been intellectual and psychological as well as physiological. "If the Eskimos were not bright and adaptable, they could not have survived," comments Dr. William Campbell Steere, Director of the New York Botanical Garden, who has spent a great deal of time in the Arctic.

When he first worked in a laboratory at Point Barrow, Alaska, he noticed that some mornings all the Eskimos who helped him were gloomy, and on others all were cheerful. One day he realized that they were reflecting each of his moods. "The Eskimos have had to become this responsive," says Steere. "It is a survival mechanism. The man who sensed the storm five minutes before the others was the one who survived."

As an example of the native ability to learn essentials rapidly, Steere cites the case of a dentist who was about to return to the United States after spending two years traveling from one Eskimo village to another. The Eskimo boy who had accompanied him as guide offered to buy the dental tools. "What for?" asked the dentist. "Do you want to carve whalebone with them?" "No," replied the boy. "I will be the dentist now that you're going away." "But do you realize that it took me years of school, then college, then dental school to learn to become a dentist?" "Maybe you're slow, Doctor," replied the Eskimo.

"I have seen an Eskimo get into a tractor or car he had never been in before and drive off," remarks Steere. "Again, people who are not able to manage quickly with whatever comes to hand could not survive in the rigorous climate."

While it might seem that immigrants from warmer countries would seek to imitate Eskimo ways of dealing with cold, this did not happen for years. A basic distrust of a culture so foreign prevented it. Eskimo-type clothing has only recently been generally accepted. For years Americans and Europeans went to frigid areas wearing garments that were bulky, heavy, and restrictive of all movement. In photographs taken in the 1930's Rear Admiral Richard E. Byrd and other members of his Antarctic expeditions look more like chunky polar bears than fit explorers. At the beginning of World War II the military command ordered the Quartermaster Corps to prepare for possible Army action in Greenland, Iceland, Alaska, and the Aleutians. The Corps was known to possess huge stores of cold-weather clothing and the soldiers went to claim them. To their dismay they discovered that the stock consisted of huge buffalo and ponyskin overcoats. A soldier was asked to put one on and stand at attention. His clumsiness made it look like a comedy act, only nobody felt like laughing.

Sir Hubert Wilkins, the famed polar explorer, was hurriedly called in for advice. Sir Hubert had been with Vilhjalmur Stefansson's expedition in the Arctic and with Sir Ernest Shackleton's in Antarctica and had led a number of polar expeditions himself. These experiences had shown him the value of Eskimo-style clothing and he brought some to the Army laboratory and prepared for a "march on the trail" in an experimental cold room where the temperature was held at -89°F. Sir Hubert put on his loosely fitted suit without underwear. The garment had adjustable closings at waist, neck, wrists, and ankles. The only concession to modernity that he made was the substitution of fabric for the natural animal products used by the Eskimos. The outer shell was of windbreaker material and it was lined with two thin layers of alpaca pile.

Sir Hubert's companion on the march was Dr. Harwood S.

Belding, a physiologist, dressed in the Army's latest cold-weather outfit. This consisted of long woolen underwear, a pair of overalls, and a jacket lined with heavy wool blanketing.

A treadmill was set in operation for "mushing" at three and a half miles per hour up an incline of nine percent. Sir Hubert was elderly and soft—after all, he had gone off with Stefansson in 1913—but he mushed with far greater ease than his younger companion. At the end of an hour rations in the form of box lunches were brought in. Belding, who was exhausted, suggested that they stop to eat. "Let's eat on the trail," said Sir Hubert, trudging on. After two hours of mushing the men lay down to rest. Sir Hubert was asleep in five minutes, while Belding was shivering and shaking miserably. "If I had only had the Eskimo suit," he remarked later.

The Eskimos had applied a principle of insulation that the Army was just discovering independently. Without waiting to see what Sir Hubert with his knowledge of the Eskimo would turn up, the Army sent a group of mountain and Arctic specialists to a nearby mountain to try out the cold-weather clothing equipment. But the month happened to be May and the nights on the mountain were balmy. The mountaineers, therefore, left the great outdoors and spent nights in the laboratory cold room. As it could neither control the weather nor fit everyone into the cold room, the Army dispatched a group to Mount McKinley, in Alaska, where temperatures run to -20°F. or so even in the spring. More than a hundred items were tested there.

Reports on their findings could revolutionize cold-weather clothing for civilians, too, should warmth rather than fashionable appearance ever be given priority by anyone besides Eskimos, soldiers, and people going to the Arctic and Antarctic to work, prospect for oil and minerals, or explore. Weight, they learned, was not really significant in keeping cold out. The buffalo overcoat and its successor, the heavy wool overall, and the mink coat of the lady of fashion are not worth their weight in warmth. Although no woman is going to abandon her mink, she would be more comfortable in garments based on the Army, or Eskimo, design. The principle applied is that trapped, still air is a remarkably efficient insulator. The best cold-weather clothing, then, consists of a series of layers, rather than just one heavy fabric. The insulating capacity is increased with every layer, because of the air trapped between it and the next. Ideally, the outer shell of the garment should be windproof and waterproof like the animal pelts used by the Eskimo or the fabric of Sir Hubert's parka. The inner layers should be of the lightest possible material. A sufficient number of layers to keep a man warm in -65°F. cold weighs three pounds or less. The layers—with warmth, not beauty, in mind—are loosely fitted, a sharp contrast to the tight stretch pants favored by skiers at resorts. Drawstrings close the garment, keeping the wind out and body heat in.

The test performed by Sir Hubert and Belding proved the Eskimo clothing to be not only warmer when the two men were resting, but also cooler when they exercised. The loose clothing provided ventilation so that Sir Hubert sweated less and little moisture collected in his clothing.

Heat has turned out to be an unexpected problem of living in the cold. Men working in frigid areas used to complain that they felt hot nearly as often as cold. They sweated when they were not shivering. For many years the designers working in comfortable offices thousands of miles away did not believe them. But the evidence became so overwhelming that at last heat dissipation became a recognized aim in design of cold-weather outfits.

The same garment must be comfortable in a temperature range of 130 degrees, that is, from 65° to -65°F., and whether the wearer is exercising violently or is just sitting still. All these requirements can be satisfied by a basic suit with a series of layers to be added or subtracted according to need.

In order to calculate the amount of warmth these garments could give with all layers on and vents closed, an arbitrary unit of measure, the clo, was set. One clo is the amount of insulation needed to keep a seated man comfortable when the temperature around him is 70°F. The average business suit measures one clo, and the clothing designed by the Army for Arctic and Antarctic wear measures 4.3 clo.

While present cold-weather clothes are more than adequate for the kind of weather encountered by people in temperate zones, they do not provide quite enough protection for extreme conditions. The Quartermaster Corps has yet to meet its goal for clothing that will keep an inactive man safe, if not altogether comfortable, for eight hours at a temperature of -40°F. What is particularly frustrating, as one officer has pointed out, is that the goal has been reached for all but five or ten percent of the entire body. And what makes up that percentage? The feet, hands, and face.

Of these, the foot problem is the closest to a solution. Sealed thermal boots have been designed to utilize the same principle of trapped air that has revolutionized clothing. Before putting on his boots and going out into the cold, a man must blow into a rubber tube which sends the needed insulating air between layers of sponge rubber. There are a number of drawbacks, however. As the boots weigh from nine to ten pounds, a long walk is exhausting. In addition, the boot is so well insulated that it does not let moisture out. Fungal and bacterial infections, therefore, are apt to run riot. But as the boot fulfills its major requirement of protecting against frostbite, there are times when it must be worn.

The hands are in some ways more critical than the feet. A person can walk on chilled, stiff feet, but he cannot use chilled, stiff fingers. Gloves have been designed that keep the hands in a more or less working position even when cold. The palms and fingers are curved and the back of the glove is one and a half inches longer than the palm so that cold air will not enter when the hand is bent. In the Arctic two men were checked while taking magnetic observations with an instrument requiring such delicate manipulations that they could wear only the thinnest of gloves. In -4°F. cold, the task took them fifteen minutes. On another day, when the temperature was -33°F., the same delicate work took fifty minutes. A good part of the extra time had been devoted to rewarming the stiffening fingers. The fifth finger tip is half-jokingly known as the "weakest link," because it gets the coldest and is the slowest to rewarm.

No matter how well gloves are designed and insulated, it still appears to be all but impossible to keep the hands really warm, or to rewarm them after they have been chilled. Men who must be out of doors in the cold for any length of time are advised to keep small heaters in their pockets. When hands begin to stiffen, the alcohol in the heater can be lighted. Then a heater is placed inside each glove.

This somewhat amateurish method is simple and convenient. The very best way of providing heat, however, has neither of these characteristics. It consists of an electrically powered heating system; socks and gloves, for example, are wired and then operated by batteries attached to the inside of a vest. The unit, however, adds seven pounds to the cold-weather outfit. And the wearer would not dare to leave off extra layers of insulation. In the cold regions there must always be a margin for error. If the batteries were to go dead when he was far from shelter, he would rapidly freeze to death. This problem will ultimately be solved by the development of batteries so light in weight that many spares could be carried.

The face and head are next to hands and feet in what one researcher described recently as the "hierarchy of weak links" in the armor against cold. Fur hoods and knitted masks that fit over most of the face are commonly worn. When it is very windy a hood edged with an extendable wire stiffener is helpful. It is bent so as to shield the face in the direction from which the wind is blowing. A heated helmet greatly increases the ability to stay out of doors for long periods on temperatures of -50° or -60°F. Such helmets are so expensive that they are seldom issued to expedition members, unless conditions are intolerable.

The coldest place on the face of the earth is Vostok, a

Cold As an Environment

U.S.S.R. Antarctic station, which is 11,200 feet above sea level. And the coldest time of year in Vostok comes in late August just when the sun is beginning to make its appearance above the horizon. At that time the thermometer dips to -103°F., to -112°F., to -125°F., and lower. Yet, as Vostok is a research station, it is necessary for men to go outside to check equipment regularly. They wear both heated suits and a protective mask developed by Soviet scientist V. A. Morov. The mask is made of compressed, foamed polystyrene and has a shield containing a tiny electrical heater. A silver-zinc storage battery powers the heater for as long as six hours in temperatures of -112°F.

A heated suit has recently been developed to protect divers in icy waters. One suit recently patented makes use of sea or river water that has been heated by steam and then pumped through an umbilical hose. The diver can keep as much warm water as he needs in the suit and send the rest back to the sea. The Atomic Energy Commission has designed another type of diving suit heater based on radioactive isotopes. Water is heated by the isotopes and pumped through the suit. Some auxiliary source of heat is essential if divers are to remain underwater in frigid seas for more than a few minutes at a time.

On land, the concept of insulation by means of trapped air has been applied to housing. A double floor to shield inhabitants from the icy ground was developed for the Second Byrd Antarctic Expedition of the mid-1930's. More recently, Robert C. Faylor, Director of the Arctic Institute of North America, noticed a fabric-covered geodesic dome covering an outdoor swimming pool. Attuned to cold-region problems, he quickly envisioned this dome lined with foam. "The lightweight fabric and galvanized steel frame can be flown by helicopter to inaccessible parts of the Arctic and dropped there," says Faylor. Such housing is now being tested in the Yukon.

For field trips away from carefully constructed housing, sleeping bags are essential, and those intended for use in frigid areas consist of a series of layers of fabric. A bag must fit the body as closely as possible, because a resting person puts out no more heat than a seventy-five watt or, at best, a hundred-watt bulb, and cannot warm a large space. The Army once experimented with a bag divided in two below the hips, so that the soldiers could get up and walk in an emergency. Whatever was gained in mobility was lost in warmth. The men in these bags were cold even in a typical night temperature of 20°F. Actually no sleeping bag is sufficient for a whole night when it is very cold. Should the thermometer drop below -20°F., the sleeper will awaken in discomfort after a few hours. Sleeping time can be extended by exercise just before bedtime. The hotter the individual, the longer it takes him to cool off.

The major source of body heat is metabolism, which is increased by the food eaten. Whatever the climate, most people like a snack before bedtime. They enjoy a late-night pizza, doughnut, or frankfurter. In temperate zones this may result just in an expanded waistline or a rise in blood cholesterol level. In extremely cold climates, however, a late-night snack serves a valuable function. Because it raises the body's heat output for several hours, it prolongs sleep. This has been a casual observation of campers on cold nights and members of polar expeditions. It has also been tested scientifically. A group of men were given a small meal—a hamburger or sandwich, cake, or milk—in an amount to total 500 calories, just before they crawled into a sleeping bag in a laboratory cold room where the temperature was -30°F. These men slept one to one and a half hours longer than they had on previous nights when they had eaten nothing since supper.

Day or night, most people have a greater desire for food in winter than in summer. The heat drains them of hunger, while the bracing air of winter increases the appetite for roast beef, French fried potatoes, and apple pie. But does the body really require more food in cold weather?

"Men are habitually hungrier in the Arctic," says Colonel Clark. "When I was stationed in Greenland, I ordered one and a half rations—5,000 calories—for each of my men per day. The men ate it and they did not get fatter."

In a test run by the Quartermaster Corps, it was found that men who spent twenty-four hours a day in a room where the temperature was held at 50° F. ate 250 to 350 calories more than others in a room at 70 to 75°F. Still, this cannot be taken as proof that cold of itself produces additional calorie requirements. People who are chilled make both voluntary and involuntary movements. The men in the colder room shivered for a while; then they got up and stamped their feet and waved their arms, and occasionally ran in place to keep warm. This extra muscular activity was probably the reason for the greater fuel need. Colonel Clark's men in Greenland were engaged in strenuous labors. At one time it was commonly believed that men in frigid climates really required 7,000 calories or more a day. Today that theory is in disrepute. It holds true only in exceptional circumstances. On days when making dives into Antarctic waters of 28°F., Lieutenant Lavallee and Dr. Carleton Ray, who was then Associate Curator of the New York Aquarium, consumed between 5,000 and 7,500 calories. But their output of energy was extraordinary.

Natives of cold climates do not eat any more than people in Atlanta or Los Angeles. The Eskimo consumes about 3,100 calories a day and the trapper in Greenland only 2,800.

Some years ago a simple study was made of soldiers transferred from a warm to a cold climate. The amount they consumed when stationed at Fort Knox, Kentucky, was carefully measured, and averaged 4,000 calories per person a day. That winter the same men were sent north to Fort Churchill. They performed about the same amount of work and were equally active in both places; the only difference was the outside temperature. The men took in no more than the 4,000 calories that had been their diet in warm Kentucky. The food intake of infantrymen in the Arctic was then evaluated, first in summer and then in winter. Again, it was found that the men ate just about the same amount—some 3,200 calories—

regardless of the temperatures around them. Eating habits are governed, for the most part, by the amount of activity engaged in and a host of psychological and economic factors.

The hope that certain types of vitamin-rich food would help increase resistance to cold has not been borne out. Laboratory animals were fed large quantities of vitamin C and became better able to endure low temperatures. But men have not reacted in the same way. They suffered just as much from cold after eating a diet weighted in favor of foods containing vitamin C.

There is a widespread misconception that the need for butter, cream, and other fats is greater in the cold weather. This is particularly illogical, because laboratory tests show that protein provides considerably more excess heat than fat can. Eight tons of meat and 60,000 eggs provided this necessary protein for the 126 men aboard the icebreaker *Manhattan*, making its way through the dangerous waters of the fabled Northwest Passage in 1969. The meat supply, however, included more pork—"because of its greater fat content," explained a spokesman—than is normally carried on journeys through temperate waters. While it does appear that animals may be helped by a high-fat diet, man is not. Americans who visit cold regions show no physiological evidence of "fat hunger," despite eating no more fats than they did in temperate zones.

Cold has no direct effect on caloric or nutritional needs—a fact that probably will not stop people from continuing to eat more than they should in winter and less in summer.

4

Animal Adaptations

It is a world of bone-chilling cold. Ice cliffs rise high above the dark and frigid waters. Every so often a piece breaks off with a thundering crash and floats away to join the towering icebergs on the sea. Beyond the cliffs the icy plateau stretches on, its whiteness broken by dark seams of crevasses and by the blue shadows cast by mountains in the distance. The scene is stark and desolate, but it is not dead. Fat seals awaken from a sleep on the ice shelf and dive into the icy waters. The skua gull spreads his wings against the brilliance of a sky lit by the never-setting summer sun. Penguins waddle awkwardly but with great determination across the ice to reach the food-filled waters.

For the icy sea is not devoid of life. Huge whales swim by spouting the bitter-cold water through their air holes. Silvery codlike fish, squid with tentacles seven feet long, starfish with curving limbs, sea spiders, and large, slimy, blue-gray jellyfish live and die in polar seas.

Unlike man, whose naked body can endure only a limited temperature range, other animal species have evolved so as to survive under the most brutal conditions. There is hardly a place on the globe so hostile but that some form of animal life can make its home there.

Polar creatures are not necessarily freakish or one of a kind. Most species contain some cold- and some warm-weather varieties. The relationship is easily recognized, but the demands of the specific environments usually make them look and act differently. Does low temperature of itself change living things in a predictable manner? Are animals of the cold related to one another in some manner that transcends species or even genus?

The polar bear, the Arctic fox, the snowy petrel, the Beluga whale, different as they are, do resemble each other in one particular: they are white. No Arctic or Antarctic bird bears the brilliant plumage of the tropical peacock or bird of paradise. No musk ox or seal has the bright coloration of the giraffe or tiger. And the human natives of equatorial Africa are dark-skinned, while the people who live in temperate zones are fair. Such observations led a scientist in the 1830's to suggest: "In mammals and birds, races which inhabit warm and humid regions have more melanin pigmentation than races of the same species in cooler and drier regions." Since melanin is the substance that protects the skin from the ultraviolet rays of the sun, it stands to reason that a bit less is needed in frigid areas. Still, this does not go very far in explaining the effect of cold.

Over the next few years other similarities between animals of the cold as a group were diligently sought. Scientist Carl Bergmann in the 1840's began to explore similarities in size rather than color. At first glance, variations in size seem to have neither rhyme or reason. The huge sea lion and polar bear of the cold climates are equaled or surpassed in size by the rhinoceros and elephant of the tropics. The Arctic hare is bigger than the mouse of temperate zones. Bergmann then tried a completely new approach. Instead of comparing the sea lion with the elephant, he compared a polar animal with a related species in warmer climates. This line of reasoning turned out to be remarkably fruitful, and he was able to formulate a new law: "The smaller-sized geographic races of a species are found in the warmer parts. of the range, the larger-sized races in the cooler districts." The Kodiak bear of Alaska is indeed huge in comparison to the Malay bear, and the Antarctic skua is bigger than the European seagull.

Following Bergmann's line of reasoning, J. A. Allen, a zoologist with the American Museum of Natural History, in

1877 pointed out another difference between cold- and hot-weather members of the same species: "Protruding body parts such as tails, ears, bills, extremities, and so forth, are relatively shorter in the cooler parts of the range of a species than in the warmer parts."

For some years the assumption was that Bergmann's and Allen's rules applied to warm-blooded animals only. Then in 1960 Dr. Carleton Ray, Associate Professor of Pathobiology at Johns Hopkins University, tried to apply the rules to cold-blooded creatures as well. He selected a wide variety—worms, flies, platyfish, toads, frogs, spiders, mites, and bumblebees—seventeen species in all. Four of these were studied in their natural environment in southeastern Alaska; twelve were grown at a variety of temperatures in the laboratory. One, a toad, was studied both in the field and in the laboratory. And thirteen of the seventeen species of toads, worms, flies, and other creatures became larger in size and heavier in weight when grown in cold temperatures. What is more, the protruding parts were shorter in eighty-one percent of the species of cold-blooded animals reared in the cold.

It is easy enough to recognize the positive advantages of having small paws, ears, tails, and noses in cold weather. Any parts that stick out and are the farthest from the internal organs get the coldest and are the hardest to rewarm. It stands to reason that a bird with a neck like a swan's, or a mammal with a trunk like an elephant's, or a tail like a monkey's, or a snout like an armadillo's would be hard pressed to keep these protuberances warm. The reason for the larger size, on the other hand, is not so easy to find. Bergmann had based his law on the principle that most heat is lost through the skin.

"The larger a body, all other things being equal," he wrote, "the smaller the ratio of skin surface area to bulk, since the first varies as the square and the second as the cube."

A small, thin animal, then, has more skin per pound of body weight than a thickly built, big one. In cold climates the short, stout penguin is able to retain the heat of his inner organs no matter how cold the weather outside.

Bergmann's explanation has not won unanimous support among scientists. Physiologist Per Scholander maintains that insulation and vascular adaptation are much more important in helping an animal to conserve his body's heat. According to this view, size is simply something that happens to animals exposed to low temperatures. They grow bigger as a result. But their size does not help them to resist cold and, therefore, cannot be described as a cold adaptation.

Of all vascular adjustments, none is more helpful to creatures of both hot and cold climates than cold-bloodedness. The polar areas abound with cold-blooded fish, insects, and animals. In the frigid waters below the southernmost tip of South America, starfish are forcing their strong, curved arms through the cracks of scallop shells to scoop out the cowering little creatures within. The anemone, which looks like a strange plant with long, tonguelike petals, is really an animal. Its tentacles are armed with poison darts to paralyze any fish unlucky enough to swim by. A few sponges sit on the sub-Antarctic ocean floor, straining gallons of icy water in and out of their bodies, retaining the bits of food within. Worms slither their elongated bodies along the dark mud bottom or burrow within. At least a few snails, crabs, clams, lobsters, squid, and fragile pink urchins can endure the cold of sub-Antarctic waters. A giant crustacean gobbles up its weaker relatives with cannibalistic relish. Even an occasional coral, the strange creature that wears its skeleton on the outside of its body, has been found near the Straits of Magellan.

In addition to the many familiar marine animals, there are some cold-climate fish—particularly in the Antarctic—that are seen nowhere else. Fifteen minutes of trawling outside the South Shetland Islands will bring up several hundred fish, say ichthyologists. It takes a good ten hours for trained men to sort them out and identify the ten percent that are unique to the area. About half of all species of the lantern fish family are found solely in Antarctic waters. Many Antarctic fishes have adapted in a manner remarkably similar to that of the

Tierra del Fuegans and Pangnirtung Eskimos. The metabolism is higher than that of similar fish in slightly warmer waters.

Many hints about the nature of cold-water fish have come to us from the observations made by sealers, whalers, and explorers. Many years ago whalers returned from a trip to the Antarctic with a strange tale. When fishing off South Georgia Island, they had caught a fish whose blood was white, not red. This story was repeated by other whalers from time to time over the years. Some of the men dared to eat the abnormal fish and found that it was delicious, despite its white blood. At last, in the early 1950's, fish of that family, the *Chaenichthyidae*, were studied scientifically. And the legend was proved to be reality. The blood of these fish has neither red blood corpuscles nor hemoglobin. As a result, the oxygen consumption of the *Chaenichthyidae* is only one-third to two thirds as great as that of other polar fish with red blood. This makes it particularly well suited to an oxygen-starved life beneath the sea ice.

The ships *Erebus* and *Terror* sailed into the Antarctic Circle in the early 1840's. A storm blew up and the gale-force winds threw a fish onto the deck of the *Terror*. The fish was frozen solid and members of the expedition decided to preserve it in that state and bring it back to England for later study by experts. The surgeon on board, John Robertson, was just making a rough sketch when one of the ship's cats darted in and seized the fish. Before anyone could stop him, the cat had bolted it down. Robertson, unfortunately, was no artist. His picture gives only a faint idea of what the fish looked like. Still, as the cat remained well, it was at least clearly wholesome.

This is one of the few documented frozen fish stories. There is a plethora of tall tales based on the theoretical fondness of animals for frozen fish. A dog swallowed a frozen Alaska blackfish whole, so goes one version. The heat within the dog's stomach was sufficient to thaw the fish and it began to flop around. The movements made the dog queasy, and at last he vomited up the fish. The dog's master tossed the regurgitated fish back into the water and was astounded to see it promptly swim away. This tale is so ubiquitous that it eventually reached the scientific community. Several biologists set out to prove it once and for all; they froze some blackfish and then tried to revive them. The fish remained dead. Still, they concede that the tall tale could have a germ of truth, minus the dog and the vomit. The blackfish and many other species can survive partial freezing. A goldfish was rapidly dipped in liquid air until it appeared to be brittle. Yet, all the water in its tissues had not frozen, and when put back in the bowl of water, it revived and began to swim around. Fishermen on Nova Scotia's Bay of Fundy tell inexperienced men never to leave the herring catch, even if it looks frozen, near the water's edge. They have often seen fish slip back into the bay and swim away.

The very fact that the body fluids of a cold-blooded creature attain the temperature of the surrounding air or water would seem to preclude active life in deep ocean water that is colder than the standard freezing point. Polar waters far beneath the ice are saltier than at the surface, and salt lowers the freezing point of water to below the classic 32°F. Some species of fish can remain active in water that is a bitter 29° or 28°F. and that has driven the temperature of their body fluids down to the same point. They should freeze, but they do not. Instead, they retain the liquid in what is known as a supercooled state. Some Arctic fish are so well adapted to cold that the freezing point of the blood plasma becomes lower in winter than it is in summer. And it tends to be lower all the time than that of fishes in temperate zones. The substance in the blood that reduces its freezing point has long eluded ichthyologists. The known chemical constituents could not have sufficient effect. The missing ingredient was found recently when scientists studied the physiology of three species of the Antarctic *Trematomus* fish that swim in tunnels within the sea ice. The freezing point of the blood varies among the different species, yet each, it was discovered, possesses a certain protein containing carbohydrate. The higher the concentration of this glycoprotein, the lower the freezing point of the fish's blood.

Fishes in the oceans that bound the American and European continents display nearly as startling cold-resistance when conditions demand. Walk along a New England shore on a bleak winter's night. When the tide goes out, scores of shellfish are left washed up on the beach. As the hours of the night pass, the temperature drops to 12°F., to 5°F., and sometimes to zero or lower. The molluscs lie there for hour after hour, while the tide goes all the way out, turns, and slowly flows in again. Some clams, unable to endure cold below 20°F., burrow under the wet sand to find protection. But the oysters, periwinkles, and other molluscs seek no shelter. By the time the temperature has reached 5°F., well over half the water in their bodies has frozen. If they are cut in two it can be seen that the muscles and internal organs are distorted. A warm-blooded creature could never recover from such a physical change; but the molluscs can take it. As soon as the water, which is warmer than the air, flows in and catches them up, they thaw out. Within seconds they have returned to normal. Every day for months on end the cycle repeats itself, and the shellfish freeze at low tide and recover at high.

The reason they survive is that between twenty-four and twenty-nine percent of the water in their tissues remains permanently unfrozen. A possible explanation based on a recent controversial Russian discovery is that a certain proportion of the "bound water" in the tissues of cold-hardy animals and plants might be "polywater." This has been described as a mysteriously modified form of water that does not freeze and only hardens when the temperature is -40°F. or lower. Even then, it does not expand as much as ordinary water.

Another theory holds that the bodies of molluscs contain some sort of natural protective substance that guards them from freezing. This substance has not yet been identified. It does not provide unlimited protection. The shellfish can endure cold of 12° or 5°F. for hours on end, but they die when the thermometer remains below -4°F. for too long. In the course of a particularly cold winter, shells with dead animals inside can be found lying on the beach.

Even when conditions are not quite so rigorous, animals are constantly required to adapt anew or perish. How does the same creature survive in both warm and cold climates? The blue crab, for example, lives as comfortably in warm tropical waters as it does in the colder ones of the northern part of the temperate zone. A theory has been suggested to explain its ability to acclimate: when it gets cold, the makeup of its body fat changes. The saturated fats, the type that raises blood cholesterol levels, decrease, and the amount of un-saturated fats increases. Crabs—and other animals—may also burn glucose with greater efficiency under the stress of cold.

Insects adapt more easily to cold than do crabs and mol-luscs. The cold-hardiest insects secrete glycerol or another alcohol, sorbitol. Both are protective substances which may be produced in the autumn in preparation for the winter. The role of these chemicals in insects is confusing at best. Some hardy species do have a lot of glycerol in their systems. Yet Eizo Asahina, the famed Japanese biologist, reports that many insects capable of recovering after freezing do not con-tain any of the substance.

The body of the insect changes in a number of ways that help it to survive a bitter winter, regardless of glycerol con-tent. In 1899, scientist P. Bachmetjew observed that insects with little water in their tissues had very low freezing points. Since then it has been learned that many insects prepare for the winter by dehydrating. The potato beetle loses about twenty-seven percent of the water in its tissues every fall. The water content of a cold-climate ant's body is as high as seven-ty-six percent in the summer; it drops to sixty-one percent in the winter.

In a laboratory experiment certain microscopic insects, the tardigrades, were first dehydrated and then cooled in liquid helium to within a fraction of a degree of absolute zero. The tardigrades recovered from this utterly unnatural, all-but-total cold. Asahina has tested larger and more complex insects, larval slug caterpillars and butterflies. They were gradually cooled over a period of an hour and a half from 23° to -140°F. The lowest temperature was maintained for forty-five minutes. One-third of the larvae revived after re-warming. The secret of their endurance, Asahina maintains, is that the insects had become somewhat dehydrated by the slow chilling.

This same type of cold-hardiness can be observed in nature. If one looks from a distance at certain glaciers in the Alps and on Mount Rainier, the ice seems to be covered with soot. But the blackness is alive; it is made up of countless wingless glacier fleas. They obtain nourishment from pine tree pollen blown to them by the wind. During most winter nights the insects freeze right into the ice. But when the following day dawns, the rising sun rewarms them to life.

Many insects are able to endure freezing best when in the pupal or larval state. In 1896, for example, a scientist was traveling across Scoresby Sound in northeastern Greenland on a winter's day when the thermometer stood at -40°F. Glancing down casually, he saw a tiny frozen object lying on the ice. He bent down and picked it up. In his gloved hand lay a frozen butterfly larva. He kept the larva and, to his surprise, it survived the cold and eventually metamorphosed into a butterfly. More recently an entomologist pulled an insect larva off the ice covering an Arctic pond. Fully ninety-six percent of the water in its body was completely frozen and it was obviously brittle. Yet when warmed up, it came to life again.

Some adults can survive similar experiences. The Arctic beetle, *Pterostichus brevicornis*, which dies at subzero temperatures in the summer, can easily endure winter freezing to -30°F. or lower.

An Arctic expedition in 1831 wintered in bleak Boothia Peninsula at the very northernmost point of North America.

The second-in-command, James Clark Ross, who was later to make a name for himself as an Antarctic explorer, amused himself by collecting and experimenting on tussock caterpillars. He put thirty of them in a box and left it outside for three months. When the insects were returned to the warm room, all were frozen solid, yet all revived. Ross put the caterpillars out into the Arctic night for another week and then brought them back inside. This time twenty-three of them recovered. These survivors were kept in the warmth for four hours and then were placed outside again for a week. The procedure was repeated four times, and at the end, two were still alive.

A strange little creature that looks something like a cricket lives in the glacial debris near Lake Louise in the Canadian Rockies. Mountain climbers say that if it is picked up and held in the warm palm of the hand, it burns up and dies within a few minutes. This may be exaggeration, but there is no doubt that the insect is comfortable only when temperatures are around the freezing point.

Most cold-hardy species escape an icy death because their bodies adapt to chilling in ways that keep ice crystals from invading the cells. Dehydration plays a part, as crystals are much less likely to form in a cell that has little water in it. Sugar substances in the cells also help to prevent internal freezing. The salts in the cells of certain insects, such as the goat moth, are replaced with sugars as winter approaches.

The bodies of many insects remain free of crystals long after the temperature has reached the freezing point. Their adaptation can be compared to that of the cold-water fish. The fluids in their bodies become supercooled, remaining liquid at temperatures as low as -31°F. This mechanism, however, cannot always be relied upon. If the insect has eaten recently, the water in his tissues is affected and is much less able to become supercooled. The glutton thus is first to die, and moderation may become an inherited characteristic.

Not all insects are cold-hardy; the majority of species are, after all, tropical. In Africa, Asia, and the South Pacific islands mosquito nets are a necessity. Insects are so numerous in the United Arab Republic that a number of superstitions about them survived into the twentieth century. Uneducated Egyptian mothers would not brush flies off the faces of their sleeping infants, convinced that flies bring good luck. The scientific fact, of course, is that they bring disease. Sleeping sickness, endemic to tropical areas, is carried by the tsetse fly and yellow fever by *Aedes aegypti*. Many of these tropical insects are so vulnerable to cold that they die before the air around them is at the freezing point. But some warm-climate insects are perfectly capable of becoming acclimated. The yellow fever mosquito in its larval stage adapts rapidly. When larvae are put in cold water for a day and a night their ability to endure cold is greatly enhanced. The despised cockroach crawling around in a 76° kitchen will go into a coma if it meanders onto the windowsill where the temperature is 42.4°F. If the weather outside is any colder than that, the roach will probably die ... unless it has been conditioned. Unfortunately for extermination efforts, the roach can learn to like cold. A roach was held for twenty-four hours in a cooled box with a temperature of 59°F. After this it was able to move around comfortably in 35.6°F. cold. Similar situations occur frequently in nature. This type of acclimatization is easily lost. Restore the cockroach to the warm kitchen and it will again become comatose should it wander out onto the windowsill.

The cold-endurance of insects in Arctic regions had been astounding both travelers and scientists for many years before they discovered that even the temperatures common to Antarctica are not below the limits of survival for insect life. "On the Antarctic continent insects and their relatives (mites, ticks, tardigrades) appear to be the dominant animals and the largest animals," says J. Linsley Grissett of the Bernice Bishop Museum, Honolulu.

In this surprising statement, Grissett is referring to the actual land area only; he points out that the seals, whales, penguins, and skuas really belong to the sea. Even the fish are of the salt-water variety; no fresh-water species have been found in the ponds made in the few places where the ice melts.

Dominant though they are compared to other animals, insects themselves are few in number. The frigid temperature of the air, the ferocity of the wind, the stark, ice-covered terrain, the lack of shelter, the scarcity of plants all keep the insect population in check. Those insects that do survive find nourishment in places where there would seem to be none. Members of an Antarctic expedition stumbled onto a dead Adélie penguin one day. More than 10,000 mites were clinging to the feathers, living off the algae growing there. Mites were the very first Antarctic insects discovered when explorers in 1897 turned over a rock near the coast and found a colony living there. Since then the mites have been trailed farther and farther inland. In 1965 an eight-legged pink mite, only one one-hundredth of an inch long, was found closer to the South Pole—a mere 309 miles—than any other animal yet seen. There on the Robert Scott Glacier it ekes out a precarious existence, waiting for melting snow to encourage the growth of lichens and algae for it to eat.

Only sixty species of terrestrial insects have been found on the Antarctic continent, and most of these are mites. Eighteen species seek shelter under stones, where they find algae, fungi, and lichens. Another six species live as parasites, gorging their tiny bodies on seals and birds. The nasty little lice comprise the next most numerous group. Fifteen species of biting lice torment birds, while another six of sucking lice obtain their nourishment from seals. There are ten species of springtails, which live in mosses or on stones covered with lichens. All are minute, no more than a millimeter in length, and they are as fragile and light as a spider's web. The unlovely flea makes its home in petrel nests. Two species of midges live in the fresh-water ponds in the Antarctic Peninsula-South Shetland Islands area. Aside from these, the ponds are surprisingly devoid of life.

Wings, the one attribute most commonly associated with insects, are a handicap in frigid areas with strong winds. No butterfly hovers gracefully over the snow. Insects on the Antarctic continent are wingless. Entomologists have studied winged insects on Campbell Island, which lies south of New Zealand. Campbell, like the other sub-Antarctic islands, is swept by fierce gusts of wind. Insects seldom fly at all on windy days, and a good percentage of those few that make the mistake of doing so are blown into the sea. Many have stopped flying even when the air is still. In time, the entomologists believe, the evolutionary process will lead to smaller wings. This has already happened on Heard, another island in the area; none of the insects living there can fly anymore.

One might question how these insects came to such unfriendly lands in the first place. Grissett suggests that the insects were trapped as a result of major changes in the topography. Perhaps at some time in history the sub-Antarctic islands were part of a larger New Zealand. This would explain why the same kind of insects are found in both New Zealand and the sub-Antarctic islands. When the islands drifted away, the insects that happened to be there could not get back to the mainland. They lacked the strength to fly such long distances in the strong winds. As for those insects that live on the Antarctic continent, it is possible that they are left over from the period in prehistory when conditions in the Antarctic were not so hostile. In the millions of years since then they have evolved adaptations to cold.

In both polar areas, where the winter's night lasts for months on end, the insects have acclimated by a prolonged period of dormancy. Some spin their own shelters, cocoons, in which to pass the winter night.

As soon as the summer warmth returns, the active insects come out. This resurgence produces a major health problem in the Arctic. The World Health Organization expresses concern over the prevalence of biting insects—black flies, horse flies, biting snipe flies, lesser house flies, mosquitoes, biting midges. These injure animals as well as humans. Reindeer suffer from the attacks of blow and warble flies, while geese and ducks are infected by the blood parasites carried by certain biting flies.

Insects are not the only link between animals and parasites. Seals and penguins probably pick up theirs by eating heavily infested fish and crustaceans.

"You name a parasite, they have it," a scientist describes the infested bodies of polar creatures.

"When you cut open a dead animal, it's unbelievable. We took the stomach out of an Antarctic seal for laboratory study," says Dr. Jacob M. Hiller of Beth Israel Hospital, New York. "Nematodes, the tiny worms, grew on it so heavily and so close together that the stomach looked as if it were covered with hair."

Repulsive though this is to the fastidious, the parasites have not been found to be harmful. They live together in apparent comfort with the cold- or warm-blooded animals that give them house room.

5

Migration, Hibernation, or Mass Death

What is the temperature of a seal? The answer to this seemingly frivolous question has been sought by biologists for many years. The adaptations of such an animal as the seal or bear are far more complex than those of the insect or fish. While it is obvious that the body temperature of a warm-blooded creature cannot undergo the wide fluctuations of the cold-blooded breeds, it would seem logical for thousands of years of extreme cold, or conversely heat, to bring about at least a moderate change of body temperature.

It has not been easy to prove this one way or the other. Antarctic explorers decided to start with the temperature of the seal. They first had to catch him, then hold him down, avoiding the hard blows of the flippers. Locating the proper body opening in which to insert the thermometer turned out to be far from simple. The anus and vagina of a female seal are separated by a thin membrane. The male seal may know which is which, but the scientist often makes a mistake. Determining even so elementary a matter as sex turns out to be not so elementary. A trained biologist kept a seal under observation for four years under the impression that he was a male. At the end of that time "he" became a mother.

Seal temperature, when finally taken, was found to be just about the same as that of man. Mammals the world over have temperatures of between 98.6°F. and 103°F. Birds have slightly higher ones. The Arctic fox stays out for an hour when the thermometer registers -112°F.; nothing happens to his body temperature. Metabolism, on the other hand, may vary according to external conditions. Rats were caught at the city dump in Fairbanks, Alaska, and studied. Their metabolism rose markedly as the temperature dropped.

The metabolism of polar creatures, as one might expect, tends to be high all the time. The seal, for example, has one of the highest rates among mammals. Still, neither seal, nor rat, nor Arctic fox, nor husky dog can increase his metabolism sufficiently to produce enough heat to counteract an outdoors temperature that is 100 degrees or more colder than his body. He would have to exercise ceaselessly and eat voraciously and constantly all winter in order to obtain sufficient body heat. This would be impossible for a number of reasons, including the most practical, that food is less rather than more abundant during the winter in icy lands.

Instead, polar creatures have evolved in a different manner and keep warm by means of coverings. What clothing does for man, a heavy pelt does for animals. Hairless creatures, like the Arctic pig, are protected by a thick coat of fat. Many animals have a two-layer covering, one of fat and the other of fur. In order to build up the fat layer for the winter, animals consume inordinately great amounts of food during the brief season they can get it easily. The baleen whale gains several tons of blubber each summer. This fat keeps him warm, and in addition, he can live off it during the compulsory austerity to come. Even in more temperate zones animals must prepare for the winter. When the woodchuck continues to search for food until very late in the fall, old-timers in New England predict a long, cold winter. The chuck, they say, knows instinctively that he must gain extra layers of fat to see him through.

The pelt of most furry animals gets markedly thicker in the course of the autumn months and then thins out again in spring. Some animals, like the seal, undergo a complete molt, losing both hair and surface skin. If a seal is pregnant, the embryo will cease its development during this period and stay in the fallopian tube until the fur is replaced. The fur of cold-climate animals is more dense and luxuriant than that of related animals that live in warmer climates. The coat of a husky dog, for example, is thicker by far than that of the Boston terrier. It is so heavy that the husky can snooze comfortably on the snow all night while the thermometer drops to -40°F., and not increase his metabolic rate in the slightest. It is far more difficult for the dog to get rid of the excess heat that builds up when he wakes up and starts running around. Heat prostration would result but for his furless paws and nose. These are an escape route for his body heat. The dog, caribou, and other well-insulated animals pant so as to lose some additional warmth by means of evaporation through their tongues.

Could man survive naked in the cold if, like the husky, he were covered by a thick growth of hair? Some people are convinced that he could and does. In 1920, Lieutenant Colonel C. K. Howard-Bury was climbing Mount Everest when suddenly he saw a set of footprints in the snow. They looked curiously human, except that they were three times the size of a normal man's foot and the toes were widely separated, with the second being longer and wider than the big one. The Sherpas, the native porters who were accompanying him, recognized the prints at once as having been made by a strange "snow creature" that they said was almost human. Their words were mistranslated as "abominable snowman," a name that has stuck ever since.

Many travelers both before and after Howard-Bury claim to have seen such tracks, and some insist that they have seen the "yeti," or abominable snowman. According to one such account, during World War II a Soviet army doctor was stationed with an infantry unit in the snow-covered mountains of Daghestan. One day he was asked to come to the police station to examine a man who had been captured nearby. When he arrived there he was astounded to see that the man was covered with dark brown hair as thick and shaggy as that of a large bear. The face was lightly coated with hair, too. The man—if man he was—was obviously hot and miserable in the house and so the doctor led him outside and completed the examination standing in the snow. The naked, hair-covered creature was clearly more comfortable in the below-freezing air.

Sixteen years later, a Soviet expedition was exploring the Fedchenko Glacier when all at once an animal that seemed at first glance to be a bear came out of a cave. The creature, however, stood up and walked away on two legs, eventually disappearing behind some rocks. The startled scientists reported that he too, was heavily covered with thick reddish-gray hair, and after thinking about it some more, decided he was manlike, not bearlike.

Commenting on these and other abominable snowman sightings, Dr. Boris F. Porshnev of the Historical Institute of the Soviet Academy of Sciences suggested that there may be remnants of Neanderthal man. Somehow a few hardy individuals survived to modern times in the frigid mountain heights, protected from the cold, like animals, by the hair that modern man has lost. Most other scientists consider the abominable snowman to be a furry animal seen by highly nervous people with vivid imaginations.

Returning to polar animals that everyone agrees exist, one learns of adaptations that seem almost as incredible as Neanderthal survival. Who has not puzzled over the way dogs and seals rest poorly insulated extremities on the ice without a trace of discomfort? The secret, physiologists have discovered, lies in what has been aptly named the *rete mirabile*, a Latin phrase meaning "wonderful net," in this case formed of blood vessels. There is a network of veins and arteries at the juncture of limbs to body so arranged that the warm blood flowing out from the internal organs through the arteries heats the cool blood from flippers or paws flowing in through the veins. Artery and vein lie side by side, with the blood in one flowing in the opposite direction from that of the other. The seal rests his flippers on the ice. The frigid blood coming into the seal's body from the flippers is warmed before it reaches the heart, and so the seal's body temperature remains unchanged.

Cold As an Environment

The clumsy manatee slowly makes his way through the coastal waters of Florida. This tropical creature needs the protection of the wonderful net. Even though the climate is warm, the manatee gets chilled during the long hours spent in the water, because more body heat is lost in water than in air. Certain tropical land animals, such as the sloth and armadillo, also possess the network of blood vessels. Their exceptional sensitivity to cold makes this adaptation necessary for their survival. The sloth shivers when the night air falls to below 80°F. The same, to be sure, is true of naked man, and he does not possess the wonderful net.

Travelers who come upon the Arctic pig think that he looks rather pathetic in the cold, as his skin bears an uncanny resemblance to that of man. But unlike man, he does not suffer. To discover what lies behind his apparent comfort, scientists stuck needles with thermometers attached through the pig's skin. Not only the skin, but also a four-inch layer of body tissue was cold. A mechanism similar to that of the miraculous net shunts the warm blood away from the surface. This entire area thus serves as an insulating layer against the frigid air.

The whale, seal, and walrus are protected from the freezing ocean water in this way, too. The layer of fat that covers their bodies is even thicker than that of animals who inhabit the land. The blubber of the sperm whale is fourteen inches thick, and the Greenland whale, who swims in icier oceans, has a blubber coat of twenty inches. About thirty tons of a seventy-ton whale's weight consists of blubber.

The Weddell seal of the Antarctic must have a blubber coat that is three inches thick to protect him from a sea temperature averaging 28.6°F. and an air temperature that can fall to far below zero. The Antarctic world, which seems so harsh to men, is not inimical to him. Even his enemies are comparatively few—the killer whale and vicious sea leopard. The Weddell serves as an almost perfect example of how complete adaptation to a hostile environment can be.

From the very moment of birth he shows a truly incredible

acclimatization to cold. When the membrane ruptures and the pup slips out onto the ice, he goes from the warm 99.6°F. comfort of his mother's body to the zero temperature of an Antarctic spring day. Ice crystals form on his wet little body and his skin temperature falls to 70°F. His shivering mechanism is so efficient that it warms him rapidly and in about three-quarters of an hour his skin temperature is 93.4°F. and his thick baby fur, the lanugo, is fluffing out. The pup is nourished on his mother's milk, which is richer than heavy cream, being half butterfat. On this diet he gains some 250 pounds in just six weeks and his fat coating is thick. The nursing mother hardly eats at all during this period, obtaining the energy she needs by burning her reserves of fat.

By the time he reaches adulthood, the seal is equally comfortable atop or beneath the sea ice. He dives through a hole in the ice cap, plunging deep into the dark waters. Some Weddells can reach a depth of nearly two thousand feet and then travel through the water for about two miles. One seal was clocked recently from the moment he went beneath the surface. He rose to his breathing hole after sixty-five minutes. Pregnant Weddells have been seen to dive with all the abandon of maidens. They, too, have stayed under the water for as long as sixty minutes with no ill effects.

A most unusual physiological quirk gives the seal his ability to perform these seemingly impossible feats. During a dive the blood in the seal's body is shunted away from the surface of his body and his flippers, so as to become concentrated in the vital organs. The heart and brain thus have a steady supply of oxygen. The blood flow to the uterus continues unabated, which explains why the fetus is not hurt when the pregnant female dives.

To prepare for the dive, the Weddell seal must make a breathing hole to which he can return. He selects a natural fissure and saws across the ice with large incisor teeth. His mouth can open almost 150 degrees to facilitate this work. However dark and murky the water, the seal finds his way back to his hole. How he manages to do it remains a mystery.

A form of sonar, the sending of sound waves through water, has been suggested. Or perhaps the seal can actually see well enough to locate the opening. His vision is believed to be very good, and the adaptation from light to dark is exceedingly rapid. Biologists have looked into the eyes of captive seals. In the daytime the pupils are infinitesimal dots; at night they are enormous.

Sonar appears logical, too, because the voices of seals are among the most powerful of all sea creatures. Little has been written about the intelligence quotient of seals, but they are clearly capable of communicating with their peers. One seal signals to another underwater with a variety of whistles, buzzes, beeps, chirps, gurgles, bubbles, and guttural snorts. Do these sounds mean anything specific? Scientists who have gone beneath the sea ice in steel capsules believe that they do. Recordings have been made of a loud trill given by the mature male Weddell in mating season. This sound was first described in the early years of the century by a member of Scott's first expedition. He compared the trill to the "tinkling of water in a cistern." This sound appears to mean that the male has claimed a certain area and certain females as his own. Should another bull seal ignore the trill, a savage underwater battle takes place, and the strongest male wins. When a bull drives away a competing seal, he emits a loud "rr whmp," while the loser responds with a sad "chnk, chnk." Another type of trill on a descending note indicates that a seal is finding his breathing hole. But men in the underwater chamber have heard this noise so often that they believe it must have other meanings, too. And perhaps all the sounds have more than one meaning.

Although seals appear to hear one another, efforts to test the seal's hearing in captivity were hampered in the past by the difficulty of understanding the animal's response. Did the seal hear, and not choose to show it? The recordings of seal cries made in the sub-ice observation chamber at last provided a way to test hearing accurately. The first time the recordings were played by a zoologist in the chamber, a nearby seal hurriedly swam over to investigate and began to imitate the sounds. Another, who had not even been in sight, rushed in and began to bite the transmitter and to hit it furiously with flippers. Perhaps the scientist had recorded a particularly nasty or insulting sound. The one thing certain was that the seals could hear under water.

Each physiological test reveals how well suited the seal is for his rigorous life. The blood is remarkably high in hemoglobin, the red pigment that combines with oxygen and carries it to the cells. If a seal is cut, the blood that flows out is a deep scarlet; the flesh beneath the blubber is maroon.

While the seal or whale can live off his fat for long periods, other, smaller animals must forage for food in the bleak snowy terrain. Like the squirrel in temperate climates saving nuts for the winter, the Arctic fox stores the bodies of lemmings and birds, and eggs, in cracks in the rocks before the winter night closes in. The stored food is carefully covered with pebbles so that no other animal will steal it. A zoologist once found a fox's warehouse. It contained forty-two little birds, all frozen and neatly arranged in a row. Eggs were placed around them. This simple natural freezer allows the fox to have his summer diet in winter, just as Americans eat frozen strawberries in January. Once winter comes, the fox would be hard pressed to find fresh birds to eat.

At a recent symposium on cold acclimatization, Per Scholander told fellow scientists of birds that begin to shiver at temperatures of between 50°F. and 68°F. Their shivering mechanism is effective enough to increase their metabolism by threefold or better. So accustomed are they to being cold that the shivering does not awaken them from sleep.

But these birds are rather exceptional. Cold-hardiness is not an avian characteristic and relatively few can get through an Arctic, let alone an Antarctic, winter. The ptarmigan is conspicuous among those who do. He endures the three-month-long winter night of northeastern Greenland, subsisting on the poorest and most sparse vegetation. Lacking both fur and fat, he is shielded from the cold by a heavy coat of feathers that extends all the way down to his feet and claws. The female is concealed from enemies by a color adaptation. Her feathers are brown in summer and turn white in winter. In this manner the perpetuation of the species is assured.

In the southern hemisphere only one, the most primitive of birds, is equipped to remain near the pole all the year around. The Emperor penguin is a magnificent creature, standing three feet tall on his black flippers and weighing what is for that height a hefty ninety pounds. The penguin is typical of Antarctic creatures in one particular—his low reproductive rate.

On a day in late autumn when the sun appears only briefly in the southern sky, the Emperor penguin mother drops her single egg directly onto the ice cap. She has not built a nest and the temperature is already far below zero, with winter yet to come. But she will not provide warmth to shelter the embryo during that winter night. In fact, before long she will be gone. Soon after giving birth she sets off on a long journey across the frozen terrain to reach the sea and find food. But she does not leave without making provision for her unborn chick; she turns the egg over to a faithful nurse, her mate, the male penguin.

The father Emperor rolls the egg up into the fold of skin that lies above his feet and below the rolls of fat on his stomach. The newly laid egg measures four inches in diameter and weighs just about a pound. The egg is protected from the cold, but the male penguin is not. The winter storms begin and the temperature drops to -70° and -80°F., but still he stands there, dutifully keeping his charge warm. The winds screech mercilessly across the plateau and heavy snow falls from the black winter sky, but the penguin does not go in search of a cave. He does not even bury himself in the snow. When the weather becomes unendurable, he joins with the other incubating males and stands close to them in a tightly packed oval formation, somewhat like a football team in a huddle, presenting his back to the elements. If the ice breaks up, the father penguins in a group move on to a new location and take a stand there. The days go by, and weeks, and still the penguin is faithful, although he has nothing to eat.

At the end of two months the female returns sleek and fat and full of food. Although one penguin looks just like another to a man, she identifies her own mate immediately by his cry. Even if he has moved to a new location during the winter, she will track him down. As if she had a calendar and were checking off the days, her return all but coincides with the moment when the chick, after sixty-two days of incubation, bursts out of his shell.

But the job of the parent Emperors is not over. The chick is frail and almost sure to die if he leaves the protective body of the adult. Still, the foolish chick does try to escape and sometimes succeeds in getting out of the restrictive fold of skin. Any childless penguins who happen to be around converge on the little bird, trying to capture him. The pleasure of cuddling a newborn baby is as strong in the penguin as in any human mother. And each mother or father can recognize his own chick out of a nursery of hundreds or thousands of others that are all the same size.

When the chick is hungry, he puts his little head out of the confining folds and whistles. The mother then regurgitates some of the fish she has eaten and feeds it to the chick. The male, ravenous by then, turns the chick over to the mother and takes his turn in going to the sea. By the time he reaches his destination he will have fasted for three months, a longer period than any other bird can endure. Again the round trip takes two months. Upon his return the male assists the female in feeding the growing chick by regurgitating some of his food. He will not eat again for another two months, until the sea ice breaks up and there is open, fish-filled water near the rookery. Luckily he has enough fat to sustain him.

Like other polar warm-blooded creatures, the penguin's body retains a normal temperature no matter how long he stands fasting upon the ice. Scientists placed a pair of adult Emperors in a pen on the sea ice and induced each to swallow a thermometer. The temperatures of all birds are higher than those of humans, and the penguins were measured at 101°F. Two of their larger chicks were tested, too, and the thermometers read 103°F.

The Adélie, the other species of penguin on the Antarctic mainland, has great cold endurance, but not on a par with the Emperor's. He escapes the worst of the winter night by moving to the outer edges of the ice pack, a little farther from the South Pole. The Adélies mate during the Antarctic summer. When the male sees a female he likes, he rushes to gather pebbles to build a nest. Then he returns and drops the pebbles at her feet, bowing low before her, as if presenting her with pearls and diamonds. The result of this courtship is a fertilized egg laid in summer and incubated for thirty-five days. The embryo develops far more slowly than in birds of temperate zones. By the end of three or four days, the fetus within the egg has barely reached the stage approached by a chicken in a mere fifteen to eighteen hours. Mortality is high; one-third of a group of eggs opened by scientists contained dead embryos. Early in the winter of 1967–68 a severe storm blew up with winds reaching a velocity of 100 miles per hour. Hundreds of adult birds died in the storm; but the death toll among the unborn was greater by far. Thousands of eggs were shattered. Even during a normal fall and winter chicks that are hatched alive are vulnerable to wind and weather. Only one out of every ten of a group of banded chicks lived to the age of three.

Like all newborn animals, Adélie chicks can be transformed into cold-blooded creatures very easily. The turning point comes at nine days of age. Birds that old and older can maintain their body temperatures when the air around them is 32°F.; those who are younger cannot. The younger the chick, the more rapidly his temperature drops to match that of the outside air. Even before that point—when body temperature is anywhere from 42.8° to 53.6°F.—his heart will stop. If the chicks are taken inside, as has been done by scientists at Cape Crozier on Ross Island, the heartbeats resume. Out on the ice shelf, however, the chicks are doomed, unless the parent penguins do as well as the scientists. The older the parent, the better the chick's chances. Penguins seem to learn by experience. After producing and losing one or more chicks, they take better care of the next one.

Mature penguins are remarkably faithful to each other. One couple marked by aluminum bands attached to the legs remained together for five consecutive seasons. About eighty-three percent of couples reunite in breeding season, if both manage to get to the rookery at the same time. It is quite different with young birds. The males, unlike those in other species, are monogamous. They return hopefully to within three feet of the exact spot where they found love the year before. But though they wait, their chances of finding their former mates are not too good. The young females are looking for someone new. Three out of five do not even go to their former site, and those who do may ignore the partner of the past. The divorce rate among young birds is seventy percent.

It may be debatable whether this adds to their curiously human status; everyone is agreed that a penguin resembles a man in a full-dress suit. This is the basis for a story about the Nazi expedition sent to Antarctica in 1938–39 by Adolf Hitler. The German explorers were marching across the ice when a majestic bird waddled out to see what was going on. The Germans hastened to give a Nazi salute and shouted "Heil Hitler," their breaths freezing in the frigid air. The story does not go on to give the penguin's response. On another occasion an Adélie mistook an American for a penguin. The bird rushed to deposit a pebble at the feet of the startled man, apparently thinking him a particularly unusual and choice kind of female penguin.

Studies of Adélies have shown that they, like humans, respond to excitement by a rise in temperature. When a male penguin approaches a female, the temperatures of both climb 1.8°F. in fifteen minutes. Sex is not the only such stimulant. When helicopters fly overhead, the penguins respond in the same way.

The Adélies show an almost human nervous system in other ways, too. A bird may not behave normally for a full week after being caught and banded for scientific study. He will lose interest in his mate or temporarily forget to head to the sea in search of food. Most penguins, fortunately, are banded in infancy. Of 32,748 Adélies banded at Cape Crozier in a seven-year period, only 2,665 were out of the chick stage.

Penguins often share their rookeries with skua gulls, who are hardly ideal companions. At Cape Crozier the rookery held 300,000 penguins and 2,000 skuas at last count. The skuas are bold, hawklike birds with strong, hooked beaks and sharp, curved talons with which they seize their prey. They swallow eggs, tear chicks to bits, and steal food out of the mouths of penguins. Like vultures in other areas, they swoop down viciously on the dead and the dying, as well as on smaller, weaker creatures. Though less is known of skua than of penguin habits, the older birds seem to be as faithful to their mates as are the Adélies.

Fierce though the skua is, scientists have succeeded in taking eggs from his nest for study. One of the two eggs in a skua's nest was sawn in half. The yolk was then replaced with a radio transmitter, batteries, and temperature sensor unit. The albumin was injected back in; then the egg was sealed up and restored to the nest. An antenna fastened overhead picked up the information from within. The temperature inside the egg varied between a low of 87°F. when the parent bird first sat down on it and 103.5°F. when it was fully warm.

Even the skua cannot stand the Antarctic winter and vanishes from the continent with the sun. Like birds in other regions, he responds to cold in just one way—escape. The typical avian adaptation to cold is migration. Birds like cold so little that they flee winter in temperate as well as frigid zones. They fly away from the housetops of London, from the trees in New York's Central Park, to regions of warmth and brilliant sunshine. In spring and summer the Arctic stillness is broken with song, chirping, and the rustle of feathers. The clear voice of the lark rises over the flowering tundra. The eagle, falcon, owl, ptarmigan, raven, and a host of other birds stretch their wings and fly over the green fields and forests. But all these birds vanish in the fall.

Many birds migrate incredible distances—going much farther than they really need. That banded skuas have been found in New Zealand and Australia is not surprising, but how is one to explain why others turn up in Japan and in India? Some years ago a British ornithologist captured and banded a giant petrel chick on one of the South Orkney Islands, just north of the Antarctic continent. When caught, the baby bird could not even fly. Yet only two months later it was seen in Fremantle, Australia, 10,000 miles away. A young petrel was found lying exhausted on a beach in the Easter Islands and another was caught in a fishing net in South Africa. The reason for this erratic pattern is that the fledglings leave their nests and fly away at random. To be sure, any place they reach is likely to be warmer than the one they left and so they may stay there for the winter. Petrels do most of their traveling when young. They mature at six or eight years and from then on journey only relatively short distances from the areas where they breed. And no matter how far they may wander, most of them eventually end up close to the place they began.

The Arctic tern flies 22,000 miles from the Arctic to the Antarctic and back in a ten-month period. In order to do this, he must travel at a speed of more than seventy-five miles a day. The American golden plover, found in summer in the Arctic and northern Canada, flies even faster, covering from 18,000 to 20,000 miles in a six-month trip that takes him to southern Brazil and Argentina and then back along a different route. The related Pacific golden plover of Alaska and Siberia makes his way to Hawaii for the winter months. The curlew and sandpiper leave Siberia each autumn and fly halfway across the world to Africa.

But birds are by no means the only migratory creatures. Huge herds of Arctic caribou gather each spring for the trip from winter grounds in the lichen-covered mountains to the grassy plains below. In the autumn they move en masse again to the seacoast, where they graze on the seaweed.

The fur seal of the Arctic heads south along the coast of California each fall. In May and June he returns and a drama of sexual combat is played out. The great bulls climb out of the water and vie for a good position on the beaches of the Pribilof Islands. Each victor holds a patch of land that is from ten to fifteen feet square. Then the females arrive and the bulls fight again even more desperately, each wanting as many wives as possible. The cows are pregnant and give birth soon after reaching the islands. The male, fearing to lose his mate if he leaves her alone, stays right there all summer, living off his fat.

The fur seals of the Antarctic Falkland Islands migrate in the opposite direction. After breeding during the Antarctic summer, they head north in late April, return briefly in June, and then leave again for the north.

The Pacific gray whales journey from the Bering Sea all the way down to lower California, where the female gives birth to her single twelve-foot-long pup. The sperm whale travels along routes that are so definite and unchanging that they are called "veins." He swims down the veins from the North Atlantic around the Cape of Good Hope to the Pacific. While some fish burrow under the sand to obtain shelter from the cold, others, such as the cod and salmon, travel upstream regularly to their spawning grounds.

What is the secret of migration? No one is altogether sure. Cold alone might be accepted as a cause, because most migratory birds cannot survive low temperatures, but it fails to explain why the fur seal and whale, who can endure almost any degree of cold, nonetheless journey on. The explanation that fits both types of migrator is that cold is the indirect cause. It affects the food supply, which in turn affects the animals. During the winter, food becomes scarce and hard to find. If all animals remained in areas where there is bitter weather, all would starve. Even in reasonably temperate climates, trees lose their leaves before the winter, berries vanish, and the grasses dry up. The competition for the available food would be too great unless some creatures left the area. Both those who migrate and those who stay behind benefit from migration.

But the question remains as to what starts off migration. How does an animal know that there would not be enough food for him and his young if he did not move on? Above all, how does he know when it is time to leave? One might assume that cold of itself serves as the stimulus. Both air and water temperatures do drop slightly when autumn begins. But again, while some creatures set off as soon as the first chill is felt, others anticipate and start their journey some days before the temperature has begun to fall.

Perhaps, said biologists some years ago, the change is within the migratory animal; the size of the sex organs varies with the seasons. They get larger in the spring and smaller in the fall. An increase in reproductive capacity might then be the stimulus for migration. Most animals do migrate before they breed; this is quite essential for the survival of many species. The infant whale, for example, has too little blubber to live in icy seas. The mother could not know this, unless whales possess more highly developed intellects than is generally believed, yet she heads for the warmth to give birth.

These observations led scientists in the early years of the twentieth century right back to changes in the outside temperature, as they assumed that the sex organs declined in size in the cold and grew in the warmth. In September of 1924 juncos were trapped in Canada for an experiment. Each day they were exposed to a decline in warmth and an increasing period of light. The temperature in their cages was dropped, falling slowly from 32° to -52°F. Nonetheless, after a three-month period the juncos' sex organs had grown to the size normally reached in the spring. These birds were released on a day in late November, and immediately flew off to the north, the direction to which they would normally migrate in the spring. This was the first documented proof that increasing day length rather than temperature is the stimulus for migration.

Unfortunately for migrators, day length is not always a sure sign of a change in weather. During April and May of 1967, scarlet tanagers, warblers, and rose-breasted grosbeaks fell dead by the thousands in the countryside of New York and Connecticut. Some had starved and others been killed by cats and dogs who had taken advantage of the birds' stupefied state. The tragedy was a direct result of a failure in migration. The spring had been unseasonably cold, but the urge to migrate is not affected by the temperature. As the days were growing longer, the birds had returned north from their winter home in South America. The cold, however, did not of itself kill the birds; they died for lack of caterpillars, their main source of food. Caterpillars do not migrate and are not affected by day length; they will hatch only when it gets warm.

Knowing why animals travel does not answer the question of how they find their way home. One November a few years ago very young birds of a species that normally migrates from north to south were transported hundreds of miles to the east. They, nonetheless, set off for the south. A number of the birds apparently discovered in some way that they were not heading for the customary destination and changed course in time. Forty Adélies were captured on the bleak coast of Antarctica. After being banded, the penguins were flown 1,500 miles away to the middle of the Ross Ice Shelf and were left there. Two years later three of them arrived back at their home rookery just in time for the breeding season. Somehow they had swum, walked, and tobogganed on their bellies over the many miles of coast and pack ice. A man with a compass could have done no better. Scientists speculate that the penguins navigate by the sun and get their bearings by correlating the time of day with the position of the sun on the horizon. Night-flying birds navigate by moon and stars.

The lemming does not migrate, but he, too, has found a way of escape—in death. This strangest of all forms of polar adaptation—population control—is practiced most conspicuously by this little furred mammal. Most cold-climate creatures reproduce seldom and in small numbers. Not so the lemming. The female is ready for motherhood at the age of three weeks; she remains in heat throughout the summer, and a pregnancy of but twenty days' duration results in a litter of approximately seven babies. Lemmings are active all winter long. During this time the female goes on producing some more litters, although they are smaller in size. She rests from motherhood only in late fall and early spring. This exceptional reproductive capacity helps the lemming to survive the rigors of life in the cold. But every few years there is too much of a good thing: a warm spell in the spring gets the main breeding period off to an early start. The lemming population becomes so large that it would consume all the sparse vegetation of its polar home and leave none for future generations. The species would die out. The lemming does not wait for this to happen; he does not eat today and forget about tomorrow. His response is immediate and drastic: he dies. Shortly before death comes a period of madness. In a country like Norway where fjords lead to the sea, the lemmings may plunge en masse into the water. In other areas they rush about chaotically in a frenzy. The mass deaths of lemmings have stirred the imaginations of all who have observed them, particularly as the phenomenon has been so hard to explain.

Until recently almost all scientists accepted the theory that crowding of itself produces hormonal changes that make it impossible for the animals to reproduce. In more temperate zones crowding does seem to have this effect on reproduction of small mammals. Today there is a difference of opinion and some scientists believe the principle does not hold true for the polar lemming. The latest theory, presented by Dr. David A. Mullen of the University of San Francisco and Dr. William B. Quay of the University of California at Berkeley, is based on the finding that at death the lemmings' bodies contain large amounts of a peculiar blood-borne substance. A newspaper story on this research described it as a sort of "antifreeze." It enables the lemmings to remain lively in the winter at temperatures that would kill other small mammals or drive them into hibernation. Heat is unendurable to lemmings; after a period of warm weather the substance travels to the central nervous system and first maddens and then kills the lemmings.

Mullen warns that such conclusions are premature and need to be proven. He concedes that a substance has indeed been found in blood and brain of the lemming. In addition, a great deal of evidence points to the existence of a pathogen in the body of the lemming that ultimately brings about his death. Perhaps the pathogen and the blood-borne substance are one and the same, but Mullen does not care to say so yet.

There is a less drastic way of leaving a cold area physiologically while remaining there physically. Bats, hedgehogs, chipmunks, ground squirrels, marmots, caterpillars, snails, and many other creatures virtually withdraw from life, going into the state akin to suspended animation that is hibernation. As is true of migration, hibernation is an adaptation valuable not so much as an escape from cold as an escape from the need for food, which gets scarce in the winter.

The hibernating brown bat eats only 130.6 calories a year, while the shrew, which is roughly the same size but does not hibernate, must have 2,628 calories. If the brown bat rested without going into hibernation, he would still need 726 calories. A slowing of bodily functions reduces food requirements.

Hibernation is not truly suspended animation, because the heart continues to beat—three to eight times per minute— and respiration goes on, albeit at a very slow rate. The hibernating Arctic ground squirrel, therefore, needs barely 1/30 to 1/50 of the amount of oxygen he must have when awake, the marmot, 1/100, and the bat barely 1/150.

In the course of hibernation the animal becomes truly cold. Body temperature is a reflection of metabolism, and so a lowering of one results in a lowering of the other. The hibernator's temperature drops until it is close to that of the air in cave or nest. A warm-blooded creature thus behaves like a cold-blooded one. To be sure, there are differences. When the temperature goes below 41°F. the metabolism of the naturally warm-blooded hibernator will increase just enough to keep the vital organs from freezing altogether. Some cold-blooded creatures, such as the snake, also go into a winter sleep when the temperature of their body fluids is so low as to limit activity.

As with migration, the shortening days tell the hibernator that the moment to escape is approaching. Temperature, though, plays a more important role than in migration. A group of thirty-six Arctic ground squirrels was sent into hibernation in a variety of ways in an experiment. First the temperature was retained for some days at a steady 57.2°F. while the number of hours of light declined. The squirrels slowly went into hibernation. They were aroused, and next the temperature was dropped gradually and the day length remained constant. The squirrels began to hibernate earlier. At last both temperature and hours of light were reduced in a close approximation of what usually happens in nature. The squirrels went into hibernation more rapidly and remained in that state for longer than when either stimulus was given by itself. Even though diminishing light can initiate hibernation, cold is essential for maintaining it.

Each fall the dormouse scurries into the nest he has painstakingly built and rolls himself up into a tight little ball. His tiny forepaws are curled up against his cheeks and his tail is wrapped around his head and back. The animal gets so stiff that he can be rolled across the ground like a croquet ball. His tail will not even unwind.

Not all hibernators become so inert; some just appear sluggish. The northern ground squirrel and gopher, to name just two, place stores of berries, seeds, and roots near their winter nests. They awaken every so often to eat and then drowse again. Most hibernators, however, depend on the food of the summer to see them through their entire long sleep. During the spring, summer, and early fall, the hibernator eats and eats, stuffing himself until he bears a heavy coat of fat. He lives on this fat all winter long. Dormice born in the fall usually die because they do not have time to store up the needed fat.

Animals can adapt to changing climate by prolonging or shortening their period of hibernation. P. V. Byeloshyts'kyy of the Ukrainian Institute of Physiology reports that when susliks (ground squirrels) and marmots were carried from their habitat on the steppes to the high Caucasus mountains, their period of hibernation lengthened to take them all the way through the bitter winter. They slept thus for eight and a half to nine months of the year. Vegetation is so scarce there even in summer that the land could not support an animal's active life for more than a few months.

If a man's temperature falls many degrees below normal, nervous activities cease. Quite the opposite, surprisingly enough, is true of the hibernator. Back in 1808 scientist J. A. Saissy stimulated a nerve in a hibernating marmot and watched in wonder as the animal responded. The obvious conclusion that he drew was ignored by his colleagues until nearly thirty years later when Marshall Hall set the record straight: "All writers on hybernation [sic] agree on stating that the sensibility is greatly impaired; it is impossible to commit a greater mistake." The hibernating animal may look insensate, but he is not.

The rising temperature of approaching spring is the stimulus that arouses the animal to complete awakening, whether he has hibernated for one or six months. The heart responds first and beats faster and faster. The increase in the rate of heartbeats is greater than the rise in body temperature would warrant under any other circumstances. It is needed here to provide the first internal warming. Then the muscles begin a quivering so slight that it cannot be seen by the naked eye. It was discovered by means of instrument measurements. Shivering follows. The blood vessels soon constrict in such a way that the warming blood flows first to the head and the vital organs and later to arms and legs. The thin, hungry creature then gets up and comes out of his nest, cave, den, or hole, shakes his head and looks around before beginning his search for food.

There are many degrees of hibernation. The rabbit, fox, wolf, and wolverine extend their night of sleep in the winter months to about fifteen hours. This reduces their food needs markedly. The sleep, though, is not as deep as that of the true hibernator, such as the marmot or chipmunk. The pulse rate goes up, rather than down, during those cold hours.

Certain bears, among them the polar, black, and grizzly, will go into a strange state of semihibernation or winter lethargy. Unlike true hibernators, their body temperatures seldom fall more than four, five, occasionally nine degrees. A scientist shot a hibernating sub-Arctic bear and hastened to take the rectal temperature with a long mercury thermometer. It measured 91.4°F. Others, bolder by far, have tested bears who were not only alive, but not hibernating. The temperature was 100.4°F. A polar bear's den is usually about 40 degrees warmer than the outside air. Unlike the long night sleepers, the bear's heartbeat rate slows gradually over a period of about a week to reach eight beats a minute at night. The number of heartbeats is greater each day at noon, and perhaps this is the time when the female polar bear arouses and suckles her young.

Polar bears, like all cold-climate animals, count on the summer plenty to compensate for the long hunger of the winter. But if the weather remains cold for longer than is normal, food may remain scarce all summer long. The bears can adapt even to that. They dig summering pits and lie in them in a state of estivation, a summertime condition of torpor in which food needs are reduced. This condition is more common among fishes, crocodiles, alligators, tortoises, and frogs, who lie in the mud when summer heat dries up the water they live in. The same adaptation thus serves both tropical and polar animal.

In addition to going into estivation and winter lethargy when necessary, the polar bear may also migrate when food is scarce. No one has yet determined this for certain. Bears are seen in one region and then another, and it has been impossible to tell whether these are the same or different animals. The truth will soon be known, because bears are now being marked like penguins and skuas. The job of tagging, is, to be sure, much harder. The bear is trailed by helicopter and shot in the rump with the immobilizing drug Sernylan. Not sure that the bear is immobile enough, the biologist administers a tranquilizer with a hand syringe before going to work. Then he tattoos a number on the lip of the bear and also marks the back or side with a purplish black dye. This large mark can be spotted from the air. In the future bears might also be tracked by satellite. The National Aeronautics and Space Administration and the Arctic Institute of North America have developed a tiny radio inducer which can be attached to a collar fastened around the neck of an immobilized bear. Readings would reveal the animal's temperature as well as his position. The bear's wanderings are limited to the northern hemisphere, in any event; despite his name, he belongs to but one pole.

A host of adaptations help him to survive there. His heavy snow-colored fur coat, like the feathers of the ptarmigan, fulfills two purposes—insulation and camouflage. The fur coats of many small animals turn white in winter and so they escape capture by larger creatures. The protective coloration of the bear, on the other hand, serves rather to conceal him from his prey than his enemies. The food requirements of the awake, active bear are such that the barren region he lives in can hardly support him. Seals are the chief item in his diet and he can down 150 pounds of blubber at a single meal. This is hardly gluttony for an animal who weighs between 700 and 1,000 pounds and stands eight to ten, rarely twelve, feet high. When he spots a seal sleeping on the ice, the bear will inch his body forward, folding his forepaws under so as to make no noise, and finally pounce. Sometimes the cunning bear will dive into the water, swim under the ice, and tap on it close to the seal. When the frightened seal dives into his hole, the bear is there waiting. He can also find and raid the snow-covered lairs where seal mothers place their pups. Should seals be scarce, polar bears will turn to lemmings, and go so far as to steal eggs from the nests of the elder ducks and snow geese. If even these are lacking, the polar bear will consume grasses, sedges, sorrel, berries, and seaweed. In his hunt for food, a polar bear once came upon a hunter's decoy intended to attract game. He pounced upon the decoy and when he got only a taste of papier-mâché, his rage was terrible to see.

For all his great size, the polar bear is particularly agile. The soles of his paws are covered with stiff bristles and his claws are sharp and pointed so that he does not slip on the ice. Membranes over his eyes filter the glare of sun on snow and keep him from being blinded. Should the bear break through the ice, he will not become chilled by the cold seawater, because his undercoat is waterproof. Although his hearing is poor, the sense of smell is so keen that he can scent a whale or seal from far away.

Still, no matter how well an animal is adapted to meet the rigors of life in a cold climate, he remains in danger, vulnerable to his greatest enemy, man. Hibernation or lethargy may bring him through the winter, but the warm weather brings him out of his lair and into the open, where he can be hunted down for food, for sport, or for profit. A bird may migrate to escape the cold, but hunters live in warm climates, too. The great whooping crane flies 2,500 miles from his summer home on Great Slave Lake in the Arctic to spend the winter in the sunshine of Texas. As the species is in danger of extinction, conservationists are trying to protect it. A safe place has been set up at Aransas National Wildlife Refuge in Texas. Not long ago a hunter shot down one of the world's remaining forty-nine birds as he flew out of the refuge.

What good is the thick pelt of the polar bear, the hairy paws, the membrane over the eyes against a hunter's gun or spear? The polar bear has been considered fair game for centuries. The Romans in the declining years of the empire had hungry bears battle seals in the arena. In the Middle Ages bears were brought to Europe as gifts for kings. They were so highly valued that a single bear could be traded for a loaded ship. In their natural habitat bears have been victims of the Eskimo hunters who seek them out of a need for food and pelts. Not all of the bear's insides are edible. A polar bear liver stew might seem a delicacy, but people who eat it get sick. The bear's liver contains some nine million units of vitamin A, a concentration that is more than the human system can endure. This excess of vitamin A has not helped to save the bear either. During the nineteenth century whalers brought back bears to satisfy the demand for polar bear skin rugs. Until quite recently, an average of 1,000 was killed each year. Travelers to the Arctic now report that bears are not as numerous as they used to be. According to rough estimates, 10,000 to 12,000 survive. The European hunters at least have had sufficiently long-range vision to go after the weaker animals, leaving the stronger to improve the breed. Americans, however, have steadfastly gone after the best bears.

Over the years the bear has been hunted on foot, by dogsled, by boat, and by airplane. Until this last refinement was outlawed, two planes would go after an animal, herding him to an ice floe, where one would land. While the hunter took aim, the other plane would fly around, confusing the bear. The creature's best hope of survival lies not in his native strength and adaptability, but in the restrictions at last being placed on the number of bears that may be killed in a year.

Hunting regulations, unfortunately, can come too late and do too little. The great blue whale is a superb creature, larger and heavier than an elephant. Only thirty years ago 14,500 blue whales swam in the oceans near Antarctica. Whaling has been regulated since 1932, yet today barely 600 blue whales are left. The Southern Right whale was once a valuable source of oil, meat, and bone. American whalers killed 100,-000 of them in Antarctic waters during the nineteenth century. Not long ago skin divers off the coast of Australia found a mother and baby of this breed. These may be all that is left of the Southern Right whale today.

The Steller's sea cow, a whalelike relative of the manatee,

was first seen in the Bering Straits in 1741. He was thirty feet long, reports tell us, and weighed three and a half tons, with a thick layer of fat to keep him warm in the polar water. But the fat was not thick enough to save him from extermination. No one living today has seen a Steller's sea cow. Within thirty years of the first sighting, the breed was wiped out. As for his surviving relative, the manatee, that has now been placed on the U. S. Department of the Interior's list of rare and endangered species.

The seal's fur and blubber—adaptations to the polar environment—have enhanced his value to men. Antarctic sealing became an important enterprise in 1784, and reports of the period reveal that "millions were taken during the next fifteen years." By 1800 barely a fur seal was left on the Falkland Islands, the first major hunting ground. A generation later hunters had turned to the elephant seal and had practically wiped him out when they learned that the fur seal herds had recovered, so they returned to this more profitable species. It took only four years for the herds to be again decimated to the point where four ships were able to catch a total of only 110 seals in an entire season. And while all this was going on, sealers were systematically devastating the seal populations of the northern hemisphere as well. Strict international hunting regulations are now in effect to save the seal from the fate of Steller's sea cow. Still, they allow 100,000 fur seals to be killed in a year.

The sea otter owes his survival to hunting quotas, too. This little mammal's fine coat of fur protects him from becoming chilled by the sea waters, yet in order to put that fur on the backs of women, kings, and mandarins, the sea otter was hunted with ferocity. Only 500 remained extant by 1912. That year Russia, Canada, Japan, and the United States agreed to stop capturing sea otters. It took fifty years for the herds to grow to 40,000.

The future of otters and other animals, too, may depend upon human activities that would seem to bear no direct relation to them. The Atomic Energy Commission has been conducting underground nuclear tests since 1965 on the remote island of Amchitka off the coast of Alaska. With bigger blasts planned, the National Audubon Society and other conservation groups have protested the possible danger to wildlife, particularly to the 2,500 sea otters. While insisting that the tests do not hurt the otters—and anyway there are too many of them in the area—the AEC has arranged for the trapping and transportation of 360 otters to other Arctic regions.

The pervasive effect of man reaches into areas where he is outnumbered by animals. In order to protect crops and people in temperate and tropical zones from insects, large quantities of insecticides have been used. The number of insects in Antarctica is small and insecticides are not applied there. Yet biologists recently found traces of DDT in the bodies of Adélie penguins, crabeater seals, and Antarctic fish. The harmful effect of pesticides on animals is now being recognized and use of DDT is being outlawed in many parts of the world.

A few years ago a small party of scientists drilled deep into the ice sheet at the Army's remote research station, Camp Century, in Greenland. When the ice core they had pulled up was analyzed, lead was found. Lead is a by-product of automotive exhaust. There are no highways in that part of Greenland, yet the lead undoubtedly came from automobiles. Exhaust fumes were carried on the wind from the heavily traveled roads of cities that lay far to the south. Air pollution is bad for everyone. The amount of lead in Greenland is minimal so far, but perhaps some day it could affect the health not only of man, but also of wolves, seals, and husky dogs. The implications for the future are there for all to see. Where on this earth can animals now hide from man?

6

Growth in Cold Soil

On a July day in 1954 Harold Schmidt, a mining engineer, was walking along Miller Creek in the Yukon Territory of Canada. He looked down and there ten feet or more below the surface he spotted some rodent burrows. These, he realized, had been laid open by the mining operations. Suddenly curious, he dug down with difficulty into the frozen soil and uncovered first the skull of a rodent and then about two dozen seeds. He carefully lifted these out and took them home with him.

Schmidt mentioned this finding to some of his friends, but none of them was much interested in what seemed like a very ordinary experience. Yet without quite knowing why, Schmidt could not bring himself to throw away either seeds or skull, but kept them in a dry place. The years went by and then in 1966 Dr. C. R. Harington, a paleontologist and member of the staff of the National Museum of Canada, came to the Yukon for a visit. He asked everyone he met whether there had been any significant finds and in time he heard about Schmidt. The skull and seeds were removed from their storage place, and Harington began to feel that he was on to something big. Schmidt let him take these objects back to the museum in Ottawa for study.

He had already identified the seeds as lupine, a flowering plant that has grown freely in the tundra for thousands of years. But when had these been laid in the burrow? The seeds had been beneath the skull and must be at least as old. It proved easier to set a date for the rodent's skull. It had belonged to the little collared lemming, which had disappeared from the central Yukon 10,000 years ago.

Harington and an associate, Dr. A. E. Porsild, selected the seeds that were in the best condition and put them on a piece of wet paper in a dish. Six of them sprouted within two days. These were later moved into pots in a greenhouse, where they continued to grow like any normal plants. Eleven months later the first of them began to flower. These are the oldest viable seeds ever found. They are more ancient by far than the 2,000-year-old sacred lotus seeds taken from a peat bog in the Far East, or the common weed seeds that sprouted after lying dormant in Denmark for 1,700 years.

What happened to keep the soil around the Canadian lupine frozen for 10,000 years? In the normal course of events the lemming's burrow would have become damp each summer during the thaw. Perhaps a landslide or a volcanic eruption deposited earth or ash over the burrow, smothering the lemming inside and covering the seeds of the flowering lupine. The burrow then sank down into the ground until it reached the permafrost level which remains frozen all year around. There it remained over the centuries. One season after the other passed overhead, while seeds and skull were preserved by the natural refrigeration.

It may be that beneath the frozen soil of other icy lands some seeds from the distant past are lying yet, needing only a moment's warmth and damp to bring them to a new life. One plant, *Rorippa barbaraefolia*, appears only in areas after mining operations begin. It may spring from ancient seeds released from the permafrost by the miners' equipment.

Seeds could survive indefinitely in dry and frozen soil, provided that, like the hibernating animal or larval insect, they are in a state of dormancy. The sleep of the seed is deeper by far, for all metabolism ceases. In addition, the skin or coating gets harder and thicker and the cell becomes dehydrated. Electron microscope photographs of inactive pea seeds show the vacuoles, the tiny sacs of fluid in plant cells, lined up in rows alongside the inner cell walls. They probably protect the cell against the cold and are in a good position to reabsorb water later.

Plants are less cold-hardy than the seeds they spring from. About one-third of the 1,800 varieties of fruit trees grown at the Department of Agriculture's Cheyenne Horticultural Field Station were killed by the cold in the course of a test run continuously for twenty-eight years. Oats have a high winter mortality rate. Farmers in the northern states must be satisfied if half of the oats they plant in the fall survive to produce a crop in the spring.

About once every ten years comes what botanists call a "test" winter when the weather is unusually severe. Many plants fail the test miserably and entire crops are wiped out or severely injured. Sudden extraordinary cold waves are even more dangerous. Completely unpredictable, these can strike in fall, winter, or spring, with devastating effect.

On November 10, 1918, the orchard growers of Iowa and Missouri were content as they looked over their leafy trees and watched the workers picking apples. The following morning, Armistice Day, brought a blizzard and a sudden drop of temperature to zero and below. The men stood by helplessly as their trees died one after the other; three-fourths of the apple and pear trees in the area were destroyed. The peach, cherry, and plum trees were even more frail; only an occasional hardy specimen survived. Within the next fifty years three more late autumn freezes decimated the orchards of the Pacific Northwest—one in 1919, one in 1935, and the most recent in 1955.

One of the worst winter freezes in agricultural history came at the worst possible time—at the height of the great depression of the 1930's. In New York State alone, 2.5 million fruit trees were killed and 3.8 million injured, and the greatest damage, ironically enough, was to trees in the very prime of life. Apple-eating habits of Americans were changed by the freeze. Until then the Baldwin had been the most popular of all with farmers and consumers alike, but as the Baldwin trees died, the hardier McIntosh took their place. In

New York, for example, only two percent of the tart, delicious McIntosh died of the cold.

The South is not safe from an occasional major freeze. A "common place book" kept by an Alabama planter in 1828 tells of an April cold wave—"The most severe ever experienced so late." This man was the first to recognize that some of the plants believed to be dead recovered when they were left alone. This is the one aspect of a freeze that can give a farmer any grounds for hope. The yellowing pages of Georgia newspapers of 1849 describe another April freeze that damaged farms and gardens in all southern states.

The question of why some plants live through cold and others die of it has been baffling scientists for generations. At one time a simple and seemingly logical explanation was given: plant cells contain a good deal of water; because water expands when it freezes, the ice crystals break the cell wall and kill it. This sounds logical, but it does not happen. This theory was overturned in 1830 when a German scientist studied hundreds of frozen plant cells and discovered that not one of them had ruptured. Years later the reason for this was found. The plant cell has a logic of its own. As it freezes the cell contracts and becomes dehydrated. This leaves space between the cells and the ice crystals form outside there. Extracellular ice, observations of all living things reveal, is not lethal.

But eliminating cell rupture as a cause of death does not eliminate death. And the theory favored by most botanists today is far more complex. When a cell is frozen, the cellular water contracts. This subjects the protoplasm within the cell to a series of stresses and strains that are beyond its endurance.

One difference, then, between plants that live and those that die in the cold is the presence of some mechanism to reduce the strain on the protoplasm. Sugar provides some defense against cold for plants as well as animals. Cells with a high sugar content hold their shape better than others and do not contract as much. Plants which become relatively dehydrated in the winter have an advantage. The cells change less in size when frozen. In 1903 botanist F. T. Shutt was able to show that shoots of frost-resistant apples contained less cellular water in the winter than apples that were easily injured by cold. Plants, however, provide frustration for those who would like to make hard-and-fast laws. Rye is a notable exception to the general rule of dehydration; it is frost-hardy, although its cells have a high water content.

Frost-hardiness is a well-chosen word, because cold-climate plants go through a process of "hardening." If grains, for example, are planted in the spring, they will never become able to resist the cold. But fall planting enables the very same wheat to change in ways that will allow it to live through the winter. As the temperatures gradually decline, the plant "hardens off" and becomes steadily more cold-resistant. One farmer complained that his cabbage seedlings were killed when the temperature fell to 26.8°F. shortly after planting. Yet it is well known that such plants have endured chilling to -4°F. without injury if they have first lived through a six-week period of slowly falling temperatures.

Frost-hardiness varies not only from species to species and variety to variety, but even in a single plant depending on the season, points out Dr. J. Levitt, botanist at the University of Missouri.

Like most living things, plants can stand much more cold when dormant or resting than when they are actively growing. Snap off an evergreen needle in January; it is obviously frozen stiff. But if one returns to that same tree in late spring, it is alive again. Ice crystals had formed but could not do harm while the tree remained inactive.

The roots alone remain sensitive when a plant is dormant. Fruit and nut tree roots are injured if exposed to temperatures lower than 20°F. Fortunately, as they are covered with soil and possibly snow, they are seldom exposed.

The words "dormant" and "resting" are not synonymous in the plant kingdom. Although these conditions are identical, the cause can be different. A rest period is brought about by the internal workings of the plant only, while dormancy is a response to the external world as well. The resting period is an extra safety device. Some days in fall or early winter are balmy enough to allow unseasonal growth. Nothing could place a plant in greater danger. Frost is sure to come soon. If the plant put out tender young shoots, it would be instantly destroyed in the first cold spell. The rest period, however, keeps a plant inactive regardless of the weather outside. The rest period must end naturally before the plant is ready to respond to the coming of warmth and moisture. After resting through the winter, it awakes in the spring.

S. H. Rumph, the botanist who bred the Elberta peach, in 1890 described some strange aftereffects of an unusually warm winter in Georgia. The peach trees usually bloomed in February and March, he reported, but that year the first flowers did not appear until April and had hardly any petals. Stranger yet was the fact that the trees did not put forth their leaves, though the month was May. Rumph concluded that this was "the most peculiar and disastrous season ever witnessed." The reason for the peculiar spring was made clear thirty years later when botanists discovered that the peach, like many plants, cannot grow, flower, and produce a crop if it has not been chilled during the winter. The Elberta peach will flourish only if it has been exposed to 850 hours of temperatures of 45°F. or lower; the pecan must have 500 to 800 hours, the apple between 900 and 1,200.

The length of the rest period is not the same for all species and is one of the criteria by which frost-hardiness can be measured. A short resting period is highly desirable in the South, where it promotes a long growing period; in the North, this could be disastrous. The few warm days in late winter or early spring will encourage an ill-fated growth spurt. The number of balmy days needed following the rest also varies among the species and varieties. Plants that bloom late are likeliest to survive in areas where winters are cold and are the best choice for farmers and gardeners there. The number of variables make selecting plants for cold-resistance very difficult. Theoretical knowledge does not lend itself easily to practical application. As sugar has been found to give protection against freezing, botanists selected wheat strains with high sugar content and bred them together. These should have produced cold-resistant wheat, but the offspring turned out to be in no way remarkable in their ability to get through the winter.

The only way of being sure that a tree, grain, flower, or shrub is frost-hardy is to plant it and then see what happens. In 1949 plant breeders began the development of a hybrid bromegrass. This is the chief perennial forage crop of Alaska, yet every winter much of the acreage dies off. Many varieties of the grass were gathered and planted at Matanuka Farm, an experimental area open to the fierce Alaskan climate. The winds blew violently across the fields, scattering the snow that might otherwise have provided insulation against the below-zero temperatures. Some of the bromegrass died and was weeded out. The hardiest plants remaining were bred together and set out the next season. And so the years went by. The winter of 1961–62 was a particularly severe one. Nearly half of the bromegrass in that part of Alaska was wiped out. But the hybrid on the experimental farm stood firm. A satisfactory crop was harvested, and the breed was adopted commercially. Only after such a rigorous test can any frost-hardy plant be safely recommended to farmers.

Plants indigenous to cold climates are naturally desirable for breeding stock. An ornamental evergreen vine was plucked high up on Mount Tsukuba in Japan by Dr. John L. Creech, a plant explorer for the Agricultural Research Service of the U. S. Department of Agriculture. He brought it back to the United States, where it was planted and grown, and in time cuttings were taken and sent to horticulturists in the northern states. This vine proved capable of living through temperatures as low as -25°F.

The privet hedge that provides privacy and an air of formality to gardens in states with moderate winters has always been vulnerable to cold and could not be grown in the northern prairie and eastern great plains states. A privet hedge discover :d in Yugoslavia offers the first hope to gardeners in those areas. It is the only privet that ever survived several winters at the Horticultural Field Station in Cheyenne. A hundred years ago cold-hardy pear trees were brought to this country from northern China. Most of the pears now grown in the eastern states are hybrids of those trees. The Department of Agriculture is always looking for frost-resistant plants. Several years ago it advertised a prize of $25 to anyone who could bring in a hardy fruit tree. That tiny reward proved enough of a lure to obtain an apricot tree from Michigan that not only produces delicious fruit, but also can endure the severe winters of the northern states.

Cold snaps kill plants in south as well as north, so warm-climate crops must also be bred to a degree of frost-hardiness. Between 100,000 and 200,000 tons of sugarcane have been lost to freezing in Louisiana in recent years. Because cold comes to Louisiana infrequently, cane for breeding is shipped to Meridian, Mississippi, a southern area with surprisingly cold winters. Smaller test crops are raised in a refrigerated room where the temperature is maintained at about 23°F.

Only the fittest survive at all in a rigorous breeding method used by the Department of Agriculture. The seeds of many different breeding lines of a crop such as wheat are planted and eventually the seedlings come up. These are cut down and the crown root, the place where stem and root are joined, is removed. The crown roots are sealed in plastic bags and first frozen and then thawed. Those that slowly put out stunted tendrils are discarded, while those that grow vigorously are selected for fall planting.

Some of the methods for protecting plants from cold are nearly as old as agriculture itself. Who can trace back through the ages to the farmer who first thought of planting trees or shrubs as a windbreak for young and delicate plants?

And how many times, in how many countries, have farmers whose crops have been destroyed a number of times moved out of an area altogether? Some years ago a severe freeze killed many of the orange trees in northern Florida. The planters, wishing to protect themselves against such hazards in the future, moved their groves farther south. The years went by and the trees grew and bore fruit. There were no cold spells and the size of the orange crop increased from season to season. Eventually some of the orange growers began to worry that the price of oranges would drop because of the oversupply and to hope that a freeze would reach down to the groves and injure some of the trees—those belonging to the other planters, of course.

In time, to be sure, a freeze did come; no area is immune. Temperatures dropped to 17°F. The extensive use of heating devices saved the citrus crop. In ancient times fields were warmed during cold spells and chilly nights with charcoal braziers or small twig or turf fires. The heater used now is different, the technique the same.

Many plants have curious adaptations that enable them to live in climates that are actually too cold for them. On a walk through the northern woods in winter, one will never come upon the little strawberry plants; yet they are there, hidden beneath the snow or a mulch formed of rotting leaves and mud. In the summer the luscious-looking little red berries will peek out again. Strawberries are not really cold-hardy; they can endure the winter because they grow so near to the ground that they can easily be sheltered by an insulating layer of snow or mulch. The brilliant red cranberry looks like a fruit of the tropics, yet the bogs where it grows are in northern climates. The bog environment is the secret of the cranberry's endurance. The swamp water covers the plants and protects them from the cold air during the winter months. The cranberry farmers of Massachusetts, Wisconsin, and Washington create artificial bogs and, if necessary, artificial rain. Frost may come late in the spring and kill the frail cranberry blossoms. Sprinklers, therefore, are placed alongside the synthetic swamps. During a cold snap, a fine spray of water plays over the bog and protects the growing leaves.

Some regions are so frigid that neither natural adaptation, breeding, heaters, nor windbreaks can make it possible for food crops to flourish. In northern Canada and other areas close to the Arctic Circle, the fierce climate makes it particularly difficult to raise wheat, vegetables, and fruit. The winds are high in the polar spring, and the soil, after the heavy weight of snow has melted, is too wet for planting to begin for three or four weeks. A good percentage of the short growing season is lost right there. Two scientists at the University of Manitoba, Winnepeg, Dr. Lucien J. LaCroix and Dr. Kurt Schreiber, have suggested that seeds of many crops be coated with protective substances and planted in the fall. They would thus be in the soil ready to sprout at the first moment of warmth, regardless of surface conditions. When the ground freezes, the outer layer, made principally of polystyrene plastic and beeswax, cracks. The seed is still covered with a thin coat of methylcellulose and another innermost layer. The scientists call this the "spring jacket," and it is composed of loam, talc, sugar, glycerin, and other substances prepared so as to dissolve when the ground thaws. The coats are timed, like the slow-release drugs, to disappear on schedule when the seed can begin to germinate—late April in Manitoba. Early experiments with coated seeds have gone very well. This method may someday make farming possible in areas even colder than Canada, regions where crops have never been raised.

Right now, in any event, farm and garden losses could be greatly reduced by proper selection of plants. The Agricultural Research Service has prepared a "Plant Hardiness Zone Map" of the United States and Canada that tells which crops, trees, shrubs, and flowers can survive the cold in any given area. This vast region has been divided into ten zones, according to the average annual minimum temperature of each. Examples of the types of plants that can be grown successfully in each zone are given. Some plants can get through the winters in zones colder than the one recommended, but they are stunted there and slow to bloom. Consider Zone 10, then, that warm, almost tropical region of southern Florida and California, where the temperature rarely falls below 30° to 40°F. even in winter. This is the land where the bougainvillaea blooms, where the royal palm stretches its fronds skyward, and the heavy clusters of fruit cling to the banana plant. Moving northward, we come to Zone 6, where the thermometer reading on a winter's day can range from zero to -10°F. This zone runs across the continent in a huge semicircle from Newfoundland in the north, across to Kansas, down to New Mexico, and up to Washington and British Columbia. This is still good country for plants, and one can see the flaming leaves of the Japanese maple, the green of English ivy clinging to oak or wall, and the tiny red berries of the American holly. The boundaries of the United States reach up to Zone 3, to minimum temperatures of -30° to -40°F. In this region grow the Japanese barberry, common juniper and Siberian crabapple. The coldest zones the map presents are in Canada. Winter temperatures fall to -40° to -50°F. in Zone 2, which spreads over much of that country from Quebec to British Columbia. It, too, is not devoid of plant life and the American elm, paper birch, and American cranberry bush are among the many varieties that can thrive. Higher plant growth takes place even in truly frigid Zone 1, where the thermometer drops below -50°F. in the long, dark winters. The dwarf birch, the quaking aspen, the netleaf willow, and the Lapland rhododendron are barren of leaves for the major part of the year, but they are alive.

No climate the earth has to offer is too harsh for some kind of plant to withstand it. Even beyond the earth some simple forms of life may grow. Lichen and moss might be clinging to the dry, red soil of Mars. On earth the Arctic itself is known to botanists as the "friendly Arctic."

"The Arctic tundra is full of plants; it is plant rich," says Dr. William Steere, of the New York Botanical Garden.

Some of the soil above the permafrost thaws each summer to allow plants to revive. During the long days of the brief Arctic summer, the flat, rolling plains are brilliant with the blue larkspur, the yellow mountain saxifrage and dandelion, the red fescue, and the green fern fronds.

"The number of species is small. Many more evolve in the tropics," comments Steere, "but the plants that are found there, like the animals, are more unusual in their adaptations."

Plants are opportunistic and seem almost to seize upon the summer to grow twice as fast as similar species in more temperate climates. Shoots are put forth swiftly; they achieve a full, albeit brief, maturity, hurrying through the growth and reproductive portions of the life cycle before the warmth departs.

The northern end of Greenland is bone dry, yet its plant life is far richer than that of any desert. As far as the eye can see are the high prairie grasses and sedges, the small tufted shrubs and trees, the type of growth found in the Alps or the high Rockies.

No trees can grow beyond a certain latitude in the far north and in the far south. The tree line extends close to the Arctic Circle and at some points, as in Norway, goes well north of it. In the lonely Arctic forests the striking white and black spruce, the graceful birch, hemlock, pine, fir, and red cedar rise tall and thin, pushing their topmost branches toward the sunlight.

Throughout the Arctic the velvety mosses hug the ground. Crusts of green, orange, or black lichen cover tree trunks and rocks. They do not look like plants, lacking as they do true roots, stems, leaves, and vascular systems. The physiological needs of the lichen are so easily satisfied and they are so sturdy that they can survive under conditions that would seem to preclude life. In certain areas, therefore, they are the only plants to serve as forage for the caribou, which are in turn a major food for the Eskimos.

It is surprising to most vitamin-conscious Americans that even in places where plants are plentiful, the Eskimos have never cared for them as food. Today the Arctic is no longer so isolated and the Eskimos' dietary habits are changing. But they are still animal rather than plant oriented. Their only concession to a vegetable diet in the past was a tradition of eating a kind of cress that grows along the shore each spring. This provided an antiscorbutic and digestive aid. For the rest of the year they staved off vitamin-deficiency diseases by eating every part of an animal.

Plant diseases, particularly rusts, are fairly common in the Arctic. Botanists view this as a good sign: "It seems paradoxical that plants must be both numerous and healthy enough to support disease," declares Steere. "If they were unhealthy, the disease organisms would kill them all off. In the Antarctic so few plants grow that there are few plant diseases."

The Antarctic appears bare and hostile to a botanist or plant lover. "As far as the eye could reach and glasses range, not a particle of vegetation existed," wrote J. D. Hooker, a botanist accompanying an Antarctic expedition in 1843. He was apparently ignoring the lichen that had been described twenty-two years earlier by Captain William Napier. Soon after putting down his gloomy observations, Hooker found a few lichens himself.

Today we know that Hooker was too pessimistic. Plant life is more sparse than anywhere else on the globe, but some has emerged on the continent wherever the ice is broken, in the sea, beneath the ice. There are even two flowering seed plants in the Antarctic—a grass and a pink. They are small and grow in clumps hugging the ground in wet, protected places on the northern part of the Antarctic peninsula. Like the Antarctic insects, the flowering plants have some close relatives in New Zealand, South America, and South Africa, providing another hint of an ancient linkage.

The main vegetation is made up of the hardy lichens and mosses. When he began his study of Antarctic lichens thirty years ago, 208 species had been identified, recalls Carroll W. Dodge of the University of Vermont. In the course of his work he learned of more than 400, and many areas on the continent have not yet been investigated. Some species exist in the Antarctic only. Perhaps again, like the insects, they are survivors of an earlier, less frigid era in Antarctica. Unlike the pink and the grass, lichens do not require protection from the elements. Let a rock peek out through the snow, and they will rapidly appear on it. Their reproductive cells are carried by the wind or by skua gulls from one area to another, catching hold wherever they can. Their need for water is smaller by far than that of higher plants and in some areas lichens absorb water vapor from the air. When the air is too dry, as is true of most of the Antarctic, they take water from infinitesimal trickles of melting snow. While the Antarctic never loses its ice cover altogether, a little melting occurs each summer. As the sun shines without cease, the rocks and the surface of the snowfields are warmed at least occasionally to above the freezing point. Every so often a summer snowstorm blows up, and the snow falls on the warm rocks, melting at once. The lichens live on just such moments. Temperature variations of 50 degrees in a single day do not disturb their growth.

Little like plants though they seem, lichens must have sunshine in order to perform photosynthesis and grow. They can find enough light not only in the height of summer, when the Antarctic sun never sets, but also in the fall, when sunset follows sunrise by a mere four hours and the temperature drops to 14°F. Only in the endless night of winter do they cease all metabolic activities. In some parts of the Antarctic, dormancy lasts a mere two months—for June and July. In August the lichens are beginning to awaken and by September, with just a few hours of sunshine, they are growing vigorously again.

The mosses, which comprise the second large plant group in the Antarctic, are nearly as resilient. Moss is usually described as a small green plant. This definition would be true, but not the whole truth, in the Antarctic, where the mosses take on startling colorations. The ultraviolet rays sent down by the never-setting summer sun are so intense that they would injure pale-colored plants. Displaying what Steere likes to describe as the "inventiveness" of living things under rigorous conditions, the mosses have evolved in red, brown, or purple colors that act as a filter.

Mosses were collected by Hooker, the gloomy botanist, in the 1840's. They had actually been observed some years earlier by James Eights, who served as naturalist to an Antarctic expedition in 1829–30. This finding of Eights was then forgotten for many years. Eights had given a passing mention to his collection of mosses in a paper about a new crustacean that he wrote in 1833 for a small journal. Both journal and paper remained in obscurity until they turned up again by chance recently. Eights had been a man of quite exceptional efficiency, and so botanists began to look for his collection of mosses. If he had gathered mosses, he had surely made some provision for their preservation. The curator of the Herbarium of the New York State Museum was called on and asked to look through his folders. It was not long before he triumphantly pulled out a folder of Eights' botanical specimens, but to the dismay of the interested scientists, not a moss was in it. Some time afterward a botanist borrowed the master folder of Antarctic mosses from the Herbarium in order to do some research. When he opened it, two packets of dried mosses, labeled as belonging to Eights, fell out. Three species were in the packets. When water was added to them, they came to life at once. These mosses of a century and a quarter ago are identical to species that are abundant in the Antarctic today. "If you took Eights' samples and threw them on the ground near McMurdo Sound, you would not see any difference between them and the mosses that are now there," declares a botanist.

The general botanical classification of mosses includes another group of flowerless plants that grow flat against the ground. Known scientifically as hepatics and popularly as liverworts, at least twelve species have been found growing along the Antarctic peninsula and at the east end of the continent as well.

No one knows exactly how many different species of mosses have been found in the Antarctic. Every so often, the leader of a botanical field party will announce that a new species has been discovered, and he gives it a new name. The moss is dried and brought back to a laboratory for more careful study, and in time it appears that the only thing new is the name. A succession of scientists with Antarctic expeditions has discovered the same species over and over again. Some of the early researchers were convinced that each part of the continent had its own plant life that was completely different from that of all other regions. They refused even to consider that the same species might be found in more than one area. In their writings, therefore, one species of moss may have half a dozen names if it was found in half a dozen places. Botanists today are trying to pull together all the data and determine just how many there are.

Antarctic mosses, like the other plants on the continent, are much smaller than their relatives in other parts of the world. The harsh climate supports marginal, not luxuriant, growth. The mosses there do not reproduce by means of spores, as most others do elsewhere. The reproductive organs are present, it is true, but the males do not get together with the females. The dryness of the climate may be responsible; many plants lack a film of water in which one organ could swim to the other. As a substitute for sexual activity, many of these mosses reproduce vegetatively by budding at the tips.

Telling the age of an Antarctic moss is an impossible task for botanists. Tufts growing in the United States and the Arctic contain seasonal growth lines, something like tree rings, that can be detected and counted with a little care. These are not present in the south polar plants. The environment is so harsh that mosses must grow when and if they can. Should the temperature rise a little and a bit of moisture become available, they function. But this friendly world can change in a moment. The Antarctic summer does not offer a succession of favorable days. All at once the temperature falls, the water dries up, and the bitter winds howl. The mosses then simply stop growing and wait for the next opportunity.

"Mosses are so marginal that they live on the very edge of life," explains Steere.

Perhaps that is why they are protected by decree. As the Antarctic became more accessible to man, a legal code was drawn up. It contained no law against murder on the Antarctic continent. Yet it is illegal to walk upon the mosses.

Part Two

Cold and a New Era in Medicine

✳

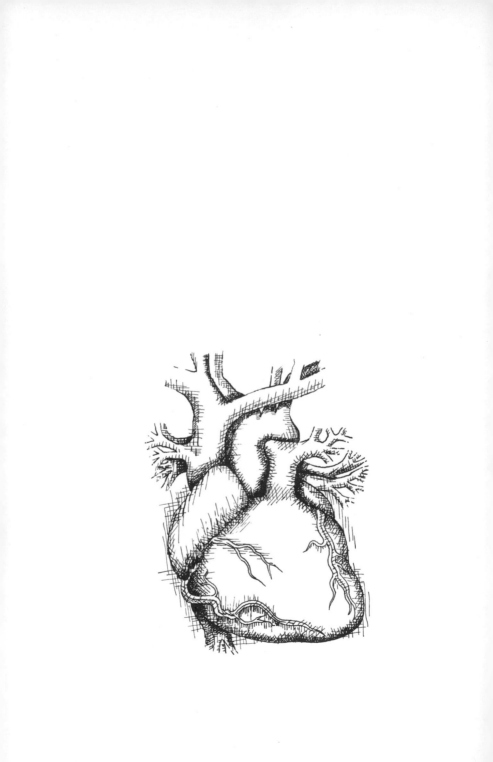

7

Take a Cold Heart

"On 3 December 1967 a heart from a cadaver was successfully transplanted into a fifty-four-year-old man to replace a heart irreparably damaged."

With these simple words Dr. Christiaan Neethling Barnard of South Africa began his description of the most famous operation of our time.

Barnard's patient, Louis Washkansky, was a wholesale grocer, married, and the father of a fourteen-year-old boy. The first of the heart attacks that were to damage his heart "irreparably" took place in 1960. By the time he was admitted to Capetown's Groote Schuur Hospital in the early fall of 1967, he was a dying man. In November, Barnard came to Washkansky's bedside and suggested the substitution of a strong heart for his weak one.

"I was petrified," Washkansky's wife, Ann, said later, "but my husband had such confidence in medical men that he inspired me as well."

Once he agreed, there was nothing to do but wait for someone to die so that Washkansky could have another chance to live. On the first Saturday in December, pretty, dark-haired twenty-five-year-old Denise Ann Darvall ran across the street to reach a bakery where she meant to buy a cake. Struck by a car, she never arrived. Instead, still alive, she was rushed to the emergency room at Groote Schuur Hospital. Doctors found that she could not possibly live for more than a few hours. Barnard was called, and he seized the moment. He went to Denise's father and asked for the young woman's heart.

"I gave the doctors permission to remove my daughter's heart and kidneys and donate them to other persons if it could save their lives," the father told reporters. "It was shortly before midnight that I was informed she was dying."

Less than an hour later Denise was pronounced dead and Washkansky began to receive anesthesia. Now the donor's heart had to be kept from deteriorating. In the natural course of events, a dead body will become cool given enough time, but by then the internal organs have undergone harmful changes. To prevent this, Denise's body was chilled until the thermometer registering the temperature in the esophagus stood at 78.8°F. The heart itself was cooled further, to 60.8°F. Finally the organ was taken from the dead body. "The excision," reported Barnard, "had taken two minutes." The heart was placed in solution in a bowl and chilled to 50°F.

The critical phase of the operation was approaching. In a neighboring operating room Washkansky was hooked to a heart-lung machine, which was to circulate the blood through his body without the help of any heart. And at this moment when it was necessary to help Washkansky endure the stress of the surgery, Barnard turned to cold. The patient's body temperature was lowered to 76°F., then to 71.6°F., and finally to a low point of 70.88°F. The very changes in metabolism brought about by a low body temperature, known clinically as hypothermia, are those that transform a dangerous operation into one that is at least reasonably safe. Hypothermia is a medically-induced form of hibernation and it produces many of the same effects: the colder the body, the more slowly it functions. The time spent between hearts, therefore, can be less damaging. At 86°F. metabolism is only half that of normal. The need for oxygen keeps dropping. When the temperature reaches 89.6°F., which is not very far below normal, the system's oxygen requirement is down by a third, and by 78°F., it is off by between seventy-five and eighty percent.

Washkansky's heart was removed from his cold body and then the heart that had once belonged to Denise Darvall was carefully deposited in the empty space and sewn in place. The new heart was in the body, but no one in the operating room was sure that it would ever beat again. It might be incapable of supporting life for so much as a moment. A single electric shock was given to the transposed heart; it stirred in response and then began to beat. "Christ, it's going to work," muttered Barnard behind his surgical mask.

The heart beat at a rate of 120 per minute. (Barnard's, according to *Time* magazine, which apparently keeps watch on such things, was racing at 140 beats a minute just then.) The heart-lung machine was removed, and the heart kept on and circulated blood through Washkansky's body, which had been gradually rewarmed.

The next morning news of what had happened in Capetown appeared on the front pages of newspapers the world over and millions joined Barnard in following Washkansky's fight for life. The reports noted that Washkansky regained consciousness, chatted with his doctor, and became hungry enough to swallow a soft-boiled egg. His heart rate by then had slowed to 100 beats a minute. Interviewed on television, Washkansky complained that he was tired of lying in bed, and joked, "I'm a Frankenstein now. I've got somebody else's heart." (He was not being accurate; Frankenstein in the novel of that name was the doctor, not the monster.)

Everything seemed to be going well and then thirteen days after surgery Washkansky contracted pneumonia. He did not live through it; that, too, is history, but the fact that his transplanted heart had worked at all gave hope to others.

By December 21, the date of Washkansky's death, other doctors were performing or planning transplants, and the impossible was beginning to seem very possible indeed.

In the many accounts of the first operation, a great deal was written about the skill of the surgeon. "It was like watching a bullfight. Certain classical maneuvers had to be done before the grand finale," said one of Barnard's associates. Little was told, however, about the technique that Barnard had applied during the long, arduous operation—hypothermia.

Cold and a New Era in Medicine

The significance of hypothermia in heart operations had been recognized long before the initial transplant. Its life-saving properties were being regularly called upon for open-heart surgery. Even if the heart remains in the body, it beats more slowly, reducing the strain on it immeasurably. When the patient is cooled to 82.4°F., his heart rate is but fifty-eight percent of normal. The blood flow naturally diminishes as well, falling to barely ten or fifteen percent of its former speed at a temperature of 68°F.

Hypothermia alone was found to be sufficient in the early days of open-heart surgery when operations were comparatively brief. But correcting complicated heart defects or transplanting a heart takes so long that cooling may not always be enough to protect the patient. For this reason Barnard employed a machine to take over functions of heart and lungs temporarily.

The original idea for a heart-lung machine came to Dr. John H. Gibbon, Jr., as early as 1931, when as a research fellow in surgery at Harvard University, he watched a woman slowly die of heart failure following the removal of an embolism. With the help of his young wife he constructed a machine that he said later looked like a Rube Goldberg apparatus. Still, it succeeded in keeping a cat alive for thirty-nine minutes. Gibbon went on to improve the machine and to perform experiments with dogs. All of this took years and he did not feel ready to try his machine on a human patient until 1953. The candidate was then an eighteen-year-old girl with a heart defect so serious that lengthy surgery was needed. The girl spent twenty-six minutes on the machine. Then her own heart and lungs were able to take over. She recovered, and the heart-lung machine became part of standard operating room equipment.

Another of the early open-heart operations was performed at the University of Minnesota by Dr. John F. Lewis, one of the first proponents of hypothermia for surgery on the heart. Among his associates at the university was young Christiaan Barnard. Hypothermia gained wider recognition as time passed, and the number of long, complicated heart operations increased. Congenital heart abnormalities were corrected in the newborn. Even pregnancy was found to be no bar to successful surgery, and several women subsequently gave birth to normal babies. Men and women who had been clinging precariously to life for years were restored to health. In 1965 a thirty-five-year-old housewife was dying. Born with a heart malformation, every moment of her life had been a struggle. With indomitable willpower, she had managed to finish school, get married, and adopt a baby girl. Still, willpower was not enough, and at last it seemed that her battle was approaching its end. She was saved in the end, as countless others have been, by two things—a surgeon's skill and hypothermia. The operation became possible only because she was cooled to a temperature of 68°F. A month after surgery she returned home. When interviewed by a reporter for a news magazine a year later, she remarked cheerfully that she was planning to learn to play golf.

Despite such successes, the low temperatures used during open-heart surgery did increase one of its risks. When the body is cooled to below 82.4°F., certain muscle fibers in the heart may begin to quiver independently and without rhythm. Nearly a third of heart patients operated on under hypothermia between 1955 and 1958 suffered this condition of ventricular fibrillation. And during this period temperatures were dropped only moderately. Then deeper hypothermia was tried as a way of reducing metabolism further and thus increasing the safety period for the operation. Some patients recovered easily; in others, however, the extreme chilling produced the arhythmic heart quiver. Three-quarters of a group of people placed under deep hypothermia at Duke University Medical Center developed ventricular fibrillation. Fortunately, by this time methods of coping with the condition had been found; drugs or electric shock stopped the quivering before it killed the patient. Still, in the words of Dr. C. Ronald Stephen of Duke University and a pioneer in this field, "ventricular fibrillation is the *bête noir* of the hypothermic state." Whatever its drawbacks, body cooling has helped to bring mankind into the organ transplantation era.

This age of medicine began in December, 1954, when a kidney was successfully transplanted for the first time. There had been previous efforts, but each had failed. Then a patient different from all his predecessors entered Peter Bent Brigham Hospital in Boston. The difference might seem to have nothing to do with the kidney: he was an identical twin. Dr. Joseph E. Murray asked the other twin to donate a kidney. While the donor of a heart or liver must die before he can give it up, the donor of a kidney can live with the one he has left. And so the operation took place, and the patient recovered.

The reason for his survival—and the main reason for the other failures—lies in the body's refusal to accept foreign cells. This mechanism is otherwise essential to health, as it enables the system to fend off an invasion of germs. When a stranger's kidney or other organ is implanted, it, too, is recognized as unnatural and is gradually rejected and killed. Identical twins, alone among mankind, can pass tissues or organs from one to the other without triggering this mechanism. There are so few identical twins in the world that the chances are slim that anyone will both need a kidney and be a twin. The next best donor is a relative. Transplant surgeons today estimate that there is an 80 percent chance that a kidney passed from one relative to another will function for five years. Twins do better; several who were among the first recipients fifteen or so years ago are still alive.

Despite the obvious advantage of a twin or relative donor, the transplant era was barely in its second decade before a psychiatrist was darkly questioning the wisdom of taking kidneys from relatives willy-nilly. What if a child bitterly resents the sister who has given her kidney? What if he were overattached to his mother, even before she made the sacrifice? A trauma might result. No evidence exists as yet as to neurosis. And it seems highly unlikely that anyone would go so far as to decline a kidney from a relative he disliked. There was one case, however, in which a potential donor's wife talked him out of giving a kidney to his ailing brother. One of his children might need it later, she pointed out. Other wives (or husbands) might do the same if given an opportunity. Twelve donors were questioned by members of the Psychiatry Department of the University of Wisconsin's School of Medicine; eight had made the decision without consulting a spouse.

Whatever the effect on others, most donors feel that they have performed the most important act of their lives. "I had always known that God had been saving me for something." And, "The whole of my life is different; I've done something with my life."

Still, no one can foresee what giving away the spare kidney could mean. Several years ago a twenty-three-year-old woman offered a kidney to her dying twin. Before the operation could be performed, the sick sister died. The surviving twin married and was in time delivered of a baby by Caesarean section. She thereafter developed severe kidney trouble herself. Had she given away one kidney earlier, she would have been in desperate straits.

All too often the person who needs a kidney has no blood relation able or willing to provide it. The kidney must then be taken from spouse or friend, or from the dead. The kidney of Denise Darvall, for example, was given to ten-year-old Jonathan Van Wyk. Murray and his team in the United States are performing an average of three transplants a month, with two kidneys usually from living donors and one from the dead.

Even when the donor is unrelated, between fifty and sixty out of every hundred transplanted kidneys will continue to work for a period of at least two years. This can happen only if the tissues within the bodies of donor and recipient match and are, therefore, compatible. The fact that this does happen would seem to support the ancient and ubiquitous belief that each person has a double somewhere in the world. In order to find a tissue mate, a large number of tests are performed.

The closer the match, the better the chances of success. The match is graded like schoolwork, from A to F, with A matches occurring only between identical twins and B matches being relatively rare. Enough differences remain even between B matches to activate the immune reaction.

A number of drugs can delay rejection. The newest, and probably the best, of these is anti-lymphocyte serum or globulin, known as ALS or ALG, made by injecting human thymus gland cells into an animal, usually a horse. These thymus cells are a source of lymphocytes, the white corpuscles that fight disease. The animal's cells then make antibody against them. When a serum made from the animal's blood is then given to a transplant patient, it has the strange effect of preventing the white cells in his body from making antibody and rejecting a foreign organ. The problem with ALG is that patients often become allergic to it. X-rays and other forms of radiation can also destroy the lymphocytes and foil the immune reaction. Unfortunately, either drugs or radiation may leave the patient vulnerable to any kind of infection, such as the pneumonia that killed Washkansky.

Research into superior ways of circumventing rejection is continuing; as of now this remains the major transplant problem. It is least acute for the kidney. Even if the transplant is rejected, the patient can survive with the aid of an artificial kidney. The transplanted kidney of a nineteen-year-old recipient, for example, began to be rejected shortly before the end of his school term. The boy finished out the year by going to the hospital twice a week to be hooked to an artificial kidney. Not daunted, he is now waiting for a second kidney transplant. Some individuals have had as many as four successive kidneys implanted, as one after the other was rejected.

In the first twelve years after Murray's initial success about a thousand kidney transplants were performed throughout the world. Then the pace speeded, and in the next three years another two thousand were transplanted. Most of the survivors were under the age of forty-five.

Hypothermia may be employed for transplants, though it is more commonly used in other types of lengthy kidney operations. When the body is chilled to 82.4°F., the circulation to the kidney can be broken off for an hour, and at 77° to 68°F., the period can be extended for two hours. The suggestion has been made that the donor be placed in hypothermia to keep the organ from deteriorating, but with a living donor the time lag is so short as to make this unnecessary. When a kidney is taken from a cadaver, it is perfused with cold saline.

Even though the kidney was the first organ to be successfully substituted, if one were to ask people to describe the first transplant, they would almost to a man come back with Christiaan Barnard and Washkansky. The replacement of a heart seems more of a miracle than replacement of a kidney, or even of liver or lungs, which are harder to transplant and just as essential to life. No other part of the human anatomy has been the subject of so much legend, poetry, and song. Education and scientific knowledge notwithstanding, man thinks of the heart as being more than the pump logic tells him it is. No, the heart is the seat of emotions. He feels with it, loves with it. The heart is shattered, not by failing arteries or defective valves, but by a failure of love.

Many years of research with animals preceded Barnard's triumph. The first transplant was performed in the beginning years of the twentieth century by Dr. Alexis Carrel, who set the heart of a puppy into the neck of an adult dog. Techniques were improved over the next half century, and eventually both heart and lungs were transplanted together from one dog to another. By this time hypothermia had entered the transplant picture. The animals were protected by chilling to between 77° and 69.8°F., but the surgery was so drastic that none survived for more than six hours. To this day lung transplantation is done rarely, and no one has survived it for long.

Returning to the heart alone, in the 1960's a puppy named Eterna lived seven months after a transplant performed by

Dr. Adrian Kantrowitz at Maimonides Hospital in Brooklyn, New York. Eterna was about the same size as the donor but did not come from the same litter. She was cooled to a temperature that varied from 62.6° to 60.8°F., and maintained there during the transplantation. Then she was rewarmed. She walked around and took fluids the day after the operation; an additional day found her back on a normal diet. Her pulse was regular by then, even after exercise. The dog gained weight and the transplanted heart grew at a suitable rate.

Not long afterward Eterna's survival record was broken by a dog who clung to life for eighteen months after receiving a heart at the Medical College of Virginia. The dog was taken to a medical meeting by the surgeon Dr. Richard R. Lower; the animal posed for pictures, ran about, and wagged his tail.

Before becoming famous Barnard came to the United States and visited the Medical College of Virginia to observe the method used. Barnard had already been performing transplants on animals for about three years at his laboratory in Capetown.

Oddly enough, a heart transplant on a man had already taken place. When one considers the blazing light of publicity that has shone on every transplant from Barnard's on, the lack of attention accorded this one is hard to understand. In fact, the movie made of the operation was not even shown for four years. The transplant, performed by Dr. James Hardy at the University of Mississippi Medical Center, Jacksonville, on January 23, 1964, was particularly unorthodox in that the heart of a large chimpanzee was implanted in the body of a man. The chimpanzee heart managed to keep the human alive for about ninety minutes. That is not much, to be sure, but it showed that a substitute heart could be placed in a man's chest and function.

A reverse twist on this surgery was attempted some time later at the Medical College of Virginia when the heart of a human automobile-accident victim was transplanted into a baboon. The human heart was quickly rejected, and the animal died.

By 1967, although the general public was not aware of it, medical teams in hospitals separated by thousands of miles were preparing for the first human-to-human transplant. Along with the deciphering of DNA and the creation of life in the laboratory, it was one of the scientific races of the century. Most observers had been betting on Dr. Norman E. Shumway of Stanford University School of Medicine, who had developed the transplantation technique. As everyone knows, however, Barnard won it—but only by days. The runner-up was the American Kantrowitz, who was later to comment sadly on Barnard's victory—"that's why I'm not a hero in Brooklyn." Kantrowitz and his group at Maimonides had prepared for the event by operating on more than 250 dogs. Like Barnard, he had spent the last days of November waiting for a suitable donor to turn up. The patient with the failing heart in this case was no middle-aged man, but a newborn baby. This made the search more difficult; only another newborn could have a heart small enough to be of any use.

In desperation Kantrowitz sent telegrams to 500 hospitals asking that he be notified the moment an anencephalic infant (one with almost no brain) was born. Such an infant could obviously have no hope for life. While Kantrowitz was waiting, Barnard performed his historic operation in South Africa. Two days later a defective infant was born in a hospital in Philadelphia. The parents, saying that they hoped someone else would have joy out of their sorrow, agreed to donate the heart. On December 7 at 4:20 A.M. the donor infant died and was immediately chilled to prevent damage to the heart. The recipient baby was then cooled to 62.6°F., and the operation began. After the new heart had been stitched into place, he was rewarmed. The heart started easily with just one shock and continued to beat steadily while the baby's temperature returned to normal. Then about five hours after the operation the infant began to sink, and in another hour and a half, he was dead. The cause of death, Kantrowitz believes, was severe acidosis, a result of the hypothermia. The technique of cooling which has saved so many during surgery failed the baby here.

In the months after these two transplants a rush of others took place around the globe. In France, for example, priest Father Daniel, who had been bedridden for a year, received the heart of a thirty-seven-year-old man dead of a brain hemorrhage. During the operation the donor was cooled to 86°F. and his heart to 68°F. Within months after surgery the priest had returned to his parishioners and was officiating at mass, giving interviews to the press, and traveling by speedboat and light airplane. In London, forty-five-year-old contractor Frederic West was first to get a heart; in Sydney, Australia, the heart of a young Royal Australian Navy sailor was donated to a man of sixty. The Russians lagged behind a bit, with the first transplant taking place in Leningrad, a full eleven months after Barnard's initial operation. Nor was this successful; the patient, a twenty-five-year-old woman, died thirty-three hours later.

During the year that followed the surgery on Washkansky, ninety-nine transplants were performed. Some patients even received two hearts, the first having been rejected. Of the forty-one who survived the first month, nine lived more than four. By the end of the following year the total had reached 150 transplants in 148 patients. Twenty survived for longer than a year, part of that time in relatively good health.

The successes were primarily among the B and C tissue matches (A being so rare as to be negligible). So few D matches lived that many surgeons began to refuse to perform such operations. Most notable among the survivors was Barnard's second transplant patient, Dr. Philip Blaiberg, a retired dentist, who was to live nineteen and a half months. Blaiberg was given the heart of a young mulatto killed by a brain hemorrhage received while playing football on a beach. Although he was compatible with his donor for twenty-two different immunological factors, Blaiberg still required drugs to combat rejection.

Blaiberg, who went swimming a year after receiving his

new heart, hastened to write a memoir of his operation, *Looking at My Heart*. In this book he revealed that he had been able to resume marital relations with his wife about three weeks after returning home from the hospital. Barnard had urged him to write this, he said, "to allay the fears of some men who believe their potency might be impaired after cardiac surgery."

This is by no means the only psychological problem to arise after transplants. Even open-heart surgery has produced several cases of what psychiatrists have begun to describe as "cardiac psychosis," characterized by extreme anxiety. The symptoms are more acute for heart transplant patients. All have been close to death, yet it never seemed so close as immediately before and after surgery. Now there is a reprieve, troubled by the knowledge that few others have survived for long. The adjustment appears to be harder than anyone recognized during the early, most exciting days of the transplantation era. Blaiberg, however, insisted from beginning to end that his prolonged life had been satisfying enough to make up for all the pain and worry.

News of one transplant after the other appeared on the front pages of newspapers for some months before slipping to the back. The *Times* of London was moved to run a cartoon portraying a doctor lecturing to his fellows on transplantation: "Now we come to a vital part of the operation—the post-operative handling of publicity, t.v. interviews, etc."

One of the most startling facts to be publicized was the cost. A government task force studied thirty-six cases and came up with an average price of $18,700. Many, particularly at first, cost more. One patient, Michael Kasperak, who received a new heart in January, 1968, ran up a hospital bill of $28,845.83, although he lived for only fifteen days. And the surgeon had donated his services.

Although Barnard has received the lion's share of the publicity, he has not performed the largest number of transplants. The record-holder for the first year was handsome, youthful Dr. Denton A. Cooley at St. Luke's Episcopal Hospital in

Houston, Texas. At the Second International Transplantation Congress held in New York in 1968, Cooley called to the
platform a living example of his proficiency—a fifty-four-
year-old man in whose chest was beating the heart of a seven-
teen-year-old boy. The substitution had been made three and
a half months earlier; the boy's body was at 89°F. before the
transfer began. The man was notable in not being notable,
looking like any other short, stocky fifty-four-year-old. In the
early days of transplantation, this seemed incredible.

As the months went by, Cooley and his staff cut the time
required for a transplant from four and a half hours to two,
and completed the actual heart installation in thirty minutes
or less.

Cooley has stated privately that he does not consider chilling necessary. Success, in his opinion, "depends more upon
expeditious surgical technique to preserve the organ during
the period of transfer. This [hypothermia] remains, however,
one of the controversial points in cardiac surgery."

Although Cooley's team, working at great speed, has given
up hypothermia, most other transplant surgeons are still using it.

By the end of the first year of heart transplants, it had
become clear that the key problem was going to be the shortage of donors. A publication put out by a medical organization carried the wry suggestion that organ transplantation
can be continued only by a return to human sacrifice, the
establishment of heart production farms, and the commercial
sale of organs. In hospital centers where the surgery is performed, people wait in desperation for a donor to appear. For
many, he does not come in time. Newspaper reporters have
dramatically described these heart patients as being "in a race
with death." It sounds like hyperbole, but it is painfully true.
When forty-seven-year-old Haskell Karp was close to death
and no donor appeared, Cooley implanted a completely artificial heart. This kept Karp alive for but sixty-five hours, and
its use was hotly disputed.

A far more bizarre transplant had been performed some

time earlier by Cooley. Unable to locate a human donor, he followed Hardy's example and tried an animal. In this case, the heart of a 125-pound sheep was placed in a dying man's chest. It was rejected almost immediately.

Although the idea of using animal organs seems either laughable or repugnant to most laymen today, it had been tried many times before Cooley or Hardy. One of the first to turn to animals for their vigor as well as their availability was Dr. J. R. Brinkley of Milford, Kansas. One day in 1920 he announced that he had restored potency and the appearance of youth to more than 600 men and women by transplanting the sex glands of goats. With such extravagance, it is hardly surprising that the idea of using animals fell into disfavor for a time. Nonetheless, today most surgeons believe that either animal or plastic replicas must ultimately be used for organ transplants.

Nowadays even when a donor is found, efforts to make use of him may be foiled. A few months after Barnard's first heart transplant, a dying man in a Mexico City Hospital was being prepared to receive the heart of a woman close to death with a brain tumor. Her family had given permission for the operation. Then while the woman's last heartbeats were being monitored, permission for the surgery was refused by the legal department of Mexico's Social Security Institute. The lawyers insisted that no one had yet declared transplantation to be legal—or illegal, for that matter—but this was of no concern at the moment. The surgeon wept as the heart patient was wheeled out of the operating room with his defective heart struggling to beat in his chest.

An even stranger misadventure put off a heart transplant operation scheduled at Stanford University Hospital, California, in late October of 1968. The patient had been in the hospital for some time waiting for a suitable donor to arrive. At last, one night, an eighteen-year-old youth was brought in with a gunshot wound. It looked like a typical suicide, and the young man died during the night. His heart was perfect, but he was not to have the posthumous distinction of giving it away. The police telephoned the hospital. Another young man had been booked on suspicion of murder. The potential donor's body could not be released in time for the transplant to be performed.

When a good donor is found, he may be stripped of his organs. One donor could contribute organs to as many as seventeen people, Dr. C. Walton Lillehei, chief of surgery at New York Hospital, points out, provided that close tissue matches were possible. An individual could offer such parts of himself as the heart, lungs, liver, kidney, pancreas, adrenal glands, thymus, larynx, intestines, spleen and portions of the ovary. Whatever the organ, it is usually cooled before use.

One evening in late August of 1968 Nelva Lou Hernandez had a violent quarrel with her husband. She turned from him, seized a pistol that she had been planning to take to a pawnshop, and screamed: "I'm going to shoot myself." After her death, her heart, both kidneys, and one lobe of a lung were removed. Four men received the transplants. A few days later a public official in São Paulo, Brazil, shot himself to death. His heart went to the father of five children; his kidneys and pancreas to three other invalids.

In the nineteenth century criminals satisfied the needs of doctors by robbing graves. Today teen-agers wear a button inscribed DRIVE CAREFULLY; DR. BARNARD IS WAITING, and a cartoonist captions a drawing of a bum sleeping on a park bench, "Just sleeping, not a heart donor."

Not everyone thinks that is funny. A number of people are beginning to worry that their hearts and other organs might be snatched from their still-living bodies. For just when does death occur? When the heart stops beating? But it can be made to beat again with pacemakers and other heroic measures. A second indicator of death is the cessation of brain function, as revealed by the absence of brain waves on an electroencephalogram. The American Medical Association urges that the donor's death be certified by a doctor other than the one attending the would-be recipient.

Once the fact of death is agreed upon, the doctor must rush

around to get consent—usually from the nearest of kin—for the use of heart or liver. The difficulty he faces depends upon where the would-be donor lived. Laws determining who controls such gifts as organs vary among the states and are confusing at best. A number still include some of the dictates of seventeenth-century common law. A way out is offered by the Uniform Anatomical Gift Act proposed in 1968 by a National Conference of Commissioners on Uniform State Laws: a person eighteen or over may give any part of his body after death, and the next of kin cannot deny his wish. Such a law may ultimately become universal, but so far has been passed by few state legislatures.

Still, if a person wishing to be a donor were to express his desire while alive and in good health, the chances are that he would be respected, regardless of the law. A growing number of hospitals is setting up cooperative registries of donors and recipients. The tissues of each donor are typed and the pertinent data are fed into a computer to await the day when death and suitable recipient match. Each would-be donor might be given a card to carry in his wallet. This "everything" card would declare his willingness to give his all.

Might this "all" ever include his brain? It would seem logical for the brain to be the most sensitive of all organs and the quickest to reject foreign matter. Instead, it accepts graft tissue more easily than other organs do.

"Just why the brain should be so tolerant is not clear, although absence of a lymphatic system and the reluctance of the brain tissue surrounding the graft to invade the transplant with blood vessels have been frequently put forward to account for this mystery," comments Dr. Robert J. White, Professor of Neurosurgery, Western Reserve University.

Transplanting the entire brain is a feat that has been challenging scientists for many years. A step in that direction was taken in the early 1960's when Dr. Vladimir P. Demikhov of the U.S.S.R. implanted a puppy's entire head and upper body in the neck of a big dog. For twenty-nine days, Demikhov reported, the transposed head could bite, swallow, and react to pain. Although this achievement is a valuable preamble to brain transplantation, it is obviously of no benefit to either donor or recipient.

White and his associates then set out to transplant the brain alone. First, they carefully removed the brains of six dogs. Each brain was then placed within the neck of another dog and connected to his bloodstream. The blood flow was stopped for five minutes during the transplantation. The brain was protected for this period by a slightly lowered temperature. Then, within the body of one stranger, the brain of another stranger was restored to life. Some dogs succumbed after six hours, and other survived for two days. Were the animals conscious and able to think during this period? No one is sure, but brain waves produced electric signals on the electroencephalograph.

Is the next step the actual transplantation of the human brain? The concept appears more suited to science fiction than reality. But is that so? Consider the young man doomed by a deep-seated brain tumor, or the elderly woman returning to a second childhood due to hardening of the arteries of the brain. Might not their only hope for a useful life be the gift of another brain or part of a brain?

Unlike the heart, however, the brain really is the seat not only of intelligence, but also memory, character, personality, and motor control. Would a totally new personality emerge? Would the manual laborer suddenly be able to do advanced mathematics, read Greek, and speak French, because the person who originally possessed his brain had these abilities? Or conversely, would the college professor given the brain of a less-gifted individual lose his intellectual brilliance? Perhaps the worst of the eventualities would be avoided by having donor and recipient matched not only by tissue type, but also by intelligence and personality traits in a vast computer operation.

The great future of brain transplantation, though, lies not in restoring mental health to adult or aged, but in giving it to the unborn or newborn. Each year many infants are conceived who have no chance of normal survival. They enter the world with hardly a brain or with one so damaged that it will never function. A good number of defects can already be diagnosed prenatally, and ways of identifying others are being discovered from one day to the next. The techniques for embryonic transplantation would not seem to be beyond the abilities of neurosurgeons today. The normal brain from an aborted or miscarried fetus might thus be transplanted into an abnormally developing embryo. A newborn baby could utilize as a transplant the brain of another infant or stillbirth. It is true that the child with the new brain would not have the inherited characteristics of those who conceived him. He might be more or less intelligent. Nonetheless, the parents of an obviously defective baby might be willing to settle for an expedient that could transform him into a normal child.

Still, say others, what of the soul?

Leaving the brain and its myriad problems aside, there are those who are repelled by the idea of transplanting heart, lungs, liver, or other organs. Taking an integral part of another person, even a dead one, seems to them to be going against nature and, therefore, wrong. But Sir Peter B. Medawar, British Nobel Prize winner and a pioneer in transplantation research, believes that doubters will in time be won over and that organ transplantation will be a standard medical practice.

"And there is no need to be philosophical about it. This will come about for the single and sufficient reason that people are so constituted that they would rather be alive than dead."

8

Chilled Bodies

In a laboratory in Cleveland a monkey's brain hung suspended in a strange device. Nothing of the body that once housed it remained, except for two small bones to help support it. Yet this brain was alive. It may even have been conscious, had thoughts, felt hunger or thirst, experienced sensations in its absent limbs, been happy, or angry, or afraid. The brain waves, measured on an electroencephalograph, were the same as those of whole monkeys, even when awake. No arteries and veins carried blood to and away from the heart, but then, of course, there was no heart. Instead, plastic tubing transported blood from another, larger monkey. In this way, removed and remote from the living organism that had once sheltered it, the brain survived for hour after hour.

And so the disembodied, living brain, for years a popular theme of horror stories and films, becomes reality.

"I don't query the usefulness of keeping a monkey's brain alive for eighteen hours while unconnected with the monkey's body, a feat just performed at a hospital in Cleveland," went a column in *Punch*, the British humor magazine. "I only wonder what the brain was thinking about during that time."

But then, no one knows what an intact monkey thinks about either. Instead of worrying about that, researchers will concentrate on observing what drugs, bacteria, and changes in temperature do to the brain. Neurologists will see which substances the brain needs and which it manufactures, and gain understanding of how it protects itself against stress and injury.

The seemingly miraculous feat of isolating the complex brain of a higher animal and keeping it alive was made possible by cold. It does not take much at normal temperatures to destroy brain function. In three to five minutes without blood, the intelligence is lost. But when the brain is cooled only a little—to 86°F.—the safety period extends to eight or ten minutes. And when it is really cold, 59°F., the brain can remain without oxygen and blood for more than half an hour without harm.

The monkey's brain was kept at a temperature of between 82.4°F. and 89.6°F. for the few minutes spent hooking it up to the device.

The startling success with the monkey and the use of chilling to protect patients for transplant and open-heart operations are so recent that few people realize how long a history hypothermia has had. Its benefits have been discovered, forgotten, and rediscovered in one century and then another, most often by accident.

The winter of 1784 was bitterly cold, and the Scottish soldiers shivered in their threadbare uniforms as they marched from Glasgow to the highlands. Added to the discomfort of the cold was the agony and terror of smallpox; an epidemic raged among the troops. Every day the death toll mounted. Wives and children were accompanying the men to the new posting. Dressed in what amounted to rags, they limped along on chilblained feet. The smallest children, barely clothed, were covered with thin shawls and carried in open baskets attached to the saddles of their fathers' horses. It was not surprising that many of these frail children caught smallpox. Yet something surprising did occur: most of them had only a mild form of the illness and recovered.

A report on this phenomenon was published but received very little attention. No one at that time took seriously the implication that cold is of value medically. Yet doctors had learned this strange fact many centuries before the Scottish soldiers set out on their journey.

Twenty-five hundred years earlier Greek physicians had

made a practice of chilling the bodies of tetanus victims. Roman doctors also were convinced of the efficacy of cold. Aulus Cornelius Celsus, author of the nine-volume encyclopedia *De re medicina*, recommended that patients with hydrophobia be dunked in very cold water. Behind the Roman treatment, however, lay superstition, not pure science. Terrified by the freezing water, the demon who had taken possession of the sick man would flee. Although nothing— not cold, nor heat, nor modern drugs—can cure rabies, Celsus' method at least did the patient no harm and may even have relieved his torment a little.

In China many years ago the physician Ch-hua t'o had a great reputation. Whenever a patient with a fever consulted Ch-hua t'o, he was promptly stripped naked and carried to a stone trough in the garden where icy water was poured on him. The curative properties of this rigorous treatment were described in the third century A.D. by one of Ch-hua t'o's followers, Chang Chung-ching, in a learned essay.

In modern times a doctor made a study of the long history of body cooling. In the course of his research, he came upon an impressive report on this subject written by a Dr. N. A. Smith in 1874. The presentation seemed familiar to him, and then he remembered that as a student he had read Chang Chung-ching's essay. It expressed practically the same ideas. Plagiarism was not suggested. The technique has, after all, been lost and found again time after time, and in between the experience of the past has been overlooked or ignored.

During the Third Crusade when Richard the Lion-Hearted was battling the Moslems for control of the Holy Land, he was stricken with a desert fever. Upon learning of this, his enemy, the Sultan Saladin, known for gallantry as well as courage, ordered soldiers to travel to the distant high mountains with a caravan of camels. The men gathered snow and packed it in skin gourds, fastened them to the camels' backs, and returned to Saladin. Careless of his safety, Saladin entered the English camp carrying the snow-filled gourds. The surprised Crusaders, recognizing the generous nature of the act, stood by while Saladin and his men packed Richard in the snow. Soon the fever went down and the king recovered and returned to the battle. The story, a part of the romance that has been woven about these two great adversaries, lived on. But the lesson that should have been drawn from it was forgotten.

Hundreds of years were to pass before William Wright, a British naval doctor, was to discover the benefits of cold all over again. In 1767, Wright caught a tropical illness when his ship was cruising in the Bahamas. Feeling as if he were burning up, he staggered on deck to get a breath of air. While he stood there, a high wave swept over the side of the vessel and drenched him. He had never heard of cold water as a medical treatment, so he had no reason to anticipate the result: his temperature dropped and he felt considerably better. For the next few days Wright insisted that the sailors douse him with seawater. They complied, although they clearly considered him deranged. Encouraged by his own example, Wright subsequently used cold to treat malaria and published a paper about it.

Several years later a Scottish doctor, James Currie, happened upon this report. At that time there was a virulent typhoid epidemic and Currie was searching for a new mode of treatment. Wright's paper gave this to him. Currie devised a special technique for chilling and used it on the typhoid victims. Although he was quite unaware of this, his method was remarkably similar to that employed centuries earlier by the Romans and Chinese. He ordered patients to sit in tubs of icy seawater until their body temperatures dropped to about 84°F. Many of them got better.

The practice was not as haphazard as it sounds because Currie was a thorough scientist and performed experiments before treating the sick. Making use of the new mercury thermometer that was for years thereafter to be known as "Currie's thermometer," he checked temperature variations among healthy people. This provided him with a basis for comparison with the sick. Then he recorded the effects of cooling not only on temperature, but also on pulse, respiration, and other physiological activities. He was thus the first to observe that hypothermia, the dropping of body temperature to below 95°F., depresses most body functions. And this is the main reason why cooling works. The typhoid and later typhus patients treated by Currie recovered, but not because the germs in their bodies were killed by the cold. In fact, bacteria, viruses, and other microbes are far better able to withstand freezing than more highly developed organisms. The patients improved because their physiological requirements were reduced.

"Hypothermia has never cured anything, does not now, and never will," Dr. Emil Blair, Assistant Professor of Surgery, University of Maryland School of Medicine, has written in the medical textbook *Clinical Hypothermia.*

Why then does it work? It simply "modifies the metabolic environment. When used properly, this modification weighs in the patient's favor and may save his life."

This has helped many of those receiving new hearts and kidneys; the technique has also been applied to those suffering from a large number of illnesses. Septic shock, most often associated with a botched illegal abortion, can also develop as a result of less dramatically incurred bacterial or viral infections. The metabolic demands of the system are raised to a point where it is all but impossible for them to be satisfied. As a result, even when treated with antibiotics, septic shock carries a high death rate. Hypothermia reduces the body's demands to manageable proportions. In one hospital fifty-nine patients with septic shock were placed under hypothermia recently. Thirty-five of them recovered, more than twice the number that could have been expected of patients whose metabolism was not controlled.

Heat has quite the opposite effect on metabolism. Yet cold has usually had to battle heat as a treatment for disease. Doctors in seventeenth-century England heated fever patients as a matter of course. Then one cold winter's day a prominent physician, Dr. Thomas Sydenham, entered a sick-room, threw open the windows, and dipped the bedsheets in cold water. The patient and his family were stunned; Sydenham's colleagues were shocked. But the patient got well and doctors began to follow Sydenham's example. Chilling was one of the few treatments available for fever in pre-antibiotic days.

The use of warmth, which is standard for staphylococcal pneumonia, a disease carrying a death rate of at least twenty percent, was challenged by work of Dr. Ian M. Smith of the University of Iowa's College of Medicine. Smith inoculated white mice with massive doses of *Staph* germs, and then warmed them. Death followed rather quickly. And so Smith reversed the procedure and put the sick animals in a refrigerator at 39.2°F. This group lived about 120 minutes longer than mice which were neither warmed nor cooled. The reason for this is not fully understood, but it seems likely that the lower metabolism is responsible. Glucose helps the body to stave off germs. The cool body burns sugar more slowly, so more is available for fighting germs. Such an application of cooling is still highly experimental, and many doctors do not believe that people will react as the animals did.

Infants with trouble in breathing at birth are almost always warmed. This approach was first questioned by Dr. James A. Miller in 1945 when he was visiting a hospital nursery where a number of premature infants were lying in incubators. All at once, as he said later, it struck him as incongruous that babies with difficulty in breathing should be warmed in incubators. He thought it unsound to increase their oxygen requirements by raising their temperatures when they were in dire stress due to their inability to take in sufficient oxygen. He began, therefore, to do research by cooling newborn guinea pigs, rabbits, and puppies. The results strengthened him in his opinion that cold was preferable to heat. Yet, though as professor of anatomy at Emory University Medical School in Atlanta, he carefully searched the medical literature of the United States and Europe for the next fifteen years, he found hardly a mention of the use of cold for treatment of asphyxia in the newborn. And then in the early 1960's a baby was born in the Sabbatsberg Hospital in Stockholm, Sweden. When fifteen minutes of effort failed to start breathing, Dr. Björn Westin placed the infant on his back in a tub of cold running water. It was a technique reminiscent of that used by midwives rather than medical specialists, yet in eight minutes the baby drew his first breath. His body temperature then had fallen to 80.6°F. The first cry was heard seventeen minutes later, when the infant's temperature was down to 78°F. With this success on record the Sabbatsberg Hospital began to use cold more freely, and doctors reported that ten out of eleven babies treated in this manner survived. Soon afterward the Pediatric Society in Finland announced that one hundred other babies in danger of asphyxia had been cooled.

Still, most newborns placed in heated incubators also do survive. The controversy between the hot and the cold factions goes on. A number of doctors consider hypothermia to below 89.6°F. to be risky for infants. They warn that there is some danger of hardening of the cutaneous and subcutaneous tissues. Cooling may also result in severe acidosis, which the infant cannot tolerate. This is probably what caused the death of the newborn who received the world's second heart transplant. Today, however, infant acidosis is being cured.

Babies can be transformed into what might be called cold-blooded animals very easily, possibly because their heat-regulating system is immature. The body temperature of adults, on the other hand, struggles to maintain itself, mobilizing one weapon after the other against cold. Should a man be placed in a tub of ice, the surface of the body would rapidly drop in temperature to 50°F. But he would not really yet be cold. The temperature of the internal organs deep within his body would not begin to fall for about ten minutes. It takes this long for cold to break through the body's defenses. In hospitals, however, the ordeal is made shorter and less disturbing by means of medication. When certain anesthetic or tranquilizing drugs are administered, the body loses its ability to fight off cold and easily falls into hypothermia. The sedatives given a mother during childbirth cross the placenta and enter the bloodstream of the infant. This is yet another reason why babies drop into the cold-blooded state so quickly.

The cliché "there is nothing new under the sun" might well be applied to hypothermia. The observation that drugs help to prevent shivering and convulsions was made by H. Laborit in 1961, and he is generally credited with originating this method. But a study of history proves this wrong. Galen, who lived in Rome in the second century A.D., reported that certain medicines have a "refrigerant action" on the system and can be used to assist body cooling. He recommended this practice for the treatment of tertian fever and commented that he had never lost a case, provided only that he had begun chilling the patient early in the disease.

The system of dunking the patient in a tub of ice water, first employed by Ch-hua t'o and then slightly refined by Currie, survived into the twentieth century. Gradually techniques less shocking to the patient were devised. The descendant of the icy tub is the extensive ice pack or the box through which cold air circulates. Dr. Temple Fay, generally credited with being the first modern physician to employ hypothermia, in November of 1938 packed cracked ice around the torso, arms, and legs of a cancer patient and opened wide the windows of the room to let in the chill autumn air. In this simple manner the body temperature was reduced to between 88° and 90° F., and maintained there for four days. Fay's report on this and other cases, "Observations on Prolonged Human Refrigeration," was given in 1939. The manuscript fell into the hands of the Germans and gave them the idea for their infamous cold-water experiments in Dachau.

Nowadays hypothermia is most often induced by placing the patient on a mattress and passing chilled liquids through it, or covering him with a rubber or plastic blanket filled with a cold solution. An electronic device attached to the blanket, for example, links its temperature to that of the patient. This is sometimes measured in the esophagus, which has been found to be the most reliable indicator of deep body temperature. (That is why the reading of the esophagus is used in transplant operations.) The device is regulated to allow for the fact that temperature will drop a few degrees more after the source of cold is removed. When it is time to rewarm the patient, the blanket is turned off, and the temperature starts up slowly.

The body can also be chilled from the inside out, rather than from the skin in. This is known as core cooling, because the internal organs get cold before the skin does. The techniques for achieving this must be much more sophisticated than Currie's tub of ice water or the cooling blanket. A heat exchanger is hooked up to a heart-lung pump that is connected to the patient. The warm blood flows through the exchanger and is then returned to the body many degrees colder. Far lower body temperatures can be obtained in this manner than with external cooling.

With this technique available, doctors had to answer the question: how cold can a human being become before revival is impossible?

"Every time someone has placed a limit on man's capacity to survive cold," comments Blair, "he has been proved wrong."

Candidates for tests could come only from among the desperately ill. In 1955 a fifty-one-year-old woman, weighing ninety-five pounds and suffering with terminal ovarian cancer, agreed to undergo deeper hypothermia than had ever been tried on a human being before. Cooling began and her temperature dropped lower and lower until the thermometer finally registered 48.2° F. Her heart had stopped and she was no longer breathing. She lay like a dead woman for forty-five minutes. Then the rewarming was started. For the first few moments there was no change; then after fifteen minutes the stilled heart aroused and began to beat again. She regained consciousness ten hours after her temperature had returned to normal. "How cold was I?" she whispered, as her doctor bent over her bed. The woman lived for only thirty-eight days, however, before succumbing to her cancer.

At that time it seemed inconceivable that anyone could endure a temperature lower than 48.2° F., yet within the next few years this record was broken, too. Dr. C. Ronald Stephen and a group of doctors at Duke cooled a thirty-nine-year-old cancer victim to 39.56° F. while removing a malignancy from his brain. And again the patient recovered fully from the hypothermia, but eventually died of a recurrence of his disease.

The experience of these two shows that hypothermia is not life-threatening of itself; it can, however, produce a number of unfortunate side effects, such as the arhythmic heart quiver. Even when temperatures are only slightly below normal other difficulties may arise.

In 1683, Robert Boyle, the English scientist and philosopher, gave a gruesome account of the effect of cold on knights in armor: "Cold seizes men's Bodies in the reins and all about the Wast (and especially horse-men underneath the Armor of the Back and Breast) and straightens those parts so forcibly that it freezes all the parts of the Belly, especially the Guts." He described this as a "gangrene of the Guts," and added graphically that it hindered "descent of Excrements downwards."

Not until the twentieth century was a clue found that there might be a scientific basis for the suffering of those knights. Then it was observed that intestinal activity drops markedly at 93.2° F. and stops altogether at 86° F. Thus, gastric upsets are frequent following hypothermia and accidental freezing.

Just to confuse the issue thoroughly, however, cold can also relieve gastric distress. In 1894, Raoul Pictet suggested "frigotherapy" as a treatment for dyspepsia. Pictet was no physician, it should be noted; he made his reputation by being one of the first to liquefy oxygen successfully. The doctors he consulted brought him no relief from the torments of his stomach pains. One day he decided to sit down in what he called a "cold well" for fifteen minutes. That night, he later announced gleefully, he ate a full dinner for the first time in many years.

Some doctors believe that cooling helps to relieve ulcers by reducing hydrochloric acid production. Bleeding ulcers can be controlled by chilling the sufferer to 59° F. or lower. This is admittedly a bit impractical. Temperatures very far below normal can produce side effects of their own, and thus would not be induced until everything else has failed.

While cooling makes possible lengthy kidney operations, paradoxically it can have a bad effect on the kidney when employed for heart surgery, septic shock, or other conditions. The kidney does not begin to function properly for at least twenty-four hours after rewarming. Fortunately, the benefits of low body temperature outweigh the drawbacks.

For all its long history, the boundaries of hypothermia are not yet set. Each year more applications for it are investigated. Chilling is being found useful in relieving such diverse conditions as cirrhosis of the liver, emphysema, and hemorrhage after childbirth. Severely burned animals have been helped by cooling; the same may well be true for humans.

The effects of excessive heat can sometimes be corrected by means of excessive cold. During a heat stroke, the body's heat-regulating mechanism goes wildly out of control. As a result, the temperature quickly climbs to 106° F., to 107° F., and higher. Death can result unless the temperature is brought down quickly. Hypothermia is an efficient way of doing this.

Cold's ability to soothe the fevered brow has long been recognized. As Thomas Masters wrote in *The Ice Book* in 1844: "In numberless cases where extreme thirst, prostration of strength, restlessness, total want of sleep, and raving delirium prevailed, the application of ice-cooled water to the whole body by a sponge, slaked the thirst, roused the strength, calmed the patient, dispelled the delirium, and induced sleep, from which the sick awoke refreshed and comfortable; and that all this train of symptoms of excessive excitement could always be anticipated and prevented by giving to the patient plenty of ice-cold ptisans, whenever he felt inclined to take them." Masters may have been a trifle prejudiced in favor of medicinal use of ice, as his entire book was intended to promote the ice machine he had invented. Yet the idea of applying cold both to reduce fever and as a calmative has appealed to many people who had no machine to sell.

Extremely high temperatures can be a feature of the final stages of severe catatonic schizophrenia. The psychotic patient goes into a frenzy of overactivity, with his temperature rising to unendurable levels . . . until death finally claims him. Schizophrenia is a disease that continues to baffle scientists and the record for cures remains a poor one.

A theory about schizophrenia, which was first presented in 1935, has it that the illness is at least partly caused by a malfunction of the heat-regulating area of the brain. Catatonics can run a continuous low-grade fever which rises as the terminal stage approaches. Cooling schizophrenics seems a logical next step, and it was done, but the results of the treatment were not particularly promising. After ten years the attempts were abandoned.

The reports of these efforts were rediscovered in the late 1950's by two Canadian physicians, K. J. Fisher and M. D. Greiner. They felt that the method had not beeen sufficiently tested, and they began to look for a suitable candidate. The opportunity came in the early spring of 1959 when a forty-seven-year-old woman was admitted to a mental hospital. A few days earlier she had been found standing in her room, unable to speak or communicate in any way. Her husband, thirty years older than she, had died shortly before, leaving her with two children, aged four and a half and fifteen. Neighbors described her as a hard-working housewife and a good mother. Five years earlier she had had a similar catatonic episode but had returned to normal after five days. This time the days went by and there was no improvement. She was given electric shock treatment in the hospital to no avail. Her temperature began to climb from 105° F. on March 22 to 107° F. on March 24. This temperature can produce brain damage and death. Antibiotics were administered, and they failed, too. And so the doctors decided that the moment to try body cooling was upon them. The catatonic woman was given drugs to speed the chilling and was packed in ice bags. Her temperature was brought down to 80° F. and kept there for thirty-six hours.

For the first few days after rewarming, she remained mute, and then gradually she began to change. She answered questions and was able to do the simple arithmetic problems presented by her doctors as a test of acuity. In time she spoke with visiting friends and relatives, and later remembered and commented on their conversation. By May 7 she had recovered sufficiently to go home and resume her life as homemaker and mother. Fisher and Greiner attributed this success to the effect of cooling on the heat-regulating center of the brain. The chilling, they pointed out, was continued long enough to counteract the disorganization and allow it to return to normal. This view has met vehement opposition.

It would be nice to be able to say that their success heralded the beginning of a new era of treatment of catatonics. But no new era has dawned. Other patients have not shown improvement. Many doctors today say that fever, if kept within limits, can be more beneficial than cooling.

The theory that chilling would be effective against cancer, which was also first posed in the 1930's, has similarly failed to produce the hoped-for results. It was based on what seems like a reasonable premise: if the entire body were cooled to about 86° F. or even 88° F., a cancer could not grow. Researchers observed that cancer is seldom found on the hands and feet, and these are colder than the rest of the body. This enticing belief, however, was not borne out. The incredible degree of cold endured by terminal cancer victims did not cure them of their disease. At best, the cooling relieved the pain for a time.

A newer theory, now in the experimental stage, suggests that the cancer itself be kept warm, while the body is cooled. A leading proponent of this hypothesis, Dr. Vojin Popovic of Emory University, has worked with male hamsters. After human cancer tissue was implanted in the cheek pouches, the animals were lightly anesthetized and placed in a cold-water bath where their temperatures fell to 39.2° F. A little heating coil around the tumor kept it at 98.6° F., which is a normal temperature for human and hamster alike. At the end of two hours some of the hamsters were lifted out of the bath and rewarmed. They were then carefully observed: the tumors continued to grow. Clearly two hours had not been enough. A second group of animals was given four hours in the bath. The tumors shrank markedly, but the improvement was brief. Within five or six days the growths were back. Then a last group of hamsters was chilled for ten hours. The cancers of these animals shrank rapidly; some had disappeared completely in ten days, and the balance were gone within fifteen. Nor did the tumors grow back. Even more startling was the finding that only the cancer cells had died; the cheek pouches soon returned to normal.

Why does it happen? No one is quite sure. Popovic suggests that the metabolism of cancer cells may be higher than that of normal tissues. When the body around them is cooled and its metabolism slowed, the warm tumor cells may be deprived of the oxygen and nutrients they need for growth. The circulation is slower, too, so the cancer cells may be unable to dispose of their waste products. This would also hamper their development.

Heating the tumor, cooling the body, and then employing a powerful anticancer drug in a triple-pronged attack on cancer is also being tested by Popovic and a number of other researchers. The drug being used, 5-Fluorouracil, has been known for a long time, but it was not favored as it was so toxic that it killed healthy tissues along with the cancerous ones. As doctors have observed that nitrogen mustard and other anticancer drugs produce fewer side effects when administered to a patient under hypothermia the drug, 5-Fluorouracil, was given to cooled dogs with warm tumors. It apparently attacked the cancer cells alone. Only tiny amounts got into other cells. As the circulation of the cooled body is slow, the chemical could not travel far. The first tests on human beings are being performed in Europe.

Final proof of the efficacy of cooling to treat cancer will not be available for years—if indeed it ever comes.

Perhaps the most startling application of cold in medicine came when the French were conducting the war in Indochina (Vietnam). An army doctor, Lieutenant Colonel C. Chippaux, placed seriously wounded soldiers into a state of "artificial hibernation." This is the European way of describing hypothermia, and it is a most accurate one. The "hibernating" French soldiers were taken to hospitals far from the battlefield where their wounds were treated. During this entire period the cold kept the men from going into shock. In addition, a cold body bleeds less. The system worked well in the winter. A far larger number of these soldiers survived than anyone had dared to hope. But then came the Vietnam summer. The thermometer climbed to 104° F. and kept on going up. There was simply no way of keeping the soldiers cold enough throughout the long trip away from the front to a hospital. Breakdowns in communications, common enough in wartime, provided a bizarre touch to the rescue operation. Several times a "hibernating" soldier arrived at a hospital looking half dead. His heart was beating slowly and his breath was just barely perceptible. The doctor who checked him in was overworked and exhausted. The report explaining the man's condition was lost, and so a false diagnosis was made, and the man received improper treatment.

Still, the French attempt to guard the wounded from shock is a valuable contribution to the practice of hypothermia. It proved that chilling might protect people from the effects of trauma if only the conditions around them made it possible to sustain hypothermia long enough. Injuries occur in peacetime, too, in temperate climates and in areas where air-conditioned trains, trucks, and planes are available.

Hypothermia is particularly helpful in the treatment of head injuries. As with much of hypothermic history, the evidence that this might be so was available for more than two centuries and ignored. In 1740 a mason fell from a scaffold to his death. His body was taken into an anatomical theater to be dissected. The room was unheated and when the doctor, Jeannes Baptista Morgagni, opened the skull he noted that the cold air of the room had produced a surprising effect on the brain: "It was contracted, firmer, and less vascular."

This is exactly what happens to the chilled living brain, too. Inflammation, swelling, and bleeding—all are reduced. The benefits are greatest when cooling can be gotten under way within three hours of the injury. Not long ago a woman was brought to a hospital after her car had gone out of control and hit a tree. Her brain seemed so badly damaged that death appeared inevitable. In a last-ditch effort to save her, doctors lowered her temperature to between 92° F. and 90° F. It was kept at that level day after day. Two weeks later she was rewarmed. The incredible had occurred: she recovered.

Hypothermia is just as valuable for nonaccidental head injuries, such as brain surgery. And this is not only because of the extended safety period produced by the reduction in metabolism. Some neurosurgeons keep a patient cool for twelve to fourteen hours after surgery in order to avoid swelling and hemorrhage. The chilled brain, as Morgagni observed, becomes smaller. Abnormalities of the large blood vessels on the basal surface, for example, are extremely difficult for a surgeon to reach when the brain is its normal size. A study of such intracranial abnormalities made as recently as 1966 declared certain of them "to be technically unapproachable." Yet when five volunteers at Columbia-Presbyterian Medical Center, New York, were cooled to about 84° F. and their circulation stopped for three or four minutes, their brains shrank, and the corrections were made.

Cooling the entire body in order to operate on just a small part of it may seem a roundabout method. This has been the opinion of a number of surgeons, too, and a technique has been developed in which only the target organ is cooled. This has the advantage of bypassing hypothermia's side effects.

Cooling the brain alone is done by flushing it with cold blood. The blood is taken from an artery in the thigh and passed outside of the body through a pump and heat exchanger. Then, with its warmth removed, it is returned to the body at the level of the neck. The quantity of chilled blood introduced is too small to affect any part of the body other than the brain. Once the brain is cool, the flow of blood can be stopped at the level of one of the vertebrae for the actual operation. The brain is then not only cold but also bloodless during surgery.

The benefits of this method were quickly evident, as "impossible" surgery could be done. A fifty-six-year-old man was found to have a large and normally inoperable brain tumor. An operation was, however, performed when the temperature of the brain was dropped to 53.2° F. in seventeen minutes. During this entire time the thermometers showing esophagus and heart levels never went below 95° F. Circulation was stopped for slightly less than thirty minutes and the surgeons removed the growth.

Taking an imaginative approach to treatment of epilepsy, some physicians have tried cooling the brain. This has already been done for a number of those epileptics whose seizures could not be controlled with drugs. One sixteen-year-old boy, for example, was having several severe attacks daily, despite massive, almost toxic quantities of drugs. After his brain was cooled, the boy had no seizures for a year. When they did recur, it was possible to control them with moderate amounts of drugs.

Local cooling of the brain was done for a number of years before anyone thought of applying the technique to the spinal cord. This is odd, because as Dr. Juan Negrin, Jr., attending neurosurgeon at Lenox Hill Hospital, New York, remarks, "It is reasonable to expect spinal cord and cerebral tissue to react similarly under low temperatures." It seemed strange to him that motor difficulties, even those resulting from injury or disease affecting the spinal cord, were all being handled peripherally by treating the brain. And so Negrin bathed segments of the spinal cords of dogs in cold solutions. This required advance minor surgery in which tubes to carry the fluid were inserted. The temperature of the brain itself remained normal, and no ill effects of any kind appeared.

The time had come to use the method on people with spinal cord injuries and even on those whose motor difficulties had persisted for years, possibly as a result of a congenital disease of the nervous system. Negrin began by treating eight victims of one form of cerebral palsy. Aged from seven to nineteen, all were spastic or burdened with stiff, rigid limbs that were hard to lift or bend. In every case these symptoms were relieved immediately after local hypothermia of the spinal cord. One little girl who had stumbled constantly even when supported by special crutches was able to walk by herself. Another had been unable to control either hands or legs, but had clumsily groped around. She became able to feed herself and stood and moved on crutches. The improvement appears to be lasting; not one of the first group relapsed during a follow-up period of several years. Multiple sclerosis is another neurological disease often accompanied by spastic muscle movements, rigidity, and severe pain. Several patients have also been relieved by spinal cord chilling.

But Negrin cautions those who would hail this as a miracle that neither cerebral palsy nor multiple sclerosis is cured by the chilling: "It is the symptom that is cured, not the disease."

What does cold do? Negrin speculates that the chilling produces structural changes in components in or around the spinal cord that are involved in motor control. These changes persist even after warming.

As time passes, the method is being used more widely and not always with the marked success of the initial honeymoon period. A number of those with multiple sclerosis, for example, suffer relapses. "When you start a new technique, you are very selective as to the people you try it on," explains Negrin. "But gradually you cease to be so strict and try to help people who really cannot be helped, to take more and more hopeless cases.

"But when I get discouraged, I think of the people I have helped whom I could not have helped a few years ago. I have seen spastics who could not walk, walk; people who could not work, work; people in excruciating pain, relieved."

Some anesthesiologists suggest that regional cooling might relieve nonorganic as well as real pain. What they mean by this is that long after a wound is healed, the pain may live on. The leg has been removed long ago, but the amputee complains that it still hurts. This seemingly causeless pain and the phantom impression of a missing limb may be the result of a vicious circle of reflex activity that has been set up within the spinal cord. Perhaps prolonged cooling might remove the needless sensations of pain permanently.

When initiated no more than six hours after an accident, regional cooling may prevent paralysis. Dr. Robert White of Western Reserve, who has moved logically from chilling brain to spinal cord, recently startled a conference on rehabilitation of the paraplegic by suggesting that proper treatment might make rehabilitation unnecessary for accident victims. Thirty-five monkeys were subjects in a massive experiment performed by White and a co-worker, Dr. Maurice Albin. First, they caused the damage that will inevitably bring paraplegia, and then undid it by flushing the spinal cord with cold saline. The temperature of the cord fell to below 50° F., while the surrounding body remained warm. A few days after the cooling, every one of the monkeys was up and walking around. The success in such cases, says White, is probably due to the familiar fact that cold reduces the metabolism at the site of the injury so that less blood is needed. Swelling is reduced before it can do damage, and pressure on the spinal cord stopped or reversed.

The technique of cooling just one part of the body at a time has not remained limited to the central nervous system. Certain types of heart operations, for example, are performed on a cooled heart in a warm body. Similarly, kidney, urinary bladder, and other internal organs are often subjected to local cooling.

Of all uses for regional hypothermia, none has aroused more controversy than whether to freeze the stomach wall to cure duodenal ulcers. In the beginning, in 1962, the new method was hailed as highly promising. After all, if cooling the whole body reduces the production of corrosive hydrochloric acid, freezing the actual site should prevent it altogether. And this was the theory presented by Dr. Owen H. Wangensteen of the University of Minnesota Hospital. He described how each of a group of his patients had swallowed a rubber balloon. Then cold alcohol at temperatures of 1.4° F. to -4° F. was circulated through the balloon, which was by then resting in the stomach. The first patients treated said that the pain subsided following chilling and they felt much better. To be sure, the acid production eventually increased again, and Wangensteen then refroze the stomach wall.

The number of cryogenically treated ulcer patients rose, and some were not helped at all. The cheering stopped. By 1966 Dr. Claude R. Hitchcock and a number of other physicians in Wangensteen's own hospital declared that freezing was no better than the old-fashioned, tried-and-true methods of treating duodenal ulcers with milk, a bland diet, and antacid pills. They had performed their own test with the chilled balloon on 173 patients. Of these, only thirteen had been completely relieved of pain and other symptoms, and fifty had been much improved. Seventy-one patients had kept right on complaining of pain, thirty-seven had required surgery to remove part of the stomach, and one had died of a perforated ulcer. *The Wall Street Journal* in an article headlined "Sloppy Research" used a quotation by a medical school professor citing freezing of ulcers as an example of a technique of "questionable value."

But Wangensteen stands firm against all detractors. He points out that he is no longer using the exact system he originated and that Hitchcock took over. A major change is the rapid rewarming of the stomach after freezing. Complications declined markedly. Reporting on the treatment of 708 patients, he found half of them improved three months after freezing. Pain was relieved in almost every one, and the ulcer was healing. Although 167 had the freezing repeated at least once, not one died. Wangensteen urges that the method not be abandoned when it can save a number of people from the drastic surgery of having a portion of the stomach cut out.

In any event, the future of hypothermia does not depend on its producing an ulcer cure. It has succeeded often enough to survive an occasional failure.

As cooling comes into ever wider use, there is a growing understanding of just how it affects the system. In the early days of cooling, many questioned whether deliberately forcing the body or a vital portion thereof to abandon its normal temperature might bring about changes in the mind or personality. The thousands of men and women who have been chilled over the years, however, bear witness to the fact that intelligence is not lost, nor disposition changed.

And what of that more fragile component of the brain, memory? In an experiment conducted by Popovic, rats were trained to find food in a maze, and then were cooled. Upon being rewarmed they ran back through the maze to the cheese.

But would they have been capable of learning to find the food when cold? Does chilling affect the ability to think? Popovic began then with untrained rats. They were cooled to 84.2° F.—a temperature at which animals can still function—and sent into the maze where food lay hidden. The rats acted sluggish and stupid.

"I then realized that a cold rat does not care about food," says Popovic. "I had to find something that would interest him. What would that be? Heat."

And so a heat-producing device was placed in the rats' cages. Every time a rat pressed a tiny lever with his paw, a lamp would be activated to send out a two-second burst of heat. It took just forty-five seconds for the chilled rats to catch on to the secret of the lever. As for warm rats, it took them much longer to learn how to use any instrument at all.

"The brain is hyper-responsive when cooled moderately," concludes Popovic. "It can learn to do everything better and faster than when it is warm."

Part Three

Cold, a Mystery Unraveled

✳

9

The Hidden History of a Cold Continent

"Lord, we are grateful today for all you have given us . . . as we watch the melting of snow that fell the year our Lord was born. We know that was a joyful year."

This prayer was intoned by Rear Admiral James W. Kelly, chief of Navy chaplains, on a July day in 1968 at Annapolis, Maryland. Containers of this historic snow are being kept at the Academy Chapel. It is mixed with the "water from the Seven Seas" in which third-year midshipmen traditionally dip their rings each spring. One vial has gone to the Vatican for further prayer.

Scientists at Byrd Station, Antarctica, treated the ice in more cavalier fashion, dropping a chunk or two laid down in 1776 into glasses of bourbon.

These frozen souvenirs of history came from the ice cores that have been lifted from the Antarctic ice cap by a huge drill rig. Work was begun in the Antarctic summer of 1966–67, and the drill had reached a depth of 700 feet before winter closed in and forced a halt. The next year the eight-man team sent from the Army's Cold Regions Research & Engineering Laboratory in Hanover, New Hampshire, was so determined to reach the bottom of the ice cap that the drill was kept going twenty-four hours a day. The men worked in a dim underground tunnel where day blended into night imperceptibly. Every three or four hours they would lift the drill and remove the core of ice within before sending the drill down again to repeat the operation. Each core was fifteen feet long and four inches in diameter. It was marked and placed in a plastic bag and stored next to the core taken directly above it. The ultimate aim was the piecing together of a complete core going from the top of the ice cap to the bottom.

And at last on January 29, 1968, the drill reached bottom after traveling through 7,100 feet of ice and snow. Some scientists confessed surprise, because seismic soundings had indicated a depth of 8,000 feet. Why had the instruments been wrong? The difference in temperature between top and bottom ice may have been to blame. The deepest Antarctic ice was laid down thousands of years ago and is undoubtedly fearsomely cold. When the surface of ice is much warmer than the interior, false signals may be emitted from below. But perhaps the explanation really involves the most startling of the immediate findings: the ice cap was resting not on bedrock, but on a layer of water.

Not everyone, to be exact, was startled. A few men had been predicting such an eventuality for many years. Back in 1925 a scientist named Nikolai Zubov first suggested that an ice cap could logically lie on water. He was discussing Greenland, not Antarctica, however. The basis of his hypothesis was that the enormous pressure of the ice above combined with the heat rising from the earth's interior would cause some melting just above the surface. But his idea won more opponents than advocates. In 1966 the theory had its first test when a huge drill went to the bottom of the Greenland ice cap. Zubov's opponents believed themselves proven correct when the tip of the drill failed to touch water. Then two years later came the discovery of water beneath the Antarctic ice and Zubov was vindicated. Why was he wrong about Greenland? Perhaps the ice cap is not thick enough; perhaps the earth's crust is very thick there . . . no one is sure.

The Antarctic ice cap is the largest in the world, holding approximately nine-tenths of all the earth's ice and about two percent of its total supply of fresh water. Byrd Station stands 5,000 feet above sea level, and the ice cap there extends more than 2,000 feet below. At its highest point, the ice sheet is 14,000 feet thick and rises 13,000 feet above the sea. The average height is 7,500 feet, and the average thickness, 6,000 feet. There is some evidence that the ice sheet was once even thicker—by about 1,000 feet. The weight of the ice today has been estimated at 22 quadrillion tons. Experts speculate that should the Antarctic ice cap ever melt, the oceans of the earth would rise by about 200 feet, flooding every coastal city. The disaster example most frequently given concerns the Statue of Liberty, which would be covered with water up to its nose.

Within the enormous sheet of ice lie the answers to questions that seem on the face of it impossible to answer. Did prehistoric man breathe the same kind of air that we do, or was the atmosphere richer then in oxygen or carbon dioxide? How many volcanic eruptions sent lava flowing over the earth in centuries before Vesuvius spewed forth the ash that covered Pompeii? Was the world warm in 15,000 B.C.? Did it snow a lot during a winter of 40,000 years past? How many particles from outer space showered the earth 10,000 years ago? Did great ice sheets cover both northern and southern hemispheres at the same time, or did an ice age in one lead to an ice age in another? As the cores are lifted, an accurate year-by-year history of climate emerges with them. The Antarctic cores can be compared and correlated with those brought from the other frozen part of the globe—the Arctic.

When the drill brought up Antarctic ice from a depth of 4,370 feet, a layer of ash could be plainly seen, the detritus of a volcanic eruption 10,000 or more years ago. The drill went deeper, and at 4,627 feet was another layer.

But how can anyone know the date when the volcano erupted, or say that this bit of ice was laid down when the Vikings sailed the seas, and that the year the Declaration of Independence was signed? Ice is deposited in layers, and scientists can count down to get the age of each—at least for the first portion of the core—much as one can tell how old a tree is by the number of rings. It is even possible to tell which snow fell on the earth in an ancient winter and which during a long-ago summer. The winter layers of snow are thick, closely packed, and finely grained, while the layers of summer snow are thinner, more loosely packed, and coarser. A separation between layers is the legacy of a time when the climate grew warmer and some ice thawed. This has happened only once in 10,000 years of Antarctic ice history. Deep down in the ice cap the layers cannot be read. They are terribly thin as a result of thousands and thousands of years of tremendously high pressure.

When the final core was brought up, the first question newspaper reporters asked scientists was how old was the ice at the bottom. A top-of-the-head guess of 50,000 years was given. "But there is no certainty at all that this is so," says Kurt V. Sandved, who is with the Antarctic Programs for the National Science Foundation. "The ice at the bottom could be hundreds of thousands of years old. The tests that are needed for dating that far back require large quantities of ice. At this point people are very hesitant about melting down these valuable cores."

One of the more sophisticated methods of dating involves determining the ratio between isotopes of oxygen in the ice. The normal atomic weight of oxygen is 16, but the ice also contains a small amount of a heavier oxygen isotope with an atomic weight of 18. The lower the temperature, the less there is of oxygen 18. Ice laid down in winter, therefore, has a smaller amount of this than the summer ice. The ratio between them can be calculated even when the ice is packed so tightly that the layers cannot be seen.

Trapped in the cores are bubbles of the very air breathed by prehistoric man. The carbon dioxide in these bubbles can be studied and dated with radiocarbon techniques. This method, which is used most often to date fossils, is based on the fact that air, water, and organic life contain a small amount of the radioactive isotope of carbon, which is carbon 14. This changes at a known rate into nitrogen. The decaying carbon 14 can be measured in the minuscule amounts buried in the ice. But again, it takes a minimum of one ton of ice to obtain enough radiocarbon to perform the tests.

The air bubbles, valuable as a source of history, make the ice cores extremely difficult to handle. Relatively large in the upper layers, the bubbles get progressively smaller going down. The pressure on those in the deepest cores is so great that they may explode when released. The deep core then shatters before being brought to the surface. Even the bubbles in the 200-year-old ice used to cool the scientists' whisky burst in the glasses with the sound of corn popping.

The same Antarctic summer that took the drill to the bottom of the ice cap through thousands of years of history also saw the discovery of a fossil far older than the oldest ice. It was the first animal bone ever found near the South Pole. Most anthropologists were sure that fossils must be there, but with ninety-eight to ninety-nine percent of the rock surface of the huge continent covered with ice, the likelihood of finding any could be compared to the proverbial search for the needle in a haystack. The bone was found when no one was looking for it. Geologists from Ohio State University were chipping away at the frozen sediment on the bottom of what had once been a stream. Suddenly their tools uncovered a wing-shaped bone. Although it was only two and a half inches long, the men fortunately recognized its significance at once and removed it with the greatest care. In time it was identified by Edwin Colbert of the American Museum of Natural History as a bit of the jawbone of a salamander that had lived 200 million years ago. Even stranger was the fact that this was an animal incapable of enduring cold temperatures. In the era when he lived, the entire world, including the Antarctic, had been warm and friendly.

The first scientific evidence that the Antarctic had once been warm was obtained in the summer of 1892–93 when a piece of a fossil pine tree was discovered. Then in 1908 when Ernest Shackleton and his men were making their way across desolate Beardmore Glacier (named, like so much of Antarctica, for a magnate who had financed the expedition) in an effort to reach the South Pole, they came upon a small deposit of coal—proof of a past vegetation. Robert Falcon Scott also crossed that glacier on his return from the South Pole and found additional deposits of coal. As he lifted some cold slabs with his heavily gloved hands, he saw clear imprints of the leaves and thick stems of prehistoric plants—a record of a warmer, happier past. Some of the leaves resembled those of beech trees and others the seed fern that had been common in the swamplike forests of prehistoric days.

In the years since then many plant remains have been found and there can be no doubt that in the days before ice blanketed the continent, it was covered with lush vegetation. Fig trees, ferns, laurel, beech, and sequoias grew in the rain forests, and pine, hemlock, and other cone-bearing trees in the slightly cooler areas. Huge petrified logs, as much as a foot and a half across, have been found in regions close to the South Pole, evidence that the forests reached all the way there.

Some of the tree fossils are suggestively similar to trees found in Australia, New Zealand, and the southern parts of South America, and others resemble the vegetation of South Africa and India.

When the first animal fossil was found and its family tree studied, the discovery was made that it was a member of a family of amphibians, the Labyrinthodonts, believed to have existed 200 million years ago in India and Africa. Then in late 1969 another prehistoric fossil, this one of the reptilian Lystrosaurus, was uncovered in a streambed near the Beardmore Glacier. Remains of this same Triassic animal have been found in many places in South America and South Africa. How did the Lystrosaurus, Labyrinthodont, trees, and plants get from Antarctica to South America, India, Africa, and Australia, and vice versa? The closest continent today, South America, is separated by 700 miles of stormy seas. But perhaps it was not always like that; in the prehistoric past, Antarctica may not have been isolated. This theory is an old one and, prior to the animal fossil finds, had many opponents. Gradually skeptics have been won over to the belief that Antarctica, Australia, South America, Africa, and India once made up the supercontinent of Gondwanaland. (The name derives from the Gondwana region of India.) And indeed, as the most casual glance at a map reveals, the east coast of South America does fit neatly into the coast of Africa. Less obvious because of the coating of ice, but suggestive to scientists, is the way southeastern Australia could fit into Antarctica's Ross Sea, its southwestern end onto Antarctica's Knox coast, while Australia's concave Great Bight is matched by the convex Antarctic Wilkes Land. Perhaps over millions of years the continents broke up and drifted apart.

According to this theory, the continents are not fixed in unchanging position on the earth's surface. The extent of the drift is as yet unproven. Some studies indicate that the ocean floor is spreading at the rate of one to ten centimeters a year. It expands by at least 500 kilometers every ten million or so years. Supercontinents form and then gradually move apart. Gondwanaland, many experts say, must have begun its breakup about 200 million years ago for the continents to have reached the position they are in today. Or the split may have begun more . . . or less recently. Over the course of tens of millions of years Antarctica drifted slowly southward, while India moved north, South America west, and Africa rotated clockwise. Australia and Antarctica may have been the last to split, possibly remaining together up to 40 million years ago.

The proof of when, where, and how the prehistoric continents moved is recorded in the rocks beneath the ocean—if only they can be read. The iron particles in rock point toward the direction of the pole. Samples are taken from the ocean bottom and tested with high-precision instruments capable of determining magnetic field. As the continents moved from one latitude to another, their positions naturally changed in relation to the magnetic poles. Nor did the poles remain constant. They wandered slowly across the globe. In addition, every so often at irregular intervals that may be as short as 30,000 or as long as 2 million years or more, the earth flips its magnetic field. The north magnetic pole changes places with the south. This is believed to have happened nine times in the last 3.6 million years, as evidenced by the belts of rock magnetized in opposite directions on the ocean floor. The Antarctic thus was not always cold, and it was not always the location for the South Pole.

Perhaps its position in part explains the ice ages. For the great ice sheets that wiped out the salamander, plants, and trees of Antarctica have covered other parts of the globe periodically. According to one hypothesis, ice ages could not take place during any period when the poles were in open ocean. Such a position would allow free interchange of warm and cold water. The ice caps could not build up and temperatures would be equalized. So it was during the ages when the world was pleasantly warm, and one season followed another, one year another, in this part of the globe or that, with hardly any change. But when the poles reached positions of isolation, the interchange of warm and cold water could not take place, and temperatures in the middle and higher latitudes could decline. Dr. William L. Donn and Dr. Maurice Ewing of the Lamont-Doherty Geological Observatory suggest that with the poles in their present positions, glaciation probably began on Antarctica and remained there throughout the Pleistocene Epoch, causing both hemispheres to become cooler. Moisture from the Antarctic made possible an ice sheet buildup in the southern hemisphere and the southern half of North America. The rest of the northern hemisphere was frozen by the moisture coming from an ice-free Arctic Ocean. Enormous blizzards formed over that open sea and fed the growing ice caps. The ice age stopped when no more moisture was available; then the Arctic Ocean froze again, and the ice cap began a slow decline.

A theory placing ice age blame directly on the Antarctic was presented in 1964 by Dr. Alexander T. Wilson of New Zealand's Victoria University of Wellington. He suggests that every so often the bottom of the ice cap melts as a result of pressure from the weight of the ice on top and the heat coming from deep within the earth. Some water even now lies beneath the ice at Byrd Station, and possibly elsewhere. As the quantity of meltwater increases and spreads, the ice breaks free and surges into the sea, covering perhaps 10 million square miles of ocean. The ice reflects solar energy back into space and the earth grows cooler. Gradually in the northern hemisphere, too, the glaciers form. The grip of the ice age will not be broken until the ice has spread and thickened to the point where it again freezes to the rock. Then it can go no farther and the ocean can begin to melt the ice around the edges until eventually the sun's heat can again be absorbed and the world's temperature rise. Wilson believes that the cycle will go on until the Antarctic drifts away from the South Pole.

Others theorize that ice ages are produced by the sunspot cycle, or by periodic changes in the tilt of the earth's axis, or that volcanic eruptions send up a blanket of dust and gases that prevents some solar radiation from reaching and heating the earth.

The number and complexity of theories and the controversy raging about them among scientists causes most people to assume that ice age study has a long history. Yet the mere fact that ice ages had occurred was unknown to Hippocrates, Alexander the Great, Leonardo da Vinci, Sir Isaac Newton, and Benjamin Franklin.

"Those who hear of this history for the first time may well be excused if they listen with some incredulity," wrote James Geikie in 1877 of the events described in his book *The Great Ice Age.*

Ice ages were suggested off and on in the early nineteenth century, but were not considered seriously until the 1830's. At that time two Swiss scientists, J. Venetz and Jean de Charpentier, declared their belief that glaciers had once covered all of northern Europe. The last vestiges of the European ice sheet lay in the Alps. This claim came to the attention of Jean Louis Rodolphe Agassiz, professor of natural history at the University of Neuchâtel and an eminent zoologist and geologist. Ridiculous, he said, but he was sufficiently impressed to go off to the Alps to examine the terrain and prove his rivals wrong. There the presence of glacial debris around the edges of the glaciers convinced him that they had once been much larger. From then on, Agassiz became the principal spokesman for ice ages and did his best to present the concept to the world. Nonetheless, pockets of resistance existed until the twentieth century. Many people remained just as incredulous as Geikie thought they might be. Yet one part of the globe then, as now, was still in the grip of an ice age.

"Antarctica is a natural laboratory of extreme conditions not found anywhere else on the surface of the earth. Here we have life surviving and evolving at the limits of endurance," Dr. Leland J. Haworth, then Director of the National Academy of Sciences, told a Senate subcommittee in May of 1965. "We have a Pleistocene condition similar to that which covered parts of the northern hemisphere thousands of years ago."

Nothing has changed significantly since the ice cap first covered the continent, and scientists now know how long ago that was. Potassium-argon dating of rocks in the dry valleys of Antarctica along with studies of deep-sea cores put the date of the original formation of the Antarctic ice cap at 2.7 million years ago.

It seems almost ironic to study Antarctic history of millions of years ago when the continent itself had not even been discovered until fairly recently. The belief that a southern continent lay waiting to be found antedated its first sighting by many centuries. Aristotle insisted that the laws of nature demanded that there be an area in the far south to balance the one in the far north. The Greeks considered it habitable and called it the land of Antichthones. And in time Cicero and other Romans became adherents of this theory. During the Dark Ages the firm conviction that the earth was flat was used as an argument to prove that Antarctica could not exist. By the fifteenth century it had been renamed Terra Australis Nondam Cognita, the southern land not yet known. But known or not, during the sixteenth century it began to appear on the maps. In some, such as the famous ones drawn by Flemish Gerald Mercator, it appeared larger than the Americas. This land was thought to be a golden paradise, lush with plants, rich in spices, another, possibly fairer, West Indies. Nothing could destroy this fantasy, even when Sir Francis Drake sailed around South America into the very area where the continent was supposed to be and found nothing.

Ships ventured ever farther south and seamen brought back tales of icebergs, seals, and penguins. But surely, said the Europeans, the ice could not extend all the way south. Go but a bit farther, and surely the warm and lovely continent will be there.

And so it was in 1772 that Yves Joseph de Kerguelen-Trémarec sailed into the sub-Antarctic waters and found an island. Now named Kerguelen Island in his honor, it was called by him, with true nationalistic fervor, South France. He was convinced that he had reached an actual continent. Storms were raging—a common climatic condition in those parts—and so he could see rather little. This served only to stimulate his vivid imagination. The land, dimly viewed through snow, fog, and mist, must conceal a wealth of minerals and precious gems. Crops could surely be grown on the rich soil. People must live there, he wrote, in a state of nature, and he added hopefully that they might be members of a different species. But when Kerguelen-Trémarec returned the following year, it was to find only a cluster of cold barren islands, always battered by storms and covered with mist. Sadly he admitted that his great discovery was in truth a "land of desolation."

When in that same year of 1773 Captain James Cook crossed the Antarctic Circle, his crew was plunged into despair at the bleak vista of ice. He returned to the area and reached South Georgia and dutifully claimed it for Great Britain, although he considered it a "savage and horrible land." Disillusioned, the tall, gaunt Englishman declared that even if another explorer should reach a point farther south, "I shall not envy him the fame of his discovery, but I make bold to declare that the world will derive no benefit from it."

But Cook was wrong in his prediction. The discovery of the Antarctic continent was duly made, and the world has been deriving benefit from this ever since. To whom does the honor of the discovery belong? The answer depends upon the nationality of the person giving it. American, British, and Russian—each has a solid basis for making the claim. To take the American first, in 1820 five ships sailed out of Stonington, Connecticut, and headed southward across the Drake Passage in search of the fur seal. The ships anchored close to the South Shetland Islands, and the leader of the expedition, Captain Benjamin Pendleton, ordered his youngest skipper, twenty-year-old Nathaniel B. Palmer, to take the thirty-foot sloop *Hero* and continue the search to the south. Palmer sailed on until he saw a long coastline with high mountains behind it. He was not able to get through the ice to the land and eventually returned to the rest of the fleet. The coastline that he sighted is now known to have been part of the Antarctic Peninsula and it was called Palmer Peninsula by Americans for many years.

The British refused to follow suit, as they declined to acknowledge Palmer's discovery altogether. Graham Land, as they named it, was discovered, they insist, by British sea captains William Smith and Edward Bransfield. The two, also in search of seals, set off for the south in 1819 and also reached the South Shetland Islands. They returned home expecting praise, but as few people—even Englishmen—believed their story, they went back the following year. This time they came upon the peninsula. The British have ever since maintained that the sighting antedated Palmer's by ten months.

The disagreement over the actual discovery has never been settled, but the disagreement over the name was ended in 1964, when both countries agreed to use the neutral term Antarctic Peninsula.

The Russian claim rests on the exploits of Thaddeus von

The Hidden History of a Cold Continent

Bellingshausen, captain of the ships *Vostok* and *Mirny*, which sailed across the Antarctic Circle in January of 1820. Oddly enough, Bellingshausen was so unimpressed by this that he did not even trouble to jot down the time and exact place of crossing in his journal. He did, however, describe a coast of ice cliffs backed by mountains that can easily be recognized as Antarctica. On his return, the Russian ships sailed past a small American sloop. It was Palmer's *Hero* coming back from its Antarctic journey. Bellingshausen did not receive a hero's welcome in Russia. The czar was no more interested than the captain himself had been. Three years passed before the Russian ruler could be induced to allocate any funds for the publication of the reports and maps of the journey. For more than a century thereafter, the Russians paid little attention to the Antarctic.

The conflicting claims of sightings and of landings were somewhat cynically put in perspective by Arctic explorer Vilhjalmur Stefansson in a speech made in the 1920's: "A land may be said to be discovered the first time a white European, preferably an Englishman, sets foot on it. If he is accredited by the Royal Geographical Society, so much the better."

The search for seals and whales continued to be the motive for Antarctic expeditions from many countries during the next few decades. The hazards of these journeys were increased immeasurably by an excessively casual attitude toward taking even the simplest precautions. Charles Wilkes, commander of an American expedition, stopped in Australia before making the run to the Antarctic. He commented on the questions asked him by the Australians: "Whether we had compartments to prevent us sinking? How were we to keep ourselves warm? What antiscorbutics did we have? And where were our great ice-saws? To all of these questions I was obliged to answer . . . that we had none." Twenty-three men died and 127 deserted, and Wilkes was court-martialed for injustices and oppression of his crew.

But injustice, danger, and hazards have never stopped exploration. If anything, they are a lure to those who would prove their courage.

"Men wanted for hazardous journey. Small wages, bitter cold, long months of complete darkness. Constant danger, safe return doubtful. Honor and recognition in case of success."

This notice placed in a London newspaper typifies the spirit of the heroic age of exploration dominated by Robert Falcon Scott and by Ernest Shackleton, author of the quoted advertisement.

The opportunity to be honored and recognized (and not to return safely) was thrust upon Scott, a naval officer with no previous polar experience. The British government, the Royal Society, and the Royal Geographical Society were then seeking a man to lead an expedition to the Antarctic. The choice was made by Sir Clements Markham. When Sir Clements was later asked, why Scott, he replied simply that Scott was a good navy man. And then he added, well, he liked Scott's looks. And indeed Scott was a most appealing figure, with a handsome, sensitive, intelligent face, winning smile, and charming manner. What is more, he was a gentleman in an era and a country which set great store on that quality. It was this very attribute that was ultimately to destroy him and his men.

Consider Scott, on his first expedition in 1902, deprecating his decision to be the first man to go up over the Antarctic in a captive balloon: "The honor of being the first aeronaut to make an ascent in the Antarctic Regions, perhaps somewhat selfishly, I chose for myself." He would not have thought it proper to mention the great danger he faced of being blown away or dashed to earth by the little-understood polar winds. As soon as Scott was back on the ice, Shackleton took his place. Shackleton was only third officer of the ship *Discovery*, but there was no question of his lagging behind when risks were involved. Bearing a camera in his gauntleted hand, he photographed Balloon Bight, now known as the Bay of Whales. These aerial photographs are used by scientists to this day when they wish to study the ever-changing Antarctic ice pack.

With Scott, Antarctic exploration entered the scientific phase that has since become the most important part of it. He combined an ambition to be first man at the South Pole with the aim of gathering scientific information about the great uncharted continent. His expedition was supplied with Bunsen burners, bottled gas, anemometers, thermometers, and scales, and some of these research instruments were carried along on the dash to the pole. Scott's chief rival, the Norwegian explorer Roald Amundsen, on the other hand, displayed little interest in anything but reaching his goal.

The race to the pole captured the public imagination in the first dozen years of the twentieth century. Shackleton, who led an expedition of his own, nearly won it. He also fit the stereotype for a hero, although very different from Scott. His body was large and powerful, and he was high-spirited, a gambler by temperament, and as a friend described him, "in love with adventure." The magnetism of his personality made him a natural leader. The difficulties of the journey to the pole were pure joy for Shackleton, as he reveled in the utter harshness of the world. Let it storm, he would rush out into the blizzard to watch the swirling snow and announce that his "imagination would take wings." As his party crossed the high polar plateau, they began to struggle for breath in the thin oxygen. Headaches were of such severity that Shackleton wrote that he sometimes felt "as though the nerves were being twisted up by a corkscrew and then pulled out." And as they were unable to carry enough food, they were hungry long before the trip was half over. On a January day in 1909 Shackleton faced the unhappy fact, "we have shot our bolt." The pole was not far; estimates of their position vary, with some placing the party at 112 miles, and others at 97 miles away from the pole. The journey back was even harder, as one after the other came down with dysentery. Shackleton, in the true tradition of the gentleman, gave a last biscuit to one of his weaker companions. Although his expedition failed to reach the geographic pole, which was the ultimate goal, a small party did get as far as the magnetic pole. Shackleton himself—no doubt to his dismay—was not among them.

No polar expedition before or after possessed the drama and poignancy of Scott's last attempt at the South Pole. Nothing went right for him. His own mistakes were compounded by a series of misfortunes beyond his control. At the very beginning of the trek across the ice shelf, in November of 1911, a summer blizzard made him lose four precious days of daylight. Of the nineteen ponies taken along, nine died right away. The motor sledges that were to carry his party easily for the first part of the journey broke down after covering only a few miles. Scott was imaginative in finding means of Antarctic locomotion. A go-cart mounted on four bicycle wheels was tried at one point. And he even packed a bicycle, used a few times by the expedition geologist.

But when it came to getting across the Beardmore Glacier and polar plateau, only one way was really suitable, and that was to use sledges pulled by dogs. Scott was by this time well enough versed in polar logistics to know that, but the way the dogs would have to be treated on such a journey turned his stomach. A team of dogs would run for a time and then when the weakest ones were exhausted, they would be killed. This saved the weight of their food, and they could be eaten by the other dogs or even the men if necessary. By starting with more dogs than were needed, the explorer would be sure of still having a team at the end. It was a brutal business, and Scott would have none of it. And so he and his men hauled their sledges themselves. It was heroic work—and it killed them.

Slowly and painstakingly they pulled their supplies across the glacier. Avalanches had made the way even more hazardous than when Shackleton had traveled there. The spirits of the weary men rose as they knew themselves to be drawing near to the pole. And then they caught a glimpse of dog paw prints and the debris of what had once been a camp. At the pole itself a flag tied to a sledge was floating in the still cold air. Amundsen had beaten Scott to the pole. And Amundsen, pulled by dogs the whole way, had not even suffered. "Great God! This is an awful place and terrible enough for us to have labored to it without the reward of priority," wrote Scott in his journal. But even as his party struggled back across the plateau, frostbitten and suffering from tendons pulled by the strain of hauling, they stopped to make a scientific study of the Beardmore Glacier. This was when they found the records of a time when the Antarctic, in sharp contrast to its present state, was warm. In addition to the plant fossils, which were at least light in weight, the party gathered a large number of rocks. These were loaded onto a sledge and the journey continued.

Each day the men grew weaker and were able to cover fewer miles on the icy plateau; their hardships spurred them on to deeds of gallantry. On a stormy night when the thermometer registered -40°F., Captain Oates, the frailest of the men, walked out of the shelter to his death. He had realized that he was becoming a burden to his fellows. As the miserable party staggered on, they kept throwing things out of the sledges so as to lighten them. But they refused to discard the rocks and other scientific specimens. On March 19, 1912, they made camp and were trapped by a blizzard; they were only eleven miles away from their depot. "Had we lived," wrote Scott, "I should have had a tale to tell of the hardihood, endurance, and courage of my companions which would have stirred the heart of every Englishman." At the very moment he was writing these words, Amundsen was being cheered in Australia.

When a search party finally located the dead bodies, it also found thirty-five pounds of geological specimens still firmly fastened onto the sledge. The expedition's scientific records described the part of Antarctica they had traversed. Among their discoveries were certain snow-free valleys where rocks were exposed to the frigid air.

From Scott's day to the present, exploration of the continent has gone on, with many governments sponsoring expeditions. American exploration was dominated by Rear Admiral Richard Evelyn Byrd, who led his first expedition in 1928 and went back repeatedly until his death in 1957. Like Scott, Byrd combined the romantic spirit of adventure with the desire to make a scientific contribution. Trained scientists accompanied all his journeys and meteorological, auroral, geological, and other scientific phenomena were studied. At the same time, field parties explored as much of the vast continent as possible.

In 1938 Antarctica came to the attention of Adolf Hitler. At his urging, Hermann Goering ordered a four-year plan of exploration to be led by Alfred Ritscher. The continent was renamed Schwabenland. In January of 1939 the Norwegians hastily declared that Queen Maud Land belonged to them. The German expedition paid little attention, and Ritscher anchored his ships offshore and sent a number of big seaplanes, the Dornier-Wal flying boats, to photograph the interior. Displaying German efficiency, photographers on board the boats took 12,000 pictures in just three weeks, covering an area of 350,000 square kilometers. The pilots dropped markers while they flew as evidence of the German claim to part of Queen Maud Land, or as they called it, Neu Schwabenland.

After the German defeat in World War II an unfounded rumor spread that instead of dying in the bunker, Hitler and Eva Braun had fled Germany by U-boat and had reached Neu Berchtesgarten in the "German colony" of Neu Schwabenland.

The negatives of the photographs taken by the Ritscher expedition were destroyed during the last days of the war, but maps, now known to be somewhat inaccurate, had already been drawn based on their findings.

For all the efforts at traversing and mapping the continent, at the end of fifty or so years of determined exploration, the Antarctic remained the mysterious continent.

"When the second half of this century started, we knew

less about the snow cover on Antarctica than about the dust layer on the Moon," wrote Colin Bull of the Institute of Polar Studies of Ohio State University in the American Geological Institute's magazine, *Geotimes.* "Perhaps 20 percent of the continent had been seen, nearly all from the air."

A few expeditions of sledges across the ice had been made during and after the Scott-Shackleton-Amundsen period of exploration, but very little scientific data about the depth or movement of the ice had been amassed. Members of a 1949–52 Norwegian-British-Swedish (Maudheim) Expedition made seismic soundings in Queen Maud Land. They then dug pits in the ice, and for the first time observed that the annual layers of snow could be differentiated, a finding that was to be the basis for the major drilling projects.

It took the International Geophysical Year of 1957–58, however, to make Antarctica an important world center for scientific study. The original idea for this project is generally attributed to Dr. James A. Van Allen. On the night of April 5, 1950, he had invited a number of American scientists to his home to meet a visiting British geophysicist, Sydney Chapman, and in the course of the evening's conversation, he proposed this plan. It took several years for it to be put into operation, and the year was extended to eighteen months— July 1, 1956, through December 31, 1958. This period was considered particularly suitable for such a project, because sunspot activity was due to be very heavy and several eclipses were expected. Emphasis was to be placed on the influence of the Antarctic on the world's weather. Scientists were to investigate the aurora australis, cosmic rays, the nature of the ionosphere during the winter night, and seismic waves. In addition, the continent was to be traversed by vehicles and completely mapped. The ice cap was to be analyzed and its movement measured. In the course of the year 60,000 scientists from sixty-six countries cooperated in the worldwide research.

Then and afterward the Antarctic has proven to be an incredible laboratory. Even aside from the ice, the Antarctic is a continent like no other. Near the pole both winter night and summer day last six months. In winter the pack ice covers the sea for several hundred miles out, and still in summer ice and icebergs extend out for between 100 and 500 miles. The winds are stronger than anywhere else on earth and the temperatures lower. The record of -126.9°F. was set at Vostok Station on August 24, 1960, and the U. S. Plateau Station has endured cold of -123.1°F. Cosmic ray studies are particularly meaningful at the poles, because these charged particles are not deflected as in other regions. The earth's magnetic field is sharply angled, becoming vertical at one place and no Van Allen radiation belts are found above this. As the Antarctic Convergency combines the waters of three oceans, the Atlantic, Pacific, and Indian, it is an ideal place for the study of deep ocean currents. The information from earth-orbiting satellites is read at stations located near the pole.

The necessity of pooling painfully gathered scientific data may be the reason why the Antarctic has been the one place on earth where international cooperation has really worked. In December of 1959 the twelve countries most deeply involved in research signed the Antarctic Treaty limiting the continent to peaceful uses, and it became effective in 1961. The treaty bypasses the complicated web of territorial claims and simply guarantees any nation the right to work anywhere in Antarctica. By the end of the 1960's forty camps were being manned by ten nations. The U. S. and then the U. S. S. R. have the most ambitious programs, but stations are also operated by France, the United Kingdom, Japan, New Zealand, Australia, Argentina, Chile, and South Africa.

Setting up these stations and continuing to live there is exceedingly difficult, because not only people, animals, and plants, but materials as well are affected by cold. At a comparatively mild Antarctic temperature of -60°F., diesel oil and kerosene are as thick as maple syrup and work just about as well in motors. Rubber deteriorates and breaks. Metals become brittle, and a heavy steel bar will snap in two like a twig. Only equipment made of nonmagnetic stainless steel, aluminum, copper, brass, and a few other alloys can endure low temperatures. Even so, engines do not start readily and all mechanisms get balky. On a September day a few years ago a field party tried to set off from Vostok with a tractor. The antifreeze froze, clogging the lines. The men worked for ten hours with a blowtorch before they could take off.

Another field party attempted to celebrate Christmas on the shores of a frozen lake where rock studies were being conducted. The bottles of whisky froze and burst, and the steak had to be cut with a hacksaw.

Putting down the results of scientific experiments can present additional difficulties. The ink in the recording machines used to freeze regularly at Vostok. The Soviet scientists returned it to a liquid state by adding one part of antifreeze and one of alcohol mixed with glycerin to every three parts of ink. This, however, made the ink blot on the recording tape. A dash of sugar proved to be the solution, at least as long as the temperature remained at or above -107.4°F.

Just keeping a station above the shifting ice can be an impossible assignment. One camp, built in 1957, is today under four to twelve feet of snow.

"It's like trying to live on a big bowl of Jell-o," says Rear Admiral J. Lloyd Abbott, Jr., commander of Operation Deep Freeze, the Navy's logistics support program in the Antarctic.

Engineers have designed prefabricated mobile units, and whenever the ice and snow move or threaten to cave in a station, the buildings are attached to tractors and dragged off to a new location.

The ice around the South Pole is moving at the rate of about 150 feet a year. A new station is being built five miles away from the geographic pole, so that it will gradually shift into the correct position. That is, if one can ever be sure of where that is. The pole is marked by a brightly striped barber pole with a globe on top, but the U. S. Geological Survey says it has been put in the wrong place. The true pole, according to Survey calculations, is about 1,000 feet away from there, and an American flag has been raised to show it. The U. S. Coast and Geodetic Survey has yet a third spot marked out.

Aside from such questionable points, Antarctica has by now yielded most of its secrets. A few bits and pieces of the continent still remain unexplored—but no large ones. In the summer of 1967–68, the last major unknown part of Antarctica was mapped by a nineteen-man American team. The expedition traveled in Sno-Cats, the big tracked vehicles found to be most suitable for Antarctic terrain, and went 815 miles across the plateau of Queen Maud Land. And what did they find in this last uncharted area? Nothing but a flat, windswept sheet of ice.

The mapping of Antarctica is a notable achievement, made difficult not only by wind, cold, and icy crevasse-broken terrain, but also by misleading atmospheric phenomena. Mountains and icebergs in polar regions can be found, lost, seen where they do not exist, and not seen where they do. The irregular peaks of Mount Vinson and Mount Nimitz have long been familiar sights to men looking out of airplanes flying over the Antarctic from Little America to Byrd Station in the heart of Marie Byrd Land. Their positions were marked down on maps and the altitudes were estimated at 20,000 feet for Mount Vinson and 15,000 feet for Mount Nimitz. Early in 1959, with the days growing ominously short, a group of scientists set out across the ice in Sno-Cats. They were taking advantage of the last daylight to cache fuel along the route of a traverse planned for the following summer. And incidentally, along the way, they thought, they could stop to study the rock structure of Vinson and Nimitz. They drove the vehicles to the points marked on the maps but found not a sign of either mountain. Traveling on, they climbed 14,000-foot-high Mount Sidley, and even from that vantage point could not find the two peaks. The next summer they flew over the area and asked the plane's crew to call out as soon as they saw the first of the mountains.

"This done, I produced a photograph of Mount Sidley,

which was unanimously identified as the same feature under discussion," reported one of the scientists, George A. Doumani of the Library of Congress. "Errors in navigation, combined with foul weather conditions and the excessive mirage displays which are frequently encountered in the Antarctic, may contribute to erroneous observation."

Such a major error in polar exploration had not occurred since Crocker Land was discovered in the Arctic. First sighted by English whalers early in the nineteenth century, these mountains, which blocked off a northwest passage between the Atlantic and Pacific oceans, were seen again by Admiral Robert Peary in the 1890's. A 1913 expedition headed by Donald MacMillan set off to explore them. Crocker Land was clearly visible, though not in the exact place Peary had said it was. Anchoring the ship, MacMillan and a party set out across the ice in the direction of the mountains. But no matter how far they traveled, they never came any closer. And then at last dusk fell and Crocker Land disappeared, and the men looked about in dismay at an unbroken panorama of ice.

It is sometimes difficult in polar regions to trust the evidence of one's eyes. During one of Scott's expeditions in Antarctica, his men saw a different type of mirage. They had made their way toward the coast, where they knew the ship *Terra Nova* was waiting for them, concealed behind the ice cliffs. All at once they saw the ship hanging upside down, and above it a second identical vessel right side up.

At Eights Station in the Antarctic on December 26, 1964, men watched a distant mountain hanging both right side up and upside down several hundred feet above the horizon. The mirage remained for several hours. On other occasions huge icebergs have been seen to travel slowly across the sky.

Mirages in polar or hot desert areas are caused by unusual atmospheric conditions. When the air above the ground is either very much colder, as in the Antarctic, or very much warmer, as in the desert, than the air higher up, the light rays are turned or bent, creating an illusion.

White-out is another optical illusion of the polar regions. Everything—above, below, and to all sides—looks white. "Flying in a milk bottle," as this is known to pilots, has been the cause of several plane crashes. In each case the flier thought he was far above the snowy ground until the very moment he hit. One pilot started to get out of his helicopter, certain that it was on the ground, only to discover that his foot was touching nothing more substantial than the air. White-out occurs when the light waves bounce back between clouds and snow and prevent depth perception.

Despite all difficulties, Antarctica has been mapped not only on, but also beneath the surface. Until this was done, no one could be certain whether Antarctica really was a continent, and if so, how big and what shape. Thousands of feet of ice conceal its contours. The rocks and land below the ice have now been charted, and the questions answered at last. Above sea level East Antarctica is a continent, and West Antarctica is a string of islands. A study of the rocks reveals that East Antarctica is the older. The two cover an area as large as the United States and western Europe combined.

Once the continent was fully explored and the scope of scientific experiments set, a search for economic benefits was begun. Geologists pin their hopes for mineral resources beneath the ice on the theory that Antarctica was once in all probability part of the supercontinent of Gondwanaland. Perhaps, like its former territorial neighbors, Australia, Africa, Brazil, and India, East Antarctica possesses uranium, lead, silver, zinc, diamonds, gold, and iron. West Antarctica, like the South American Andes, might contain lead, tin, copper, and gold.

Many minerals have been identified in the rock specimens collected all over the Antarctic. Professor Duncan Stewart of Carleton College in 1963 listed 222 minerals found in Antarctica, noting that fourteen of these produce useful metals. But even if substantial deposits of high-value minerals, such as gold, silver, uranium, or diamonds, were found, it is very doubtful that anyone would think it commercially sound to get them out of the ice sheet and ship them north.

Considerable evidence points to the existence of several sizable coal deposits, notably in the Transantarctic Mountains of East Antarctica. One geologist has described this area as "one of the world's big coal fields." But again, it is hard to imagine why anyone would go to great lengths to bring out the coal.

Petroleum may lie deep beneath the ice in the least accessible parts of Antarctica. But it would obviously be extremely difficult to prospect through thousands of feet of ice. Drilling for the oil once it was located would be nearly as hard. The ice keeps moving and the drill would have to go with it. Huge icebergs and shifting pack ice could crush the rigs in offshore oil operations.

Every one of the problems involved could, however, be solved if it were necessary. The population of the world is increasing at an excessive rate. Each additional person must be supplied with goods of all kinds. Industrialization is reaching countries that were formerly agricultural. The need for metals, for coal, and for oil is growing every year, yet the amount of raw materials is constant. Someday the mines and oil wells in temperate zones will be depleted. At that moment men may turn to the deposits that are buried deep below the ice cap cover of the coldest continent. No one will then object to the cost and difficulty of raising these needed resources and hauling them northward. The Antarctic thus is described by one economist as "the world's natural resources ace-in-the-hole."

One of the most valuable of all commodities in the Antarctic is also held in the ice; to be exact, it is the ice—fresh water. This essential is scarce, and growing scarcer, in many parts of the world. California, to take just one example, is perennially short of water. A few years ago the interesting suggestion was made that water be obtained by floating an Antarctic iceberg all the way to California and then melting it down. The logistics have already been figured out. It would take three tugboats about two months of maneuvering to get an iceberg out of the Antarctic waters and into the Humboldt Current, which runs up the west coast of South America. In those places where the current runs too slowly, the tugs would work the berg into other favorable currents. After a trip of about a year, the iceberg would finally reach Los Angeles. During the journey through the tropics the iceberg could be expected to lose about half its bulk. But if it were ten miles long, half a mile wide, and 600 feet thick—rather small by Antarctic standards—to begin with, there would still be enough left at the end to provide about 300 billion gallons of fresh water.

Climate itself can be counted a natural resource. The refrigeration that exists naturally in the Antarctic is reproduced at considerable cost on other continents. Food shipped to the south polar region would never spoil, and so Antarctica could serve as the world's frozen food locker and cold storage warehouse. Agricultural surpluses could be saved until needed, instead of being wasted. At present, as with mining operations, the cost of getting food to and from the polar region is too great. But eventually the number of people on earth may be so great that careful planning of food supplies will become a matter of life or death for millions. The giant ice cap then might be put to use.

The cold in Antarctica is such that even in summer the ice cap does not melt. While the ice and snow make the region unpleasant to work in, they might make it pleasant to play in. It could become a resort for skiing, tobogganing, sledding, and snowshoeing. The skier could stay out on the slopes all night long, if he wished, as the Antarctic summer sun never sets. Planes could land the jet set at McMurdo Sound instead of Saint Moritz.

The continent has a rare beauty found nowhere else in the world. The magnificence of the giant bergs floating on the sea, the play of light on the ice, the clear brilliance of the sky, the strange dignity of seal and penguin, all beckon the traveler.

"The Antarctic is an addiction," says a member of a recent

expedition. "Once you have been there, you are not happy until you go back."

The age of tourism is already here. It began in 1966 when a travel agency organized a tour to Antarctica from the United States at a cost of several thousand dollars per person. No longer was a journey to the south polar region limited to the young and the strong. One of the tourists was eighty-seven years old. The group was entertained en route by scientific movies, lectures, and folk dancing. All learned how to take bottom samples from the sea and examined the plankton and sediment beneath the microscope. Then with the ice-breaking vessel serving as a floating hotel, the tour group visited the scientific bases and penguin and seal rookeries. It was indeed a trip for the person who has already been everywhere else.

The coming of tourists is but a sample of the growing bourgeois quality of life on what was only yesterday the dangerous continent of adventure. Only on an occasional field trip can members of the present-day expeditions recapture something of the spirit of the days of Scott and Shackleton. "If a scientist has to spend a night in the field, it's a traumatic experience," remarks a naval officer. Should illness strike, a pilot will fly in through the mid-winter darkness and pick up the sick man. McMurdo Station has three movie theaters and three bars. Smoke from the garbage dump floats through the air over the inlet where Scott wintered during his first expedition.

Until recently only one aspect of civilization was missing. Pinned to the bulletin board at the McMurdo Mess Hall was a sign bearing a single word: WOMEN. Those in charge of the expeditions for years persisted in saying that the "facilities are not suitable for women," and the Antarctic was, to all intents and purposes, an enormous men's club. The Russians broke down first and allowed a few women scientists to work at Antarctic bases, and in 1969 the American National Science Foundation followed suit.

Back in 1683 Robert Boyle had shown why the absence of

women was particularly bad for men in polar areas: "An old Sea Captain told me when he was in Greenland and those Artick Regions, his Appetite was so great that he could eat more in one day than he could in a week or 10 days here, and that accordingly he and others found themselves stronger there than here, and more prone to Venereal pleasure."

10

Microbes in a World of Ice

Can one catch cold in Antarctica? Although convinced that cold brings on the common cold in temperate climates, many people believe that no one has a cold in the coldest area of all, around the South Pole. This view is based on the misconception that viruses, as well as bacteria and fungi, cannot live in Antarctic temperatures. For a long time the belief was not challenged because members of the early polar expeditions did not have colds. Once large numbers of men entered the area, colds did make their unwelcome appearance. Even so, colds are less frequent in polar regions than conditions there warrant. At least that is the opinion of O.G. Edholm of the National Institute for Medical Research in London. Perhaps some adaptation to cold occurs in the vascular network supplying the mucosa of the upper respiratory tract, he suggests, making it an unfavorable place for the viruses to grow.

Although the existence of a totally sterile continent has been disproven, the fact remains that the microbial population of the air over the continent is remarkably small, compared with any other part of the world. This may contribute to the good health of the relatively few human beings who spend time there. When men first arrive at Plateau Station, 700 miles north of the South Pole, where the altitude is high and the cold severe, their white-blood-cell counts are a normal 7,350 cells per cubic centimeter of blood. After they have been there a while, the circulating white cells decline sharply in number to 3,660 cells. The function of white cells is to travel through the bloodstream, fighting off attacks of viruses and bacteria. So few microbes are encountered in the Antarctic that the defense mechanism is rarely stimulated.

The paucity of microbes is such that bacteriologists accompanying expeditions in the early twentieth century were seldom able to find any at all. Scientist H. Gazert of the German South Polar Expedition of 1901–03 gathered falling snow when the ship *Gauss* was frozen in the pack ice. He did not obtain a single bacterium from the meltwater. In the course of the Scottish National Antarctic Expedition of 1902–04, J. E. H. Pirie had glass plates placed in the crow's nest of the main mast and left there for several periods of up to twenty hours each. Again, not a microbe was caught. A decade later during Scott's second expedition the first bacterium, described as "very motile," was isolated from snow. In the years since then bacteria, yeasts, and other fungi have been discovered in snow, in glacier ice, and in the air. But they are scarce, and many air samples taken are found to be sterile.

Turning to the sea, in the course of the International Geophysical Year, 1957–58, scientists on the Soviet ship *Ob* took samples from Antarctic, sub-Antarctic, and sub-tropical waters, and performed bacteria counts. No bacteria could be found in forty-three percent of the samples; only one colony was growing in another thirteen percent. The microbes appeared in larger numbers in water that was close to the land masses.

The scarcity of bacteria is particularly surprising, comments Dr. John McNeill Sieburth, Associate Professor at Rhode Island University's Graduate School of Oceanography, considering how rich the seas are in other microscopic living things. The zooplankton, or minuscule fish and crustaceans, and the phytoplankton, the infinitesimal plants, float in the upper levels of the water, going down as far as the rays of sunlight can reach. The bloom is heaviest from mid-December to March, declining thereafter with the declining day. The teeming plankton populations are of inestimable importance to higher forms of life. They are at the bottom of the food chain: small fish feed on plankton, large fish and birds feed on small fish, animals and man feed on fish and other animals. If plankton could not survive in the Antarctic seas, then whales, penguins, and seals could not live there either. A baleen whale strains out and consumes a ton or more of shrimplike krill, each no more than an inch or two long, in just a few minutes.

Whatever the reason, the bounty of plankton and the scarcity of viruses, bacteria, and fungi combine to sustain the life of larger animals in the brutal Antarctic. Mammals, birds, and fish seem to be relatively free of serious bacterial and viral diseases. (The high infant mortality among penguins is a result of storms, exposure, starvation, and attack by predators, rather than illness.) A veterinary on board a whaling ship some years ago examined 2,000 whales intended for human consumption and found illness in only one of them. But scientists have so seldom observed Antarctic animals in the wild state that they believe some existing diseases may not yet have been diagnosed. Polar literature contains many references to mass deaths among seals and penguins. The cause might very well be a viral or bacterial infection. Most of these reports, however, have never been documented.

One of the few opportunities to track down such a disease came to Sieburth a few years ago when he visited a rookery and found large numbers of penguins lying dead or dying. He diagnosed the disease in general terms as an acute intestinal infection and isolated micro-organisms from the birds' bodies. The bacteria bore a strong resemblance to the ubiquitous *Salmonella*, which causes intestinal illnesses in both animals and man. Antarctica is not so remote from the rest of the world that microbes cannot travel there. The herring gull and a number of other oceanic birds are known to harbor the pathogen, and might fly with it over great distances to reach the rookeries. Absolute proof that these penguins died of salmonellosis will never be obtained. The microbes were taken on board a ship to be returned to the United States for laboratory study. A storm blew up and buffeted the ship severely. When it subsided, Sieburth observed to his dismay that the bacteria had been destroyed.

Cold, a Mystery Unraveled

Although deadly illnesses like this one appear to be rare, minor diseases do plague Antarctic animals. Mild respiratory infections are often found in the nose, pharynx, and trachea. The crabeater and Weddell seal harbor bacteria that may very well give them sore throats; unfortunately, they cannot describe symptoms. Microbes were observed to be plentiful in the hurt nose of a sea elephant. And within the throat of the skua gull are germs of the type known to cause tracheitis in other creatures. The gull's cry, however, was not affected. Skin infections are particularly common among the more competitive beasts. On a summer's day a year or so ago two male seals were engaged in a vicious fight over a female. They fought until both were exhausted and then flopped off to rest and nurse their wounds. Scientists on a field expedition to the area had been observing the battle. Creeping up on the weary animals, they cautiously swabbed at the wounds. When the swabs were later subjected to laboratory tests, infectious bacteria were isolated. On one of his many trips to the Antarctic, the late Dr. Paul A. Siple slashed his hand while hacking at seal blubber. The cut quickly became filled with pus, and the infection spread to other bruises on his arms. A hunter infected his hand by handling the birds he shot. There had been a small cut on a finger and the bacteria had slipped from the bird into his bloodstream. An unexpected exception to the general rule of infection has been reported by men working with oceanographic gear. Their hands are constantly wet, and any cuts on fingers and knuckles stay open for months. Yet these do not become infected. One theory that would account for this phenomenon is that antibiotics formed by the phytoplankton floating in the water kill the bacteria.

The concept of a microbe-free environment dies hard. Around the turn of the century the first microbiological studies of the gastrointestinal tracts of seals and birds were made. The bodies of all animals, including man, play host to large numbers of bacteria, most of them harmless. And this was also true of many of the Antarctic animals. Yet among the birds tested the scientists found surprising numbers who seemed to have no bacteria at all. They tried again and again to culture microbes, but nothing grew on their slides and petri dishes. At last they declared these birds to be "bacteriologically sterile." Time passed and other biologists went to the Antarctic and studied the animals and every so often other microbe-free creatures would be found. A number turned up in 1955 on sub-Antarctic Macquarie Island.

By this time Sieburth was eager to see for himself if the findings were valid. When an Argentine expedition set out for the Antarctic during the 1957–58 season, Sieburth, on the trail of the sterile penguin, came along. The icebreaker reached the polar region and sixteen penguins were captured and brought on board. Some were predatory scavengers and others lived on plankton. A laboratory had been set up on the ship and Sieburth set to work at once on the gastrointestinal tracts. And before long he found that several of the birds were relatively free of bacteria. What was there in their stomachs that held down bacterial growth? Further tests revealed the presence of an antibacterial substance. The question remained as to what it was and how it got into the stomach. The birds with the fewest microflora were eaters of plankton and favored a certain tiny crustacean. They gulped this down in such vast quantities that as much as a quart at a time could be taken from the body of a penguin. It seemed logical to look for the antibiotic in the crustacean, and some was duly located in the stomach. Sieburth then went one step farther, to the diet of the crustacean. In its turn, the crustacean lived on phytoplankton, in particular on colonies of sticky green algae. Some of the algae were hauled on board and tested, and they did produce a substance capable of killing bacteria.

The antibiotic had not been identified by the time the winter began to close in, and the icebreaker had to steam to warmer waters. The following year a small Argentine ship, the *Chiruguano*, returned to Antarctica. Twenty quarts of phytoplankton were scooped up, frozen, and sent back to the United States for laboratory investigation. Sieburth worked on the plankton for an entire year, thawing a tablespoonful at a time. The active substance was volatile and kept being lost to the atmosphere. The antibiotic was eventually isolated and found to be acrylic acid. And so, Sieburth suggests, the penguin eats the crustacean which has eaten the algae. As the bird digests his meal the antibiotic is liberated.

Many other microbiologists strongly disagree with Sieburth's conclusion and insist that the original tests on the intestinal tracts of the penguins were in some way faulty. They concede that naturally occurring antibiotics and ultraviolet rays can in theory kill bacteria. Nonetheless, they doubt whether these processes are efficient enough to make any animals nearly bacteria-free. After all, many creatures who eat the identical diet as the penguins have large numbers of microbes in their systems.

"We, too, have run across some sterile specimens," says Dr. I. D. Cocioba, who has studied the microflora of Antarctic animals at Beth Israel Hospital, New York. "But I do not think that the animals were truly sterile. The bacteria may have died before the tests were run. And some bacteria will not grow in the laboratory culture."

Even if algae do not contribute to the creation of a sterile animal or environment, the mere fact that they are present in polar climates is a tribute to their cold-hardiness.

Algae appear in some unexpected places. A man walking across the snow in the Arctic happened to look back, and there on the snow behind him was an eerie sight: his footsteps were outlined in pink. No supernatural explanation was needed. The rosy glow on the snow was produced by colonies of colored algae. In other places they glow in green, orange, or fuchsia.

This sight cannot be duplicated on the Antarctic ice cap as algae live mainly on rock and in water. Nonetheless, they are a dominant form of Antarctic and sub-Antarctic plant life. A botanist froze first Antarctic and then Wisconsin green algae in a comparative test of survival. The polar algae won easily. The sea, as the penguins' diet attests, is filled with colonies of microscopic algae. Each summer patches of red, resembling the "red tides" of the Americas, dot the surface of tidal ponds off the shore of Palmer Station on the Antarctic peninsula, and there are pools where a grayish-pink algal crust skims the surface, and others where the water glows green or is a dull murky brown. Algae flourish in ponds near rookeries, taking nourishment from penguin guano. Larger seaweeds abound too, such as the giant brown kelp that grow near the shores of Macquarie Island.

Scientists have learned only recently that algae are living in the polar waters underneath the ice not only in summer, but all year around. Some actually begin to reproduce in October, early in the Antarctic spring, while it is still frigid. Aside from the cold, their growth at that season is threatened by the lack of light. Simple though they are, algae are plants and, like all members of this kingdom, require sunshine. Only three percent of the sunlight can pass through a one-meter (39.37-inch) layer of sea ice covered with snow, yet several species of algae "grow luxuriantly" there, to quote *The Antarctic Report* of the National Science Foundation. Their adaptation is so perfect that this is enough for photosynthesis.

Being neither true plant nor animal, fungi, on the other hand, need no light. Although they are more numerous in warmer surface waters, the unicellular forms can survive in the depths of the polar seas. These simple forms of life, which include yeasts, molds, and mildews, are remarkably resistant to chilling. This trait can easily be observed in homes located in temperate zones. If lemons or meat are left in a refrigerator too long, they will be covered with mold. The fungi species of the far north and south have acclimated to endure the far greater cold of natural refrigeration. Fungi grow on land as well as in the water, sometimes in the same places where algae are found.

Lichens, which are almost always described as part of the larger plant life of a region, are actually composed of an alga and a fungus living together in a symbiotic relationship. The fungus's role in the partnership is to absorb water and chemicals from rock or air. Certain species growing in particularly dry areas become several degrees colder in temperature than the surrounding rocks or ground. The relative humidity directly overhead thus is higher, and some of the vapor condenses. Whatever liquid is obtained is conserved, because the colder the plant, the lower the rate of evaporation. The alga then does its part by photosynthesizing and making food for itself and the fungus out of these raw materials.

The interdependence of living things can also be observed in the special relationship of a microscopic alga and a tiny Antarctic mite. The mite lives on the underside of rocks where algae also are clinging. The insect eats the algae and then crawls off to another area. In due course the mite digests and eliminates its food. The algae are so hardy that they survive the digestive process and begin to grow and reproduce rapidly as soon as they are expelled. The mites are reproducing, too. There are more than enough algae to serve as baby food for the larvae of the mites as they come out of their eggs. The algae continue providing food and the mites transport. And so life in a hostile climate goes on.

The successful survival of micro-organisms—algae, fungi, bacteria, viruses—is undoubtedly due to the fact that as a group they contain very little water, and dehydrated organisms of all kinds are able to withstand chilling. Some species have acclimated to the point where they can continue growing for a year at a temperature of -16°F.

In climates where the temperature is lower than that, the microbes, like the seeds of higher plants, cease their activity. As a result, decay, a product of microbial growth, occurs slowly, if at all.

This is true in the northern hemisphere, too. The woolly mammoth has been extinct for thousands of years. Yet we know the ways in which he was different from the modern elephant. His heart, lungs, and other organs were protected from the cold by a series of insulating layers. The outer hair was thick and coarse, and beneath it was first a heavy undercoat of short fur and then an exceptionally thick layer of fat. The head had a strange appearance due to a topknot of bone forced upward by the creature's large sinuses.

All this is known because frozen woolly mammoths have been found preserved in permafrost above the Arctic Circle. About 50,000 of them have been discovered in Siberia, with a single pit in Yakutsk yielding more than 1,000 frozen carcasses. The bodies are in such good condition that it is possible to determine that their last meal consisted of grasses and sedges. The penis of one mammoth was having an erection. As no female mammoth was near, physiologists believe this was a reaction to asphyxiation either by drowning or being buried alive.

Many of these mammoths were found by uneducated natives who were terrified by the enormous size and unusual appearance. Tales about the animals entered Arctic folklore. Children were told how mammoth meat was served at banquets and prized for its rare, exotic taste. Dogs were so tantalized by the smell when the mammoths were brought in close to the fires, it was said, that they fell upon the bodies and tore out large chunks of bloody meat. Scientists today believe these stories to be no more than that. The meat was either tasteless or, more likely, rotten. The mammoths had not been frozen instantly upon dying; most had begun to rot before the icy soil claimed them. The rotting had stopped abruptly and the bodies had ceased to decompose when the fungi and bacteria could no longer grow in the cold. When the carcasses were defrosted, they were restored at once to the state in which they had been frozen.

Preservation in the Antarctic is even more perfect. Not long ago members of a field party stumbled on the carcass of a dead fur seal. They could not decide whether the animal had died the day before or centuries earlier. The fur had not even begun to decompose. Tissues of a mummified Weddell seal, believed to have lived 1,600 years ago, have been analyzed in the laboratory at Northwestern University. Enzymes taken from the skin are still chemically active.

Scott's first Antarctic expedition took place in 1902. He stopped with his party for a time at Camp Evans on Ross Island before continuing the journey across the polar ice. Fifty years later a modern American scientific expedition came upon the remains of the camp. The microbiologists pounced upon a glass container of dehydrated bakers' yeast. The words on the label, "Rising up Yeast," could still be read and the seal over the cork stopper was in place. The bottle was sent to the University of Texas, where the yeast was removed and studied in the laboratory. After fifty years in the Antarctic, it was as capable of growing and making bread rise as it had been on the day Scott left it behind.

Human and animal feces remained until recently outside the campsites of Scott and Shackleton. Bacteria able to grow have been isolated from the half-century-old excrement. As they had been dormant until disturbed by the scientists, they had not caused the feces to decompose. (One can only speculate with horror on what would happen to the sewage and garbage should the Antarctic ever become heavily populated.)

Not only a record of the past, but a way to the future can be found in Antarctica. It is the place on earth most like some of the other planets and the moon. The temperatures are often 100 degrees or more below zero, and the winds sweep furiously over the plateau at 100 or 200 miles per hour; the air is dry, and most of the moisture on the ground is entrapped in ice. A current wave of exploration is taking man into space. Journeys beginning with the moon move on to Mars and ultimately to the huge cold planets far from our sun. And so scientists are being dispatched to Antarctica by the National Aeronautics and Space Administration to study conditions there. They are particularly interested in the snow-free valleys that lie in Victoria Land and some other parts of Antarctica. What little soil is exposed there is barren, rocky, and desiccated, perhaps not too different from the ground of Mars. Yet in that soil live bacteria, fungi, and algae, and even simple plants and animals.

The dry valleys of South Victoria Land support algae, particularly the blue-green; bacteria, including cocci and bacilli; actinomycetes; fungi, mainly molds and yeasts; lichens; and protozoa, such as amoeboid and flagellated forms.

When the first group of space scientists arrived at a dry valley, they picked up rock after rock without turning up any living organisms. To their chagrin a biologist who had been with an Antarctic scientific expedition for some months was able with unerring accuracy to select which of a group of seemingly identical rocks had microbes and insects clinging to the underside. In time the space experts, too, learned which rocks to turn over and discovered where the soil is richest in micro-organisms.

"We hope that what we have learned from the Antarctic can be applied to a search for life on Mars and other planets," declares a space scientist.

If these microbes can live in the dry valleys, perhaps they could live on another planet, too. The temperature in the valleys often drops to -35°F. and the air and soil are dry as bone or dust most of the year, but the microbes do not die. They lie dormant, waiting for conditions to improve. Scientists believe that in some of the dry valleys the microbes have been inactive—though capable of revival—for thousands of years. A drastic change in climate or topography may someday bring them warmth and water to awaken them. In other valleys, a trifle warmer and wetter, there comes a brief period every year when the microbes are restored to active life. Their time for growth and reproduction is pitifully brief. It lasts no more than four weeks, and in some places only two or three. The micro-organisms' active life occurs in the middle of the Antarctic summer when the sun has burned long enough to melt tiny bits of glacier. The meltwater is heated to just slightly above the freezing point, but that is enough. The bacteria, fungi, and algae are frail, barely clinging to life. The scientists must lift them carefully from the rocky soil with tools that have been sterilized.

Few of the bacteria, fungi, and algae lie on the surface of the soil. Instead they are within or near the permafrost layer, where the humidity is higher than elsewhere. The microbes in the dry valleys are most numerous in the places where the soil is comparatively young. As the ground in the frigid, windswept Antarctic becomes drier and saltier, much of the life within it dies out. Perhaps such findings could be correlated to the growing information being obtained about the soil of Mars.

However sparse extraterrestrial life might be, microbiologists believe that they will be able to detect it. In dry valley samples they have noted the presence of a mere one to ten microbes in one to five grams of soil. Improved laboratory techniques are making it possible to find micro-organisms in environments formerly believed to be sterile. The most startling such example occurred a couple of years ago when scientists from Virginia Polytechnic Institute collected soil samples near a frozen lake that had always been considered microbe-free. The soil when tested was found to contain 20 million bacteria per gram.

If the Antarctic is indeed a proving ground for space, there can be hope that somewhere on another world, as bitterly cold and dry, there, too, is life.

Part Four

Cold As a Means of Survival

✳

11

Sex without Contact

Could a baby be born to a woman who is not his mother and fathered by a man unknown to either the person who gives birth or to the true mother? This is the way it would work: the female reproductive cells would be fertilized by the male in a laboratory and an embryo would result. The embryo would then be implanted in a foster mother's womb. The reproductive cells would have been stored at liquid nitrogen temperatures to retain their vitality until the moment of use.

This incredible phenomenon is already within the realm of possibility. Human egg cells have indeed been fertilized by sperm in a test tube. Controlled reproduction of this type has been carried farther with animals. Mouse ova were taken out of the body and fertilized, and then transplanted into a female mouse. Normal young were born.

Even though humans might be able to perform like the mouse, one must ask why anyone would want a child produced in such an aseptic, unromantic manner. Perhaps it might be acceptable to the infertile woman who cannot release an egg naturally. An ovum would be taken out by a doctor, fertilized by her husband's sperm, and then reimplanted in her womb. Aside from such rare situations, the concept of laboratory-produced children seems to belong to a future world where sexual intercourse has been totally removed from procreation. Strict regulation would hold down the population. Anyone could enjoy sex with contraceptives; only the chosen could become parents. Tests would identify the most healthy, intelligent men and women among those free of hereditary diseases, and only their reproductive cells would be used. As the frozen ova and sperm would last indefinitely, the same superior genes would be transmitted to one generation after another of progeny. Limits would be placed on the use of the cells from any one man or woman or the world would be filled with thousands of siblings with the same or similar traits. Selection of followers as well as leaders, listeners as well as musicians, would be necessary.

The prospects of such a world are terrifying to us today. The degree of regulation required to make it work would bring an end to all individual freedom.

So let us settle for the smaller goal—motherhood for the sterile, the elimination of hereditary diseases leading to idiocy or invalidism, and the improvement of animal breeds. The ova of a highly qualified cow or sheep or horse could be transplanted into inferior animals. The desirable traits of the original mother would then be passed to many more calves than she could possibly bear herself. This, too, is far in the future. The female cells are at present the stumbling block— at least for higher animals—as they are easily damaged or even killed by the freezing.

Sea urchin eggs have been frozen to 14°F., a temperature at which their jelly coatings become icy. After they were rewarmed, they produced normal tadpoles. But, of course, sea urchins are a low form of life. When hundreds of fertilized rabbit eggs were frozen, only one later proved able to develop even as far as the six-cell stage. Slightly more promising results have been obtained with rat ova, which were frozen to -110°F. for as long as six weeks and then transplanted into sterile animals. Although most—99.9 percent—of the eggs died, the infinitesimal remainder developed, and those few sterile rats who were transformed into mothers gave birth to normal young. This was achieved through the magic of freezing and transplantation. Still, the percentage of surviving eggs is too small to be used for breeding stock. Freezing of female cells is now in an elementary stage.

It is quite different when it comes to the male. Both human and animal semen can be frozen and revived to the point of begetting progeny again. Attempts to freeze sperm go back a long way. In 1776 Lazzaro Spallanzani, an Italian biologist and university professor, exposed the sperm of men, horses, and frogs to "the freezing cold of winter and its snow" for half an hour. By then the spermatozoa had stopped moving. When Spallanzani rewarmed them, he observed that they rapidly revived and became active. In subsequent years, though, scientists declared that his findings were inconclusive. The degree of cold he used was not believed sufficient to freeze the semen. All he had proved, they said, was that sperm could survive chilling. It was not until 1866 that conclusive evidence was obtained. Biologist P. Mantegazza froze human semen to 5°F. and brought it back to active life. Mantegazza might be described as the Jules Verne of cryobiology. He was the first to suggest what freezing of reproductive cells could mean. If animal semen were frozen, it could be shipped from farm to farm in order to improve the breeds of cattle, horses, and pigs. Even more startling was his idea for a human sperm bank. Let us assume that a man dies on the battlefield, said Mantegazza. This need not be the end of his line. Had he left a stock of frozen semen, stored at home, he could still father an heir or heirs by his widow. Mantegazza did not suggest how a woman with a husband long dead could explain her pregnancies to neighbors skeptical of the powers of freezing.

Mantegazza sounded like an idle dreamer then. Today some of his suggestions are being carried out; the rest are accepted as possible, and probably desirable. Many scientists recommend the founding of sperm banks to preserve, as they say semihumorously, the seeds of genius. The sperm of men with outstanding gifts would not die with them but would remain in cryo-banks to be withdrawn and used for generations to come.

"Here we have nothing to lose, but we and the world have everything to gain," said the late Dr. Herman J.

Muller, geneticist and Nobel Prize winner.

Semen banks offer the opportunity to better mankind, even when an Einstein or Beethoven is not involved. A man could bank his reproductive cells in his youth, possibly before even meeting the woman who will bear his children. The likelihood of a defective child increases with the age of the parents, and so the younger the sperm, the better the chance of a healthy baby. Some men today work at occupations hazardous to their sperm. The astronaut who will endure the radiation of outer space and the scientist using X-rays might bank semen before undertaking their dangerous activities.

Infertility may result when the number of motile spermatozoa released at each intercourse is too small. In such a case a man could collect and store his sperm over a period of months. Then it could be pooled and concentrated. If it is the woman, on the other hand, who has difficulty in conceiving, her chances of becoming pregnant can be increased by repeated insemination during the fertile period.

In the first years after Mantegazza, his revolutionary idea was greeted with the same indifference that marked most early cryogenic research. In fact, hardly anything on the subject was reported until 1938. While doing research on syphilis, scientist F. Jahnel plunged test tubes containing sperm into baths of liquefied gases at -110°F., -320.8°F., and even lower. When he thawed them, he could see moving sperm, though he neglected to say how many. Some were in test tubes that had been stored for forty days at -110°F.

Where Mantegazza's report languished untouched, Jahnel's set off research into the freezing of many different types of cells. Biologists moved from sperm to blood, to skin, to tumor, to bone marrow, and a host of other human and animal tissues.

It is paradoxical that cold, which kills living cells with such ease, can yet be used to preserve life. To circumvent death requires elaborate freezing methods, and for years, failure and death were more common than success and life. The great breakthrough in the freezing of living cells came in 1949 when a woman scientist, Dr. Audrey Smith, and two colleagues at the National Institute for Medical Research in London observed that when they added a common chemical, glycerol, to bull spermatozoa, it was far better able to withstand the rigors of freezing. This is the same substance that is present naturally in the bodies of many cold-hardy insects. The discovery of glycerol's effects had been made by other scientists before Smith, and reports had been published. But again, these were almost entirely ignored.

To understand why glycerol helps, scientists turned their attention to the most basic question: how does cold kill? Although this question has not yet received a final answer, it appears most likely that death is caused either by the formation of ice crystals within the cell or by the concentration of salts when the cellular water is frozen out—or both. The protein molecules basic to cell function are arranged in a certain pattern, and water molecules help to hold them in place. When the water is lost and the salts are concentrated, the protein pattern collapses and damage results.

This does not happen rapidly or easily. Cells are far less fragile than they seem. They can endure the removal of a great deal of water without dying of dehydration. Take out a third, even a half, of the water in most animal cells, and they will survive, provided that the ice forms outside the cell walls. When the temperature is brought down slowly, the water within the cell passes out gradually and ice crystals form in the space outside the cell. When freezing is very rapid, there is no time for water to diffuse out of the cell, and so it forms crystals inside and these cause the damage. In most cases cooling at a rate of 1.8°F. per minute works best and is described by scientists as "the magical formula for success."

Biological variation among the animal cells and species is so great, however, that there is no hard-and-fast rule concerning freezing death. Red blood cells can lose four-fifths of their water while being chilled to 26.6°F., and no damage takes place. Those same sturdy red cells can also be frozen at literally fantastic speed, and yet return to life unharmed after thawing. Some cells, such as mouse skin and parakeet tumors, are so hardy that they survive even after crystals have formed within the cell walls. In contrast, others are so sensitive that they can be injured by cold before being frozen. Rapid cooling to only 32°F. is enough to produce damage. Rewarming is a hazard, too. Certain cells that live through freezing will die when they have to go through the same temperature range in reverse. The problem is that melting takes longer than freezing. Water remains solid at temperatures that would not have turned it to ice in the first place. As a result, the dehydration of the cell can become acute.

Glycerol provides protection because of its ability to hold water molecules in place, in both fast and slow freezing. With glycerol, a new chapter in freezing history began.

"Virtually every tissue of the body, including nerve and ganglia, has been successfully frozen and revived when protected with five to fifteen percent glycerol," reports cryobiologist Harold T. Meryman, Assistant Research Director, Blood Program of the American National Red Cross.

A number of other substances can also help cells to get through the freezing process. The simplest of all, egg yolk, can save bull semen from harm when rapid cooling is desired. The sperm, which has gained the reputation of being hardy, is actually quite unable to endure fast chilling; unless treated, it is damaged even before the freezing point is reached. The one preservative that has come to rival glycerol is dimethyl sulfoxide, DMSO, a chemical by-product of woodpulp manufacture. Which is better? That depends not only on the type of cell, but also on the kind of creature it comes from. DMSO penetrates cell membranes faster than glycerol, so less is required. In but thirty seconds DMSO enters the red blood cells of bulls; glycerol in this case takes two minutes. But this does not mean that DMSO is always best. It is not used in freezing either human or bovine spermatozoa because it has been found to be more toxic to these cells than glycerol. Human bone marrow does perfectly well in glycerol, while mouse marrow does not. In one experiment only twelve percent of the mouse cells survived freezing to -112°F. in a solution containing fifteen percent glycerol, while more than half were revived after DMSO had been used. No difference in effectiveness between DMSO and glycerol has been found when viruses, bacteria, and fungi are frozen. On the other hand, certain types of protozoa could not be frozen at all with glycerol; it destroys them.

Too little cold can be as dangerous for cells as too much. Some time ago a bacterium was sent from Germany to an American laboratory, where the enzymes were studied. Then the organism was frozen and stored for safekeeping. A few years later a question about one of the enzymes came up. The bacterium was taken out of the freezer and grown in a culture medium. The enzyme to be analyzed had been lost. The reason, scientists concluded, was that the temperature had not been low enough to preserve the bacterium properly.

The means to achieve the truly frigid temperatures needed can be found in the gases that make up our atmosphere. In the eighteenth century French chemist Antoine Laurent Lavoisier had theorized that if the air were cooled to the temperature of outer space, a part of the atmosphere would become liquid. Eventually he was proved right. All the gases that make up our air have indeed been chilled to temperatures that could not occur in nature on this planet, and in the process they have become liquid. Those with boiling points below -148°F. are considered cryogenic gases. In order to move from the vapor to the liquid state, oxygen must be cooled to -297.33°F., nitrogen to -320.36°F., neon to -410.8°, and hydrogen to -423.0°F.

Of these, liquid nitrogen has proven the most valuable for the freezing of living cells. Its use has simplified laboratory work immeasurably. A tumor resistant to a certain drug was investigated, and then it was frozen and stored in liquid nitrogen. Some time afterward, when additional tests were needed, it was thawed. The unhappy experience with the bacterium was not repeated. The tumor's resistance to the drug remained unchanged.

Cold As a Means of Survival

A giant step toward perfection of artificial insemination was taken when liquid nitrogen was first used to freeze human semen. In 1963, Dr. J. K. Sherman of the University of Arkansas Medical School made an electrifying announcement to the 115th International Congress of Genetics at The Hague: normal babies had been born to mothers who had been inseminated with liquid-nitrogen-frozen sperm.

Four years of storage had produced no damage in the sperm cells. Unfortunately, even with liquid nitrogen, not all the cells survive. About thirty percent of human sperm cells and forty-five percent of the less cold-resistant bull semen is lost, and so research to improve the technique still goes on.

That cells can revive from liquid-nitrogen temperatures seems incredible enough; yet even greater cold has been endured. Absolute zero, -459.69°F., has been defined as the point at which all molecules stop moving. That is, they would if they could; some slight motion of atomic particles goes on eternally. Absolute zero has, therefore, never quite been reached. A Naval Research Laboratory scientist, Dr. Arthur Spohr, has brought helium to within a millionth of a degree of total cold. How close to that point can living cells be taken? Coldest of all the liquid gases, helium does not even become a fluid until the temperature drops to -452°F. Cells were frozen in liquid helium. All life processes came to a virtual standstill. Then the cells were rewarmed and returned to life again.

"Suspended animation in isolated cells and tissues is in fact a reality," Meryman told a New York Academy of Sciences Conference a few years ago. "Man has altered the time dimension of his existence, since, for the red cell, the sperm, or the kidney, suspended at low temperature, time does in fact stand still."

Cells and tissues go into this state well before absolute zero is reached. For a long time scientists thought that they could name the precise degree at which all biological process stopped—it was -202°F. Any number of laboratory experiments backed up this theory. There was, therefore, no reason to worry about damage to micro-organisms, tissues, or food, provided that they were frozen to this point. If no reactions take place, frozen cells cannot deteriorate. When revived, they will be exactly the same as they were before. Certainty that this is so has vanished with further investigation. In 1960 two scientists chilled cells to below the cut-off point and discovered that some activities were still going on. A few years later others checked red blood cells held in liquid nitrogen for two years and found some deterioration. But this research is far from conclusive. After all, babies healthy in every way have been fathered by frozen sperm, and an analysis of sperm after four years revealed no alteration. For that matter, a number of biologists have studied red blood cells stored for ten years and declare them to be in perfect condition. As with much cold research, the definitive answer is yet to come.

From a pragmatic viewpoint, any changes that might occur are so minor that they do not really matter. Freezing works so well that it has improved our health, has changed our food habits, and has revolutionized cattle breeding.

Artificial insemination as a way of upgrading stock has long been known. Seven hundred years ago the Arabs, famed for their abilities as horse breeders, inseminated many mares with sperm taken from their finest stallions. In the nineteenth century dogs were successfully inseminated. As there was then no good way of storing semen for any length of time, artificial insemination remained an exceptional practice. This all changed with the advent of glycerol and improved methods of freezing. Bull semen loses none of its potency when frozen.

At this very moment somewhere in America a calf is being born. The mother cow has never been mounted by the bull who impregnated her; she has never watched him come charging across the fields, nor heard his bellow. In fact, the bull has been dead for three years. He was selected to serve as father in absentia because of his magnificent qualities of strength and health. This old story is acted out again and again. Every year at least four million calves are born in the United States alone to dairy cows who have been made pregnant by frozen semen. A number of breeders of beef cattle are beginning to switch from natural to artificial insemination, too. The results should soon be evident. The very traits governing growth rate and meat quality are the ones that are inherited. Good steak is a result of good breeding.

A single ejaculation can be diluted and used to impregnate several hundred cows. One bull can thus father thousands of calves in a single year. "Bulls of some species are monogamous and would otherwise pass their valuable traits on to the offspring of a single cow," explains an animal breeder.

In underdeveloped countries generations of cattle have been reared with sparse rations, thus weakening the breed. Even when agricultural improvement programs are instituted, it takes years to strengthen the stock. The years can be telescoped into a single generation by using sperm from the strong bulls of richer countries. It can be shipped in frozen form. The farmers receiving the semen would not need expensive refrigeration equipment. The shipping container can be so well insulated that evaporation of liquid nitrogen is slow. The sperm in it will keep for thirty days without any attention. This is quite long enough for shipping and presenting it to the cow.

The great success with frozen bull semen raised hopes for similar results with other animals, but efforts have been foiled repeatedly. In many cases breeders cannot even decide when to inseminate. Only the male pig knows for sure when a female pig is in heat and ready to ovulate. The most experienced farmer may miss the moment altogether. If he should occasionally get it right, he would still not be likely to obtain the desired results. Pig sperm does not freeze very well; it becomes less active and less potent.

Artificial insemination of rams would be particularly desirable, because wool quality is an inherited trait. Unfortunately, when frozen sperm is thawed and injected into the female, pregnancy is by no means sure to result. The fertility rate declines to only one-third to one-fourth that of the unfrozen. Efforts to improve this record are being made in the U. S., the U. S. S. R., South America, and Australia.

Goat semen, on the other hand, does well after freezing. This is of relatively little concern in the U. S., where goat farmers are few. Two major goat breeders here do use this technique, and in Australia it is a customary procedure.

Frozen horse sperm loses none of its fertilizing power and will probably in time be used in countries like Greece where some horses and donkeys are bred for work, rather than just for riding and racing. The Thoroughbred Racing Association in the U. S. has strict rules about it. Artificial insemination is allowed only immediately after stallion and mare have copulated. Some veterinarians believe insemination increases the chances of impregnation, and others think it diminishes them by disturbing the natural progression of events.

"The economics of horse racing does not permit the use of frozen semen," declares a spokesman for the association. "A yearling bred from a famous racehorse would not be worth so much if there were 500 or 5,000 just like him. The owner of a winner counts on getting large stud fees from a few major breeders."

This being so, racehorses will go on reproducing in the old-fashioned way, and the racing stables of the world will not be glutted with foals fathered by the same prize-winning stallion.

A pedigreed poodle bred by frozen semen would usually be disqualified by the American Kennel Club. Although artificial insemination is allowed, shipment of sperm from one area to another is not. Male and bitch must be within possibility of contact, even if insemination is the method of impregnation. Breeders say that results with frozen sperm have not been favorable, although laboratory studies show that potency is retained.

What is the best size for a turkey or chicken? That depends on the consumer. The newlywed couple wants a small one with delicate bones and soft flesh; the restaurateur wishes a big one for economy; the gourmet who prefers the tender white meat will buy only a big-breasted fowl. A farmer then must breed his flock in such a way as to suit his particular customers. Artificial insemination is by no means uncommon, but it has been performed in a rather haphazard and unscientific manner. Most farmers simply pool the semen from many males, completely voiding all genetic benefits. Big, small, tender, tough—become matters of chance. It would be far better to use semen from the best roosters exclusively, and this would become practical only if it were frozen and stored until needed. A major problem to date has been that the glycerol essential for successful freezing interferes with the normal development of the chick embryo. Researchers are close to a solution.

The sex life of the herring is seldom given a thought by the diner nibbling on a smoked or pickled herring canapé. Yet in the early 1950's researchers began to freeze herring spermatozoa. Although it might seem difficult to freeze fish semen, they were successful. Since then a number of scientists and sports lovers have been urging federal and state hatcheries to use frozen sperm to increase the number, size, and quality not only of herring, but also of trout and other popular game fish.

Conservationists as well as fishermen and farmers are turning to frozen semen. The buffalo that once roamed the plains of this continent was nearly wiped out by the relentless hunting of Buffalo Bill and his fellows. New advances in freezing buffalo semen may help to save this hitherto unlucky breed from extinction.

Some years ago a scientist was performing cancer experiments on rats. He observed their susceptibility to tumors, and then tried a variety of treatments. His work was hampered by spontaneous mutations among the young. The mutants were different enough from parents and grandparents to throw off his series of experiments. There was no way for him to compare the reactions of the new generation of rats with those of the group he had started with. Today he freezes and stores the sperm of each male rat. Whenever he wishes to check back to an earlier stage of his research, he inseminates a female and produces a rat of the desired generation.

As frozen sperm has been easing the lot of workers in one laboratory after the other, scientists in primate laboratories decided to give it a try. The baboon is the troublemaker in these research centers. The large, powerful, and aggressive male sometimes hurts the female severely during the sex act. Perhaps sex relations between baboons should be eliminated altogether, suggested biologists, without considering whether the females would not rather take their chances. Instead, they would conceive via artificial insemination with frozen semen. Interfering with an animal's sex life is always risky. Danger to the female proved to be nothing compared to the danger to the scientists. The male baboons turned their wrath on the men and refused to cooperate in the unwholesome project of giving their sperm to anyone but their mates.

"Unless the basic artificial insemination techniques are made practical, frozen storage of spermatozoa obviously will be of no value to baboon breeding," said Dr. J. K. Sherman, accepting the way things are among the apes.

12

Banking Life

In the late years of the nineteenth century an American researcher wanted to compare an encephalitis virus with another being studied by Russian scientists. There was only one way for him to obtain the foreign virus: an infected tick was sent to him. Today he could receive a frozen sample of that isolated virus.

Influenza viruses are among the most troublesome of microbes. Although all flus are almost identical in symptoms, each is caused by a different virus. No one can get the same influenza twice, a fact that most people find hard to believe. One becomes immune to each flu virus in turn. There are so many of them and they mutate so frequently that no one ever seems to run out of viruses to catch. Vaccine makers are in a never-ending race with the viruses. Each season they must prepare a new vaccine that will provide immunity to the particular influenza strains that are around just then. They are helped in their work by the World Health Organization and its two affiliated laboratories, one in Atlanta, Georgia, and the other in London.

Influenza travels from country to country, continent to continent. An epidemic in Hong Kong heralds a subsequent epidemic in San Francisco and Paris. And so whenever an outbreak of influenza occurs anywhere in the world, the nearest of the centers collects and studies the virus, formulates recommendations for dealing with it, and sends it to health officials and doctors.

"Influenza viruses may be shipped by air on wet ice in the

form of infected egg fluids. If viruses will be en route longer than twenty-four hours they are frozen and shipped on dry ice or they may be dried," states Dr. Marion T. Coleman, who is in charge of the Atlanta laboratory.

Scientists studying other types of viruses and micro-organisms apply to the American Type Culture Collection in Rockville, Maryland, and receive a culture of the frozen microbe. It would be hard to name a micro-organism that is not on file in this frozen cell bank. At most recent count, the collection included nearly 6,500 different strains of bacteria, 526 virus and rickettsiae strains, about 4,500 fungi, 45 algae, 24 protozoa, and a host of others. Each year the number increases. The pathogens that make people sick are represented and so are the ones that cause plant disease. In an average year more than 13,600 cultures of bacteria, 3,300 fungi, 1,100 viruses, and 200 algae are distributed to scientists. But the collection, as its name implies, contains more than microbes. The National Cancer Institute was instrumental in setting it up, and it includes a large number of animal cells needed for basic cancer research. There are also cells displaying the chromosome abnormalities that produce mongolism and other congenital conditions.

A duplicate collection has been set up as a safeguard against disaster. Those in charge of the collection recall the fate of its predecessor, begun in 1911 by Dr. C. E. A. Winslow at the American Museum of Natural History in New York. Winslow gave it the impressive name Bacteriological Collection and Bureau for the Distribution of Bacterial Cultures. Within a year the collection included 578 strains representing 374 species of micro-organisms. Winslow cared for the collection diligently, but in time he left the museum. No successor appeared to share his enthusiasm. In 1922 a decision was made to move the collection out of the museum and take it to the Army Medical Museum in Washington, D.C. When bacteriologists checked over the cultures, they discovered that the majority had been lost or destroyed. Only 175 strains remained to make the move.

Cold As a Means of Survival

Some of the cells at the American Type Culture Collection now are preserved in liquid nitrogen; others are freeze-dried. Many people are surprised to learn about freeze-dried microbes, as they connect the process with coffee or fruit. The basic principle is the same extremely simple one that can be observed in daily life. A housewife hangs her laundry out of doors on a day with subfreezing temperatures. Soon the shirts and towels become stiff with ice. Then the wind blows through and the ice disappears. Yet the cloth does not drip with water. The ice was transformed into vapor without ever passing through the liquid stage. In the laboratory, or in the food industry, the product or tissue involved is first frozen and then placed in a vacuum chamber. The vacuum facilitates the removal of water.

The use of this process in the laboratory antedates its use in food processing by many years. William Hyde Wollaston mentioned the principle of "low-temperature evaporation of water under vacuum" to the Royal Society of London in 1813, adding parenthetically that the facts were "too well-known to need confirmation before Members of this Society."

Nearly a hundred years later two scientists were trying to improve the rabies vaccine so that it would be less painful for those who needed it. In the course of their work they took a rabid dog's brain and spinal cord and froze them in a salt-ice mixture and then dried them in a vacuum. When they reconstituted the freeze-dried tissues, they observed that the rabies virus that had sickened the dog was still alive and capable of infecting others. This proved to be the most significant part of their research; they failed to produce a less painful vaccine. Within the next few years, bacteria, blood, and other cells were successfully freeze-dried.

Micro-organisms that have been freeze-dried are particularly easy to store and to ship. The vast majority take the process extremely well, but there are exceptions. Bacteriologists at the Collection observe that forty rare bacteria strains that are damaged by freeze-drying can be held in liquid nitrogen.

"Liquid nitrogen is probably the very best way of preserving all microbes," declares M. T. Alexander, chief of facilities at the collection. "The problem is that it is difficult to work with. It is costly, and if we were to run out, the loss would be tragic. There are 30,000 ampules in a single liquid nitrogen freezer."

Freeze-dried cultures do not require such elaborate refrigeration. They are held at -68°F. "Should the temperature get any higher during the night, an alarm system is activated," explains Alexander. "It is connected to an answering service which then calls me at home. I run down here and move the cultures to a spare freezer which we have running all the time."

In many countries, however, there are no liquid nitrogen freezers, or even iceboxes. A physician visited the remote areas of South America in 1965 and was shocked to see how many people had paralyzed limbs as a result of poliomyelitis. A local doctor explained to him that the scarcity of refrigeration made it impossible to keep large enough stocks of vaccine on hand for immunization. Since then millions of doses have been freeze-dried and distributed.

Animal illnesses have also been hard to control in underdeveloped areas. A cow on a ranch in Africa, for example, would be sickened with rinderpest. Unless all cattle on the huge continent were immunized, the contagious disease would spread to other ranches and ultimately other countries. Until recently such large-scale immunization was not possible. The virus needed to make the vaccine deteriorated too rapidly. Freeze-dried virus has changed all that, and the illness can now be conquered. Today hog cholera and viruses that cause canine disease are also freeze-dried and preserved until required for vaccines.

The uses of freeze-dried micro-organisms have been varied and imaginative. The dairy industry has employed them as starters for cheeses, yogurt, and other mold- or bacteria-based products.

Antivenin against snakebite has also been freeze-dried, starting with the snakes of India and the United States. The life-saving serum can in this way be shipped to areas where snakes abound. Unfortunately, people most often encounter the cobra, rattlesnake, viper, or mamba in desolate regions. The problem remains one of getting victim and antivenin together.

Frozen human mothers' milk somehow sounds more peculiar than frozen antivenin or vaccine, but it has been in use for a long time. In 1935, long before freeze-drying became widespread, pediatricians were seeking better ways of feeding babies who could not digest formula and whose mothers had no milk to give them. Their solution was to ask nursing mothers to squeeze excess milk into nursing bottles. It was then freeze-dried and banked for later use.

The major medical application of freezing today is certainly not for mothers' milk, snake venom, or even flu viruses. It is in the preservation of blood for transfusions. Until recently blood banks operated under what was known as the "twenty-one-day tyranny." That was the length of time that fresh blood could be stored under normal refrigeration before the red blood cells began to rupture. The American Medical Association noted that in a year when 6.4 million pints were donated, only 4.7 million were used in transfusions. The rest had to be thrown away. The summer was always the worst time for keeping blood supplies high, because donors would go on vacations. But illness does not take a holiday. Women keep on giving birth; operations are performed; rivers flood, hurricanes rampage, earthquakes break houses apart, wars are fought.

Freedom from the twenty-one-day tyranny was won by that same liquid nitrogen that had saved the sperm and the bacteria. The technique involved was devised only recently. After being taken from the donor, the blood is spun in a centrifuge to separate the red cells from the plasma or fluid portion, explains Dr. Arthur W. Rowe, a biochemist at the New York Blood Center. The red cells, gradually mixed with glycerol to protect them from the cold, are poured into a stainless steel container no wider than an empty manila file folder. The container is placed in a vat of liquid nitrogen and kept there for about three minutes. By then the cells within are completely frozen. It is stored at liquid nitrogen temperature until the call comes. At that time, two minutes in a warm-water bath is enough to restore the blood to its liquid state. All that remains is for the blood to be washed and spun in a centrifuge in order to remove the glycerol. For the actual transfusion, the red cells may be combined with plasma or a saline solution, or used alone.

When this method was being developed, no one was sure whether frozen blood would be as harmless as fresh when sent coursing through veins and arteries. Before recommending that anyone else use the frozen blood, therefore, scientists served as their own guinea pigs. They drew their own blood, froze and stored it for longer than the old twenty-one-day limit. Then they transfused it into themselves. After a brief, uneasy period, they realized that all was well.

Shortly after the freezing technique had been perfected, two chimpanzees taking part in a blood research project died. Just a few months earlier, it would have been necessary for the experiment to be abandoned, as the blood could not have lasted long enough for studies to be completed. This time the animals' blood was quickly drained and rushed to a blood center for freezing. The tests on the blood could then be performed at leisure.

While Apollo 11 was traveling to the moon and back, blood samples were taken from the 250 men and women who worked in the Lunar Receiving Laboratory at Houston. This blood was then frozen and stored. In this form it could remain indefinitely to serve as a basis for comparison, showing whether handling or being near lunar matter had produced physiological changes.

Studies of blood typing, compatibility, and enzymes are performed on frozen blood. The "reference library" at the New York Blood Center contains thousands of blood droplets and occupies a space no larger than that taken up by a household refrigerator. The blood to be investigated is sprayed from a syringe onto a cone vibrating in liquid nitrogen. The frozen drops are then collected in a cup and poured into a vial which is numbered for storage.

The bulk of the blood in banks, however, is needed for transfusions. For all its advantages, frozen blood is not intended to replace fresh blood entirely. Regular daily calls from hospitals will be filled by blood banks much as they have in the past. Thousands of pints of the frozen blood will be stored for emergency use, and a good percentage of that— possibly as much as a third—will be of rare blood types.

The largest number of people has blood type O Positive, with A next, followed by B and AB, and then the rarer types. With the exception of O, which can be accepted by people with some other blood types, an individual can take a transfusion of his own type of blood only. Otherwise, a severe reaction sets in.

In early 1968 a four-day-old baby boy lay dangerously ill at Bronx Lebanon Hospital. His blood cells were being destroyed by the antibodies he had received from his mother's blood. If this process continued for any length of time, he would suffer severe brain damage or die. The baby could be saved only by having his entire blood supply changed, but the type needed was a U-Negative so rare that it is found in only one of a thousand people. A call went out to the New York Blood Center, and the information about the required blood was fed into a computer. The right type was quickly located. A donor had given some long before. Within two hours the rare blood was being transfused into the baby. When he went home a few days later, his doctor reported him as being "in tip-top shape."

One blood type, known as Bombay, is even more unusual and has so far been identified in only three people in the world, an American brother and sister and a nurse in Czechoslovakia. The man's blood type was discovered when as a soldier he contributed to a Red Cross blood drive. Soldiers had been offered a weekend pass in return for a pint of blood. This particular man's blood was first incorrectly classified as

O, an error that would have had tragic consequences for the person who would ultimately have received it. The mistake was found before the blood could be used. The Army, fearing that the man might be wounded in combat and require transfusions of a blood impossible to provide, hastened to reassign him as a personnel clerk. It would obviously be impossible for a supply of his own frozen blood to be kept close to the combat zone.

Under peacetime conditions, it is feasible for a person to be his own blood donor. The first dramatic demonstration of this came in 1966 when a fifty-nine-year-old man required surgery for relief of an extremely painful ulcer. The operation is usually not considered a dangerous one, so long as the patient receives two or three blood transfusions. But this man's blood possessed such an unusual combination of antibodies that he would reject practically any blood but his own. And so his doctors decided that if the only blood he could stand was his own, that was what he should have. The operation was put off for several months, and the interim period was used to collect his blood. The patient came to his doctor's office at regular intervals, and at each visit some of his blood was taken. Then it was frozen and stored. Just before the surgery the whole supply of blood was thawed. The patient received all the transfusions he needed, from himself.

As frozen blood came into wider use, several unexpected advantages were discovered. Slightly less bleeding occurred after surgery than when fresh blood was transfused. Massachusetts General Hospital, for one, began to use only frozen blood during and after organ transplants and other risky operations.

After the first 8,000 transfusions of frozen blood had been given, a surprising fact was recognized: hepatitis hardly ever followed. This infection has been a major hazard of transfusion. The preparation of blood for freezing apparently removes the lurking virus.

Can one pint of blood equal three pints, or four, or more? This mathematical impossibility becomes reality when blood is separated into its components. Only the red blood cells are taken for the basic freezing method. The other parts of the blood require great care and are chilled separately at a slow rate. After this has been done, each patient can receive only the part of the blood that he needs. One will get the red cells, another the white, still another the platelets—all from the same pint of blood. With this system, a person can take in great quantities of the single component he requires.

One of the first substances separated out for freezing was the clotting protein, known variously as the antihemophilic factor or factor 7. This is desperately needed by hemophiliacs. Glamorously described as the disease of kings because of a long line of royal victims, hemophilia is in truth a most unromantic condition. A minor cut, a tooth extraction, a splinter, a stubbed toe, a severe bruise carry danger, as the blood does not clot. In order to be sure that freezing had not damaged the delicate antihemophilic factor, a young hemophiliac on the staff of one of the blood centers offered himself for experiment. The scientists waited for him to start bleeding; before long he banged his head on a car door and the flow began. The factor 7 was thawed and injected into him. The blood fraction had survived, and so did the young researcher.

Victims of leukemia lack another of the blood components, the platelets. These are also essential to the clotting process. When they are missing, blood seeps out of the veins; the resultant black and blue marks are clearly visible close to the skin's surface. Unfortunately, the drugs given in the treatment of leukemia not only destroy leukemia cells, but also those cells that make the platelets.

"There is a shortage of platelets and the priority now is naturally being given to children," says Rowe. "Platelets are very fragile and it is extremely difficult to keep them from breaking during freezing. Liquid nitrogen, though, will make it possible for us to at least double our supply."

When a leukemia victim receives transfusions, he becomes able to endure larger dosages of the powerful antileukemic drugs. When drugs and platelets were administered to patients at Children's Hospital in Philadelphia a short time ago, results were far better than when either was used alone. The number of children with acute leukemia who survived that particular crisis was four times as great as for any previous comparable group.

No one knows when illness may strike or surgery be necessary, and so some doctors are suggesting that people with unusual blood types follow the example of the ulcer patient and freeze their own blood.

Some far-seeing scientists are suggesting that everyone routinely freeze and store his blood. Each person would then know that whatever befell him in the future—whether major surgery, anemia, leukemia, or radiation sickness—he would be sure of a supply of blood. Studies are already under way to calculate the cost of saving blood for the entire population.

13

Cells and Squirrels

When a child is born, a tiny bit of his skin, no more than an eighth of an inch, should be taken and frozen and stored. Similar quantities of bone, muscle, nerve, and other tissues should be saved. This startling piece of advice is today being given by a number of sober scientists. Some of these human cell banks could be buried in the Antarctic. Fifty, a hundred, or five hundred years from now, the cells would be thawed. Scientists of the future will analyze them and learn how man has changed in the interim. What has he done to himself? Have air pollution, water pollution, pesticides, excessive noise, crowding, and radioactive fallout changed the very constituents of our cells?

On an individual basis, the infant cells would serve as a means for evaluating subsequent changes produced by maturing and disease. Most of the banks would be maintained in refrigerated warehouses near the homes of the original possessors of the cells. The underlying principle is the same as for the more frequently suggested individual blood bank, which might very well be incorporated. In case of need, each contributor could draw upon whatever supply of his own skin, marrow, or liver cells he had gradually deposited when healthy. He would never be faced with the necessity of adjusting to someone else's tissues.

At present most frozen cells have fewer medical uses than they might. Ideally, all body tissues should be used, as blood is, for transfusing, transplanting, or grafting. But as the experience of organ transplants has shown, where the body will accept blood provided that the type is right, almost all other foreign cells are rejected. If an individual had given his cells to be frozen when he was healthy, he could have them back when ill. Bone marrow, for example, is badly needed by people in whom these cells have been destroyed by leukemia, congenital abnormalities, radiation, or treatment with certain cancer drugs. Transplants have succeeded when the donor was a twin, or, more rarely, a sister or brother with particularly compatible tissues. It would, of course, be better if the donor were the invalid himself. Occasionally even now the victim of cancer does have some cells frozen at the zero hour. If cancer cells have not entered the bone marrow, he can have a small quantity removed for freezing before he submits to radiation or drug therapy. Then it is thawed and reinjected later.

Animal experiments indicate a number of other potential uses for frozen marrow. Sometimes the victim of a serious accident must have bone transplanted from one part of his body to another. In tests on dogs, the inclusion of an animal's own previously frozen marrow encourages new bone to grow around the transplant.

Freeze-dried bone taken from a rib has also been transplanted together with bone marrow to repair damaged jawbones in a group of dogs. Fresh bone formed and the jaws were gradually built up. Perhaps this technique will someday be perfected sufficiently to be used for people who are unable to wear dentures because their jawbones have deteriorated too badly to hold them in.

There are already hints that freezing may alter the mechanism of rejection for certain tissues. Preliminary experiments seem to indicate that frozen bone marrow is not as readily rejected as fresh. Mice that had been subjected to lethal doses of X-rays recovered when they were given injections of frozen guinea pig bone marrow. It is too early to say whether people will react in similar manner. If so, the cell banks would have an even wider use than is now anticipated.

Although another person's skin tissue is rejected in the

end, it can be retained long enough to be of some use. Not long ago a man was severely burned in a factory fire. It was essential that the burn surfaces be covered to guard against both infection and further loss of vital body fluids. Skin is the best of all coverings, but the victim, with burns covering three-fourths of his body, had none to spare. And so freeze-dried skin cells were rehydrated and buttered over the damaged area. This type of treatment is not a true graft, to be sure. After serving as an almost perfect dressing for twenty-one days, the skin is sloughed off.

During a visit to the Central Institute for Trauma and Orthopedics in Moscow, Dr. Robert Roaf of the University of Liverpool observed a number of patients who had received transplants to replace bone removed because of deep-seated tumors. Transplants of live bone and cartilage have been performed for many years; what was different in the Moscow treatment was the source of the bone: it came from the dead, and had been frozen and stored until needed. Then it was thawed and inserted in place of the missing bone. The transplant, Roaf was told, was to serve a temporary function. It merely had to provide a structural foundation on which new bone tissue would eventually be grown by the patient himself.

A study of history reveals some even more surprising examples of transplant operations. The French transplant surgeon Charles Dubost was relaxing from his grueling work by looking through reproductions of Renaissance art. All at once he stopped to look more closely at a painting by the early Renaissance master Fra Angelico. The artist had portrayed a saint in the act of changing the entire leg of a patient.

"I don't know if this first transplant was successful," remarks Dubost.

Who can say whether the rejection mechanism of the body was overcome by a miracle?

The noble art of dueling was responsible for other Renaissance transplant surgery. When the sharp saber's edge would detach the tip of a nose or the curve of a cheek, the injured swordsman would seize the severed bit in his hand and run to the nearest apothecary to have it stitched back on.

Since dueling was outlawed, noses and cheeks have been relatively safe from detachment; legs, arms, fingers, and toes remain in danger. One day in the late 1960's a college student was washing his dungarees in a basement washing machine. Suddenly he remembered that he had left some money in the pocket. In reaching for it the unfortunate boy's arm was caught and completely severed. A friend, who was a premedical student, had the presence of mind to grab the arm and put it in an ice-filled laundry tub. It remained there until the nearest doctor, from seventy miles away, arrived. The arm was sewed right back into position and in time it healed and moved again, although it never regained all sensation. On another occasion a suburban homeowner lost his right thumb while clumsily trying to repair his power mower. A surgeon replaced it with one of the less essential fingers of his left hand.

But these cases, dramatic as they are, involve the victim's own arm or finger, so there is no question of rejection. When one belonging to someone else is used, the body throws that off, just as it does a heart or liver. The drastic immunosuppressive therapy given organ transplant patients may help, but the side effects are such that drugs would probably not be used for minor transplantations of finger or toe. Nonetheless, every so often reports trickle in from one country or another that this kind of transplant has been accepted without drugs or X-rays. The most recent told of finger transplants performed by Dr. Viktor Kalnberz of the Institute of Traumatology and Orthopedics, Riga. Cadaver fingers that had been frozen to -94° F. were defrosted and then used to replace lost fingers on the hands of five patients. The technique was elaborate. The cadaver finger was first attached to the patient's abdomen. Kalnberz claims that the fingers were reasonably useful, but most doctors here express serious doubt.

The usual rejection problem faced by transplants is happily missing when it comes to the cornea of the eye. Isolated from the rest of the body and bathed in aqueous humor instead of blood, the cornea can be passed from one person to another —or, to be exact, from one dead person to another living, but blind. The technique of transplantation was developed in 1905, but the first eye bank was not established for nearly forty years thereafter. The eye is removed within three to four hours after death, and the transplant should be made as soon as possible. The Eye Bank for Sight Restoration, New York, gives assurance, nonetheless, that the cornea can be kept for a week in a sterile container in the refrigerator at 39.2°F. As living tissue goes, that is pretty good, but it is not enough. The supply of cornea donors is seldom exactly equal to the demand. In a single recent year New York's eye bank received about 1,170 eyes, yet many blind people in the city had to wait while directors made arrangements to borrow another 337 corneas from other areas.

In order to meet their own and other cities' needs, the nation's eye banks (eighty at last count) must build up a stock to be used in lean periods. Freezing instead of mere refrigeration should be the answer, but the cornea, so easy to handle for the most part, has been surprisingly unmanageable. The cornea is impermeable, and a preservative cannot get through to the fragile layer of cells behind. If these cells die, a graft cannot be successful, because a part of the cornea becomes opaque.

After considerable research, England's Audrey Smith, who had discovered glycerol's preservative qualities, invented a special needle with which to insert glycerol and DMSO. The corneas of the eyes of laboratory rabbits were then frozen, stored at -110°F. for periods ranging from one hour to 120 days, and then grafted onto other rabbits. Between seventy and eighty percent of them took, regardless of the length of time they were frozen.

Experiments are also now under way in transplanting corneas that have been frozen to only -22°F. And some researchers suggest replacing the fragile cell lining with one made of silicone rubber. The question remains, though, whether the body would reject this.

Can transplants help the deaf as well as the blind? In 1965 a startling medical report came out of Auckland, New Zealand. The heart valves of bullocks had provided deaf people with new eardrums. The valves, declared Dr. C. B. Cornish, had been removed right after the animals had been killed and were first sterilized and then freeze-dried. Before being used in the operating room, the valves were soaked in a saline solution until they became soft and pliable. Then the bullock valve was stretched over the outer surface of the patient's eardrum. Thirty-five patients whose eardrums needed repair or replacement were operated on. Six months later Cornish checked back on six of them. All the bullock-derived eardrums were still functioning. One of the men reported that he could hear well enough to get along socially, which had been impossible for him before.

Freeze-dried heart valves from human rather than bullock cadavers have frequently been used as replacements for damaged valves. Heart specialist Brian Barrett-Boyes, also of Auckland, has gained a worldwide reputation for his work in substituting aortic valves taken from the dead and either freeze-dried or preserved in a salt solution at 39.2°F. A couple of years ago, the wife of an American broadcasting executive traveled all the way to New Zealand to have this operation performed on her. Surgeons elsewhere report successes, too. Following up the results of sixty transplants with freeze-dried valves, physicians at Guy's Hospital in London found thirty-three patients in excellent condition from one to as long as four and a half years later.

As heart valves are bloodless, the transplant seldom triggers the rejection mechanism. Oddly enough, heart valves are rejected more frequently and rapidly by animals than by humans. The reverse is true for the other internal organs. No exact correlation between the rejection mechanism in animals and man can be made.

Second only to rejection as a problem in transplantation is that of keeping the donor's organ in good enough condition to use.

"The impressive thing to me is the extreme temperature

dependence of the cadaver organ," Dr. William Angell of Stanford University School of Medicine stated at a recent conference on transplantation.

Even when the transplant is made immediately, as has been done with all the hearts, the organ is placed in a cold saline solution at about 50°F. for the brief period of waiting. A number of surgeons, among them Christiaan Barnard, also perfuse the heart with blood. Others, however, maintain that cooling alone is sufficient. A few years ago Dr. Richard Lower of the Medical College of Virginia transplanted an animal heart which had been kept for seven hours with no attempt at preservation other than a cold saline solution. This simple method, for shorter periods however, has been used by such notable transplant surgeons as Norman E. Shumway. The heart transplanted into Michael Kasperak, for example, was preserved in cold saline alone.

If a liver is removed and kept at room temperature, it will become useless as a transplant in a mere twenty to thirty minutes. Chilling changes that. In eleven liver transplantation operations performed in 1968, the organ used had been taken from its dead donor four to seven and a half hours earlier. Three of the patients were still alive five to seven months after surgery, when Dr. L. Brettschneider of the University of Colorado Medical Center reported on them to the Second International Congress of the Transplantation Society. The storage time for these livers, as for other internal organs, was extended by placing them in a cold, hyperbaric chamber and perfusing them with a diluted blood solution. With this method, Brettschneider pointed out, a liver could be stored for eight hours, then transplanted, and immediately support life.

While surgeons hold back from using livers stored for more than eight hours or so for humans, animals have received transplants kept for much longer periods. Five dogs received livers that had been held at 39.2°F. for twenty-four hours. Three of them survived the operation, and one lived for several months.

Kidneys perfused and maintained at 39°F. for twenty-two hours were transplanted into baboons in 1962. The kidneys did not begin to function unaided for several months thereafter. Today, human kidneys that have been cooled and stored in a hyperbaric chamber for twenty-four hours can begin to function immediately after transplantation.

The same technique has more recently been applied to the hearts of a group of dogs. Five out of seven animals who received hearts removed from the donors twenty-four hours earlier survived for more than a day.

Six dogs were given grafts of pancreas that had been held at 39°F. for twenty to twenty-four hours. Five of them survived the transplant, one for 169 days.

Although human brain transplants are as yet only a faint possibility for the future, efforts at preserving the brain in viable condition are already being made. Dogs' brains have been isolated, much as the monkey's had been earlier, and then they were chilled to between 35.6°F. and 33.8°F. The tubes that had been carrying blood to the disembodied brains were closed off, and the blood flow brought to a complete halt. All brain activity had ceased long before; no electric signals appeared when an encephalogram was taken. Two hours later a few of the brains were rewarmed and the blood was sent through them again. Would signs of life be recorded by the electroencephalograph? As the temperature rose to 71.6°F., the electric signals reappeared. Two hours more went by and another group of brains was rewarmed, and again the signals indicating activity resumed. Then the brains chilled for six hours were given a trial, and they, too, were restored to life. The ability of the brain to survive is surpassing the most extravagant hopes. Even those dogs' brains that had been held at near-freezing temperatures for fifteen days were eventually brought back to functioning life. They were not operating on any high level; nonetheless, they continued to take in oxygen and glucose and to release carbon dioxide.

The brain, heart, and other vital organs are at present being chilled, not frozen. The difficulty of freezing without resultant damage is the real stumbling block to the establishment of a heart, lung, liver, kidney, or brain bank. It might seem that the same techniques that have been used to freeze individual cells and tissues might similarly be applied to whole organs. This has not worked out. Each organ is a conglomeration of many different kinds of cells, and the freezing method that puts one kind of cell into suspended animation can utterly destroy another.

The many research failures, therefore, are not unexpected; what is surprising is that there should be any successes at all. Audrey Smith has taken the hearts of embryonic chickens and frozen them in liquid nitrogen. When they were thawed the normal heartbeat resumed. No mammal has done as well. A puppy's heart was frozen to 24.8°F. for fifteen minutes and beat again after rewarming. Still, neither the puppy nor any other mammalian heart has survived for twenty-four hours at 10.4°F.

The first real breakthrough is expected to come with the kidney and liver. Dog and rat kidneys have been frozen in liquid nitrogen. They looked all right when they were warmed, but the first impression turned out to be misleading. They failed to function. The most promising results have been obtained when either kidneys or livers were carefully brought to subnormal temperatures in such a way that most of the water within the cells remained liquid. In one research study, a number of dog kidneys were treated with DMSO and stored for eight hours at 11.2°F. Then they were warmed and implanted in dogs again. Three-fourths of the kidneys worked again. In other experiments, livers have been preserved for as long as five days.

Smith and a group of scientists at England's Medical Research Council's Mill Hill laboratories are working on a machine to cool the intact kidney at a controlled rate to the freezing point. It has already been found that the frozen kidney's chances of survival are greater when increasing amounts of DMSO are gradually added during the cooling process.

Successful freezing of entire organs is sure to come, say cryobiologists. And what of the whole animal? Could any mammal be frozen, and then restored to life?

"Not even twenty years ago scientists were saying that a body temperature of 59°F. was the lowest which a warm-blooded animal could survive," comments Vojin Popovic of Emory University.

Today it is known that even the highest animal of all, man, can live after being cooled to 39.6°F. And researchers have succeeded in chilling monkeys to just about 32°F. and re-warming them to life after two hours of clinical death. When it comes to less highly developed mammals, the experience has been even more startling.

In the course of his cancer experiments, Popovic brought the temperature of hamsters to 39.2°F. for ten hours, and they survived. Then he selected newborn ground squirrels, because hibernators endure cold better than other animals, and the young stand it more easily than the adult. He cooled them until their body temperature fell to 24.8°F. At that point there was no heartbeat and no respiration. Nonetheless, when rapidly rewarmed after almost twelve hours, they recovered. The temperature was then dropped to 15.8°F., and they were returned to life after five and a half hours.

This is the lowest temperature ever recorded in a mammal with complete recovery. It breaks the record of 19.4°F. achieved for hibernating bats at the National Institute for Medical Research in England.

14

"Nothing That Has an End Is Long"

"And can we, in heaven's name, call anything human long? Grant the very latest term of life; suppose we reach the age of the king of Tartessus—it is recorded that Arganthonius of Cadiz ruled eighty years and lived a hundred and twenty— still nothing that has an end is long."

Cicero's words, written centuries ago, express a regret common to all men. He went on to say that we ought to be content, nonetheless, with whatever life is allotted us. Yet most men cannot be content. The hope for immortality is as old as thinking man himself. The most primitive religions promised something beyond this life, beyond this world. But even the promise of heaven is not enough for most human beings. Man struggles against his mortality, unable to rest easily with the knowledge that this is the only turn he will take in this world. He longs for a second chance to live again in the same body he possessed on earth.

Today there are people who refuse to agree that a man is forever dead because his heart has stopped beating and his brain no longer functions. Such death, they say, is but a temporary thing. They believe that cold holds a promise of physical immortality here on earth. If we can place the sperm cells into suspended animation and yet bring them back to potent life; if we can freeze the blood and then transfuse it into the veins of living men; if we can chill the hamster, the ground squirrel, and the bat until hearts and lungs are still and bodies stiff and brittle, and even then restore them—why not man?

Their plan is disarmingly simple: the way to seek immortality starts in the freezer. A man dies. His body is frozen at once and is then stored at the temperature of liquid nitrogen, or better yet, liquid helium. He is not in a state of suspended animation, but rather in suspended death. The years go by, the centuries, while he lies undisturbed in his icy bed. Then at last the moment for his second chance is at hand. His body is lifted from the container, thawed, revived, repaired, and his life resumes again.

"Most of us now living have a chance for personal, physical immortality," declares Robert C. W. Ettinger, a former physics professor, who is leader of the immortality-seekers. "No matter what kills us, whether old age or disease . . . sooner or later our friends of the future should be equal to the task of reviving and curing us."

Unlike the smallpox victim irrevocably dead before Jenner and the vaccine, or the pneumonia patient killed by his disease before Fleming and penicillin, the man with an incurable illness today will be cured—if only he can wait until medical science advances to the point that Ettinger believes it can. The child who dies of a diseased heart would be frozen and revived when a cure is discovered or heart transplantation made routine. The cancer sufferer would awaken when malignancies are no more serious than inflamed tonsils. The person dreadfully deformed from birth or by fire or accident will be aroused when plastic surgery can guarantee a handsome face and figure. The missing, crippled, twisted, or shrunken limb will be replaced with a perfect one. Or perhaps the thawed body will be induced to grow its own replacement parts. Death comes most often to the old, and the bedridden woman of ninety does not wish an immortality in which she is forever, at least physically, a ruin of the self she was when a girl. Each person longs for immortal life in his prime— young, healthy, sexually vigorous, and attractive. Old age, it is said, is a disease that only death can cure. Not in the future, murmur the hopeful, who imagine being thawed out when science has learned not only to arrest, but even reverse the aging process. The wrinkles will disappear, the spine straighten, the hair grow luxuriant and lose its gray, the spring return to the step, and the gleam to the eye. Youth is so wonderful, remarked George Bernard Shaw, that it is too bad to waste it on the young. In that golden age of the future, the face and form of twenty would be combined with the wisdom and experience of many decades or centuries.

Immortality of this kind is a beautiful vision, but can it ever be more than that? Almost all scientists regretfully insist that it is merely a hope. No higher animal has ever survived freezing to subzero temperatures, they point out. For that matter, not one internal organ has been able to function normally after freezing and long-term storage. People cannot be guarded properly from freezing injuries. Without glycerol or DMSO, freezing brings drastic cell damage. Yet many scientists believe that these chemicals are lethal of themselves when used in concentrations sufficient to protect a human being.

"I do not know at the present time of any method which has been demonstrated to achieve your purpose," a doctor noted for his work in heart transplantation responded to a query from the Cryonics Society of New York, an organization formed to proselytize for immortality.

"I have no particular quarrel with your ambitions," wrote a leading cryobiologist, "other than that you are more optimistic than the facts warrant. And although whole body freezing is the ultimate goal of cryobiology, this does not necessarily imply that it is also achievable."

"The fact that freezing techniques are far from perfected is discouraging, but irrelevant," is the calm reaction of spokesmen for the Cryonics Society. "The only other choice is to let the organism deteriorate. Freezing is the better alternative."

"I am almost convinced that people can be frozen after death and resuscitated," declares Ettinger.

For the most part, scientists in the cryonics organizations are rare. The most prominent is, like Ettinger, a physics—not a biology—professor. He has conceded that many in the academic community "think it's a hoax, but I myself am doing what I can to spread the idea among scientists."

The proponents of freezing the dead are quick to say that scientists are more encouraging in private than in their public utterances. And they can pull out at least one letter in support of this view. A scientist wrote of his excitement about the idea but said simply that he dares not come out with this as it would injure his academic status. "Please stay in touch with me," he concluded. Another explained that freezing could not be done now but added that there was no evidence that techniques might not be developed in the future.

The cryonics groups follow the scientific journals with painstaking care, rejoicing in every bit of research that seems to promise hope, however remote. A newsletter circulated among believers hails reports that biologists in Japan have succeeded in obtaining electrocorticograms from a cat's brain frozen and stored for 203 days, that a normal frog developed from a cell injected into the egg of another frog, that human cells survived freezing for six years, that information from one rat's brain has been transferred to another.

Enthusiasts seize upon the fact that no scientist will come out and say flatly that freezing and revival of the dead will forever be impossible.

Ettinger, the man who has focused national attention on freezing, has been thinking about it for more than twenty years. While lying in a hospital bed in 1947 receiving treatment for World War II wounds, he first read about experiments being done by French biologist Jean Rostand. In these, frog sperm was protected from freezing injury with glycerol. Rostand's discovery of the preservative was for the most part ignored; glycerol did not gain general acceptance until it was rediscovered in 1949 by Smith and her associates. But young Ettinger grasped the significance at once. In Rostand's dry report he saw possibilities of the most incredible wonder. He rapidly made the jump from frog sperm to human beings. It appeared clear, he said later, that "even if suspended animation techniques were not perfected, one could freeze the newly dead, accepting whatever degree of freezing damage was unavoidable, and still have a non-zero chance of eventual revival."

The idea seemed so obvious to him that he was sure it must be equally apparent to everyone else. He assumed that it would be seized upon and promoted by influential and prominent scientists. During the next fifteen years, while following his profession as a professor of physics at Michigan's Highland Park College, he eagerly watched for news. But nothing happened. Suspended animation or suspended death remained what it had been for a century—a subject for fiction only. One writer described a soldier in Napoleon's army who was frozen solid during the return from Moscow. His body was revived years later, with only one bit of damage: an ear broke off. When it came to serious science, rather than romantic fiction, not even Rostand went as far as Ettinger would have liked. Rostand predicted that someday a way would be found of freezing the old or incurably sick until their conditions could be corrected, but he did not take the next step and urge freezing them or the dead with the imperfect methods of the present.

At last in 1960 Ettinger decided that if no one else would present this revolutionary idea, it was up to him. He set it down in book form, gave it the romantic title *The Prospect of Immortality*, and sent a copy to Rostand, his source of inspiration. Rostand rose to the occasion by writing a warm and enthusiastic introduction. The book was published privately in 1962 and was discovered and brought out by Doubleday & Co. in 1964.

Once Ettinger's book was out, it was learned that he had been right to assume that he was not the only person thinking along these lines. Another man, Ev Cooper, says he had the idea independently. His book, *Immortality, Physically, Scientifically Now*, written under a pseudonym, was published in 1962. Cooper also had organized a discussion group which was the nucleus for the Life Extension Society, largest of the organizations favoring freezing. But the movement needed Ettinger's book and the attendant publicity to spark it. Membership in the Life Extension Society quickly climbed to well over four hundred, with LES "coordinators" available as advisers to the dying in many cities in the U. S., Canada, France, Belgium, England, Italy, Mexico, Costa Rica, Venezuela, India, Malaysia, and the Ivory Coast. "Freeze-Wait-Reanimate" was adopted as the motto. Other groups of activists formed cryonics societies and eventually were able to claim more than a thousand members.

One of the men who later joined the Cryonics Society of New York describes his reaction to *The Prospect of Immortality*: "I thought it the most optimistic book I had ever read."

And optimism is the key to the entire philosophy. It is the old dream of eternal life, but with just enough scientific truth in it to be modern. Ettinger himself is not a wild-eyed revolutionary, but rather a quiet man who seems completely sincere. He has a scientific background, and he has written a scientific book. Much of what he says is valid, reasonable, and convincing. He is on sound ground, after all, in suggesting that people have various of their body cells frozen long before death. But Ettinger's plan for these cell banks is different from those of other scientists. He urges that these cells be stored with the frozen body to serve as samples to later-day scientists at revival time. At some point, therefore, the reader must make a jump to faith, to a blind acceptance of the basic premise. And like members of a mystic sect, those who believe it simply cannot understand why anyone else should not.

All physiological damage resulting from freezing, and Ettinger concedes that this will exist, will be handled by "our friends of the future." The worst freezing injury occurs when the protein molecules within the cells collapse due to dehydration. The effect of such denaturing in the brain would be devastating. Ettinger is not unduly disturbed; a way of reversing this process may be developed, he says hopefully.

Cold As a Means of Survival

Which of the stored thoughts, emotions, experiences, dreams, longings, remembered joys or sadness, loves and hates will be retained after years in the freezer? Immortality of the type desired by those who seek it in liquid nitrogen requires the restoration of the person as he was at his best. What good is it to be immortal and not know it? And so Ettinger suggests that key elements of memory and personality be fed into a computer and retained as a permanent record. With this as a guide, surgeons in the future might rebuild the vital portions of the brain "cell by cell, or even molecule by molecule in critical areas." It might take years or even centuries to complete such a difficult task, but that would not matter. Time would stretch out endlessly in this golden future.

But would the future be so golden to those coming from a distant past? Perhaps physical immortality, even if it could be achieved, would bring nothing but misery. The image of awakening young in body and mature in experience might be utterly false. Instead the formerly dead would be alone and frightened in a world he could not understand. He may have been brilliant and learned when last he lived, but compared to the beings in that advanced era, he might be as one retarded. His knowledge and experience could be less than that of the children who would gather around to see him as a curiosity. Once a doctor ... lawyer ... businessman ... he would be fit for no profession. And how would he communicate with others, find a friend, a companion, a lover? A television program of the 1960's aimed at a juvenile audience portrayed a man frozen in an avalanche in Alaska and discovered and thawed out after sixty-eight years. He was still thirty-three, while his son had become an old man. It was a puerile conceit, played for laughs. Yet there would be no laughter for the man of today, lost and a misfit among his distant descendants.

This prospect, too, does not deflect Ettinger from his missionary zeal. A transitional period would be needed; that is all. The formerly dead will ultimately adjust no matter how great the cultural gap. After all, remarks Ettinger, tribes at the level of the Stone Age have made the jump when civilization reached them. The problem of the displaced person is not new. The future society will prepare systematic reeducation and rehabilitation programs for the resuscitated.

And in the meantime: "Perhaps we might have to live in subcultural enclaves and take a subordinate place in society." Although this sounds depressing to a twentieth-century mind, it will not be troublesome in the future. "We could bear this, as we would know that it is only temporary," says Ettinger. "We have the chance of being in time brought up to the level of those around us. There would be no need for discouragement or insanity.

"I'm not afraid of such words as utopia. In that future despair will dwindle to nothing. Men will not have to regard any problems as insoluble, any injustices as uncorrectable. What is offered is time which gives hope in any situation. It removes the worst effects of present unhappiness."

Cryogenic interment may be a temporary expedient. Should old age indeed be conquered, people would go on living indefinitely and there would be no necessity for freezing. If old age is only postponed, then the freezing of corpses might remain a standard practice.

The conquest—for that matter, the mere postponement—of death would create population problems on a scale undreamed of today. Death now comes at three score years and ten, or thereabouts, yet the number of people on our earth doubles and redoubles. Add the teeming population of today to that of tomorrow and the earth would sink beneath the load. Obvious though it appears, this objection only irritates Ettinger. The earth, in his opinion, can hold billions of people —40 billion anyway. And what if that number were reached? Thousands of new planets could then be created and people emigrate into space. There is indeed nothing that would be beyond those superscientists of tomorrow. Ettinger feels that population is not a proper concern for him. He equates freezing with medical care, not very different from an iron lung, kidney transplant, or penicillin. Refusing to do it strikes him as comparable to withholding treatment from a sick person and allowing him to die. Nor does the invalid pause to consider that his death would be a small contribution to population control. Contraception and expansion of the economy are the ways to handle the matter.

War, to be sure, would solve the population problem for good and all. But war does not figure in the plans of those who seek to prolong their lives. "I think that the possibility of nuclear war might very well be reduced," says Ettinger. "There would be no need for desperation."

And what of religion? There is no conflict with any belief, Ettinger and his followers insist. Freezing is not a scientific resurrection without a day of judgment; it is merely the extension of life. And should the utopian age come into being, men would find it easier to live up to the ethical and moral codes of their faiths.

Leaving religious and moral questions aside, freezing presents some very real practical difficulties. The person who wishes to be frozen someday is given a piece of semihumorous advice by Ettinger: "Try to live a little longer." His reasoning is that techniques are improving with every passing year.

Careful advance planning is necessary for those seeking storage in liquid nitrogen. "Do not wait for the last week," urges a Life Extension Society newsletter. "Decide now." The interested person is urged to make out an affidavit: "It is firmly desired that the biological decay of my body be arrested at the moment of my death by the most advanced technological method, cryogenic or otherwise, available at the time of death."

The greatest risk to immortality is that death may come suddenly, possibly through accident. One disciple believes that those who would be frozen will be more careful of themselves during this "first life." "No chance is worth it, if it risks my immortal life." Some put the letters "M.P.G.," standing for "Member of the Permanent Generation," after their names. But even the greatest of care is not always enough, and the chance at immortality must be jealously guarded. The Life Extension Society and another group, the Immortality Research and Compilation Association, suggest that "emergency freezing cards" be carried in the wallet. A bracelet or tag could also be worn. But any of these might be overlooked. Perhaps, says an LES member, the desire for freezing could be tattooed on the body. The only part of the body that is certain to be noticed is the face and a tattoo there would be an embarrassment at any time except after death. Another possibility is to wear a "unit containing a small radio transmitter and battery-powered audible-frequency alarm." This would be activated by breathing, and at its cessation a radio signal would be flashed and a siren go off. The radio frequency would be monitored by other members of a freezing society. While they would be rushing to the scene, passers-by, attracted by the siren, would be helping. The very fact that freezing enthusiasts think a stranger would give assistance indicates their singular optimism. Let us assume that someone bends over the body and finds the card, bracelet, or tattoo. Even if a "reward" is included, it still is unlikely that he would go to work and carry the corpse off to be frozen at once. And it must be done at once . . . or never.

If freezing is the medical technique its advocates insist that it is, it should logically be performed by a doctor. But finding a doctor who is willing to cooperate is exceedingly difficult. "Many doctors say 'wait until suspended animation is perfected,'" complains a member of the cryonics society. "Well, by then anyone would be for it. Now is when it is radical."

Most doctors, however, are anything but radical. Nor are hospital personnel eager to cooperate. One man belonging to the LES died of heart disease in an intensive care unit of a hospital. Although he had told both his doctor and the hospital that he wished to be frozen after his death, no efforts to cool him were made. He lay there, deteriorating, until another society member was summoned by a friend. Freezing was then instituted, but probably too late. It is not surprising that some of the would-be frozen are urging the construction of a special nursing home "offering attention and care for those who wish to be frozen upon the moment of medical death."

Ettinger, who manages to combine pragmatism with idealism, suggests that the person who desires freezing make his appeal to a doctor friend, preferably a very young or very old one, not too afraid for his reputation. As a last resort, it is always possible to try "the pure power of money." This may be of no avail, but all is not lost even then.

"A layman can do the freezing, if he trains himself and is not too queasy," declares Ettinger stoutly.

Freezing a dead body is a ghoulish task for which Ettinger gives explicit, detailed, step-by-step instructions. He has even succeeded in convincing a national magazine to run an article containing the rules. Difficult though they sound, members of the cryonics societies refuse to be frightened. "As the person is dead, he can't be killed by bungling" is the matter-of-fact approach.

Anyone planning the job should prepare for it weeks, even months, in advance. The amateur freezing technician should assemble a "do-it-yourself perfusion and freezing kit," containing all the things he will need.

Once death occurs, cold is essential to prevent deterioration, and so the body is quickly carried to the basement or coldest room in the house. But even while this is being done, efforts must be made to maintain the circulation of the dead man. Irreparable cellular damage will take place if circulation stops before freezing has been completed. This is a truly monumental challenge for the amateur. Those with ample funds may obtain a closed-chest heart-lung machine and learn to use it. Others must rely on artificial respiration and external heart massage.

Preparedness is the key to success. At any time during the life of the loved one, the person who is to do the freezing can begin his study of the necessary techniques. If husband and wife both wish to be frozen, they can practice on one another while alive. First-aid courses in artificial respiration are a starting point. If no partner is available, a life-sized doll may be bought from a medical supply company. Mouth-to-mouth respiration can be performed through a tube instead of by breathing directly into the dead person. Such a tube might be purchased as part of the do-it-yourself kit. Then the amateur must learn how to give an injection, because a drug such as heparin is needed to prevent coagulation of the blood. And while the heart is forced to pump, the temperature of the corpse is brought down to 50°F. by means of ice packs or a special mattress in which cold water circulates.

The cadaver, Ettinger goes on to explain, must be perfused with blood plasma or a solution containing DMSO or glycerol—and this is an awesome task for anyone not engaged in the practice of medicine. While the solution can be introduced via a heart-lung machine or embalmer's pump, few do-it-yourself kits will contain either. The layman can instead, after countless hours of practice, make use of the kind of hanging bottle employed medically for intravenous glucose feeding. It takes about half an hour to perfuse a child and an hour for a larger person.

Once perfusion is completed, the body is ready for freezing. Dry ice is the recommended refrigerant for the first stage, and it can be used in conjunction with almost anything at hand. The corpse may be wrapped in alternate layers of bedsheets and dry ice, with blankets or even newspapers on top. Or the body can be covered with plastic bags that have been filled with crushed dry ice in alcohol. Ever practical, Ettinger urges that a supply of dry ice be ordered when death appears imminent. In a well-insulated box, it will evaporate at a rate of about fifty pounds a week. The cost is minimal. The body can keep for a day or two in dry ice, but the final stage of freezing requires a transfer to a box or capsule containing liquid nitrogen. Great care must be taken not to drop the body during the move to the box, because a frozen body can break.

As the description of the procedure unfolds, it becomes

clear that the husband, wife, or friend of the deceased must be possessed of a devotion that passes understanding. Love alone may not be enough; faith is needed, too. It would be all but impossible for anyone who is not himself a believer to prepare a dead body for freezing. Only the dream of immortality can make the foul task palatable. The worker must be convinced that he is saving the life of the one he loves. And perhaps, he may think, this is not the end of physical love between them. Frozen himself when his time comes, he will be reunited with his beloved on the day they leave the freezer. Instead of meeting in heaven, they will meet in, say, A.D. 2300.

Still, who can say that marriage will survive the freezer? Sex will be possible with sex organs restored to youthful vigor; love will return with the brain brought back to its former habits of thought. But there is no guarantee that husband and wife will reawaken together. The scientific world of tomorrow may not consider ancient marriage rites of any consequence. The wife who died of a disease conquered in the next fifty years may not be allowed to wait for her husband, dead of a condition it takes five hundred years to cure. Even if future scientists do respect the marriage vows of the past, a whole new set of problems arises. Should the surviving partner remarry in the years left to him before he, too, enters the freezer? With which spouse would he then be reunited on resuscitation day? Would the original mate retain his rights, even though the second or third may have been better loved? These philosophic considerations seem quite beside the point to those dedicated to freezing.

They are more concerned about where to store the bodies for their long wait. One suggestion is to ship them to the Arctic and put them in pits dug in the permafrost. The pits would be insulated with straw and dry ice. Others urge the Antarctic, where the bodies could be kept above ground in simply constructed housing. Looking to the future when they are convinced thousands or millions will be frozen, some cryonics society members suggest that bodies be shipped to the moon. Not to be outdone, others urge the moons of Jupiter.

At present, bodies are placed in cryogenic warehouses or mausoleums, sometimes on cemetery grounds. Ettinger thinks interested groups should form associations and buy shares in a cooperative storage facility. The shares would pay for the land, construction of the warehouse, and maintenance. The first storage facilities for the once and future living have been built in Phoenix, Arizona; Long Island, New York; and Orange County, California.

The bodies lie in cryogenic capsules, obtained for the most part from Ed Hope, founder of the Cryo-Care Equipment Corporation, which operates under the simple motto "Pioneers in Human Preservation." Hope is a wigmaker, which seems a profession rather far afield from cryogenic interment; still, he has moved easily from the world of beauty to the world of cold. Hope designed a capsule that works on the same general principle as a thermos bottle. It has an inner container chilled by liquid nitrogen, an outer container, and a vacuum between. After completing the first capsule in 1965, Hope had a trial run using a simulated 150-pound human body which was wrapped in a one-inch insulating cover made of cotton and synthetic aluminized fabric. He found that the temperature of the inner container required but thirty minutes to drop to the coldness of liquid nitrogen. The body itself took longer. The nitrogen gas surrounding it fell to below -100°F. very rapidly; then it took the better part of two days to reach -320°F. This was quite satisfactory, and with this test behind him, Hope was ready to offer his capsule to the first taker. The price was originally set at $3,200, but it soon moved up to more than $4,500. Should anyone be unable to raise this sum, buying on the installment plan was suggested.

What price immortality? Ettinger has been giving a figure of $8,500 for freezing and perpetual care, but inflation is rapidly making that estimate obsolete. Price depends, of course, on who does the freezing, the equipment used, and the storage facilities. Once the frozen body has been placed in its container, the only continuing expense is that of replacing the liquid nitrogen, and possibly "room-rent" for the crypt. One young man who was to die of an intestinal ailment at twenty-four in 1968 had allocated well in advance a fund of $200 a year for his postdeath care.

Each person must finance himself on the road to immortality. And the way to do that, so the cryonics societies maintain, is to take out a $10,000 insurance policy. Although the beneficiary would really be the person himself, the name on the policy would have to be that of a trusted friend. It would be up to him to use the funds for freezing and storage of the deceased. If no friend or relative is sympathetic, members of the organized groups have volunteered to serve. The Life Extension Society had an insurance company work out a possible group policy and has sent its members a list of the rates.

Over the years payments from the policy would keep the container cold but would not be sufficient for that day when, according to the belief, the body will be reanimated. The former corpse will have no possessions and will have to pay for food, clothes, and shelter, or become a public charge and add abject poverty to his problems of readjustment. Those who favor freezing have a solution for that also: take it with you. The means to do so, they say, is a trust fund to end all trust funds. It does not stop at children or grandchildren, but goes on and on. The money is to be paid "when the Grantor is restored to full life and health." As a hedge against possible inflation, the individual setting up a trust fund would invest it in stocks of basic industries, so that the value would keep pace with the changing times. The deceased could remain frozen until his trust fund has grown to the point where it could support him in his new life, Ettinger points out with firm logic.

At present, there are legal obstacles to such trust agreements. Funds cannot be kept in trust indefinitely. Lawyer members of the Cryonics Society of New York are looking into this and, with characteristic optimism, hope to find a solution.

Every aspect of freezing demands the utmost nobility on the part of all involved. The setting up of a trust fund for oneself, even if legal, requires that the relatives be totally unselfish. They must actively cooperate in losing their share of an estate. When someone dies, the next of kin traditionally determines what is to be done with the body.

Even with a cooperative spouse and children, the way to the freezer is beset with legal obstacles. In most states disposal of a body is regulated by law. The cadaver must be prepared by a licensed mortician, be buried in a legally specified cemetery, or cremated in a licensed crematorium. Should the mortician decide to embalm the body, he would, of course, destroy it. And so after getting the family to agree, and if lucky, a doctor, the would-be immortal must convince a mortician to join in, too. Ultimately, Ettinger believes, morticians will take over the entire freezing procedure.

The first effort to move freezing out of the theoretical and into the practical sphere took place in May of 1965 shortly after a woman in Springfield, Ohio, suffered a massive heart attack. As she lay in a hospital, her husband learned about the freezing procedure and decided to arrange for it. He was told that a new company, Juno, Inc., had already constructed a cryogenic container and he immediately ordered one. Word of his plan began to trickle out and a horde of newspaper reporters descended on the hospital, hot on the trail of a major human interest story. While they were waiting, the fate of the freezing hung in the balance. The woman, still in a coma, was unable to give her consent to the unprecedented happening. A number of her relatives, deeply troubled, consulted a minister and were apparently urged to abandon the freezing. Her own doctor refused to take part, and the hospital board would not give its approval. The venture was doomed, and the woman died and was laid to rest in a conventional manner after all. Juno went bankrupt, leaving the capsule field to Hope. As for the capsule, when last checked, it was still lying empty in the deserted factory.

Another attempt at freezing failed for quite another reason. In this case, the man involved, an engineer, had decided that he wanted to be frozen. But death came too soon, and his plans had not been perfected. After his burial, his relatives realized that they had not observed his wishes. They called Ettinger and asked if anything could yet be done. But as members of the cryonics societies are quick to say: "If you're buried unfrozen, it's all over."

By this time it was clear to the proponents of freezing that some highly publicized event was needed if the technique was ever to make its mark. Cooper, president of his Life Extension Society, had an idea; if the Russians could put dogs in space, why could not the society place a dog in a cryogenic capsule? The ideal time for such action would be at the third annual meeting of the group, the Freeze-Wait-Reanimate Conference, scheduled for January 1, 1966.

Hope, who had been fortunate enough to escape involvement in the Springfield fiasco, was still waiting for a human occupant for his container. He offered the suggestion that LES freeze a pig. He considered the plan to use a dog to be fraught with danger: "One out of every three or four people has had a dog at one time or another, and by comparison I would prefer to face all the pig-lovers of America." Cooper conceded the wisdom of his remark but found it easier to obtain a dog for freezing, and so the practical side won out.

On December 22, Cooper anesthetized Bel, an average-sized, black female dog, half Labrador retriever. Then with the help of a veterinarian, he perfused the animal with a DMSO solution and froze her in dry ice. Five days later Hope's cryo-capsule arrived from Arizona by trailer. Hope had by then been reconciled to the dog. On December 31 the capsule was opened and to the dismay of one and all, no liquid nitrogen was inside. Something must have gone wrong when the capsule had been filled. Rallying quickly to meet the emergency, Cooper postponed the transfer of dog to container for a day and obtained an additional supply of the cryogenic gas. Once again the capsule was filled and everything was in readiness.

A restaurant in Washington, D. C., was the scene of the LES conference. The proprietor had apparently been living in a fool's paradise, assuming that this was a typical business conference—many rounds of martinis, lunch, and speeches. He was appalled when reporters entered, demanding to know where was the capsule, and most important, where was the dog. The proprietor begged Cooper and the other LES members not to bring the capsule and, for heaven's sake, not the dog inside the premises. The group accepted this uncooperative attitude with philosophic calm and obligingly—followed by a stream of television and newspaper reporters—went outside. They were promptly rewarded for their humanity to the restaurateur by an attack from a representative of the Humane Society. He denounced their plan as "shocking, disgusting, and serving no useful scientific purpose," and went on to suggest that "Ev Cooper should go freeze himself." Once again members of the LES accepted these insults with aplomb. The police then came up and informed Hope that his trailer containing the capsule was in a no parking zone, and he had better move it. Undismayed, Hope and the group repaired to a nearby parking lot. In the confusion some of the followers got lost and failed to see the dog at all.

Finally in the parking lot, a most unromantic place to seek immortality, the dog was prepared for the long years ahead. Bel, enclosed in a plastic bag, had been resting throughout the furor in a fiberboard box filled with dry ice. This had been kept in the back of a convertible. With television and movie cameramen from America and Europe focusing on her, Bel was at last lifted out of the box and placed on a stretcherlike tray which slid directly into the capsule. The liquid nitrogen temperature within was to keep Bel forever, or until the moment of resuscitation so fervently longed for by the members of LES.

With all the publicity attending the freezing, the move from dog to human was not long in coming. A woman was frozen the following April and placed in a Cryo-Care capsule. This venture was not a success. For some reason, incomprehensible to members of the cryonics societies, her relatives decided after only a few months that it was foolish to hope, and removed and defrosted her.

The first success, if such it can fairly be called, came for Dr. James H. Bedford, a retired psychology professor of Glendale City College, California. Bedford had decided that he wanted to be frozen, and he had gone on to convince his family to cooperate. In January of 1967 Bedford was dying from lung cancer, and the time to prepare for freezing was at hand. He called the Cryonics Society of California asking members to see to it that his wishes were carried out. In order to avoid possible objections from hospital boards, Dr. Bedford entered a Los Angeles nursing home. On the night of January 11, with death clearly near, the freezing equipment was prepared. The following day the attending physician stayed close by, listening carefully through his stethoscope to the failing heartbeats. Suddenly they stopped; the physician signaled for help at once. The heart was then forced to resume its beating with artificial means until the initial chilling was completed. Heparin was injected to prevent coagulation. This was the moment of truth and members of the Cryonics Society were equal to it. Rushing to the nursing home to lend assistance, they worked on Bedford's body for the whole day, sending out periodically for additional supplies of dry ice. At last the body was frozen. Seeing this as an epoch-making event—the first such procedure performed under ideal circumstances—Ettinger flew to Los Angeles to participate in a huge press conference. For the final step, Bedford's body was flown to Phoenix, where Hope was waiting with his liquid-nitrogen-filled cryo-capsule. Two years later, Bedford's family moved him back to California so that his frozen body would be nearer them. Bedford will remain in his capsule until a cure for cancer is found, says Robert Nelson, president of the Cryonics Society of California.

The next candidate for the freezer was Marie Phelps-

Sweet, a life-long campaigner for liberal causes, and first LES coordinator in California. She died unexpectedly in her sleep in a hotel room in Santa Monica, California, on the night of August 26–27, 1967. Instructions concerning her own freezing were found among her possessions. With touching optimism, she had enclosed a photograph of herself taken twenty-seven years earlier. "This Is As I Wish To Be Restored!" she had written, adding in tiny letters, "I believe it can be done in time!" But her death was not fortuitous. She died alone and three days elapsed before her wishes could be carried out.

Members of the Cryonics Society of California together with Los Angeles LES coordinators rushed to the dead woman's side to perfuse and freeze. Ettinger stayed by the telephone for hours on end, giving advice. Although there was considerable doubt as to whether she had left any money to cover the costs of freezing, an LES coordinator advanced some of his own at once, members of the organization sent more, and dry ice and other necessities were purchased.

Her fellow LES members fear, nonetheless, that some damage to her memory may result from deterioration during the delay before freezing. But they allow themselves the "wild hope that Marie can eventually be rebuilt into a person very similar to her old derring-do self." Her frozen body attests to that hope.

After Mrs. Sweet came a fifty-five-year-old Michigan businessman whose family was said to have no hope of his eventual revival, but who did not want his body to rot. The next person remains in what has been described as "a state of cryogenic limbo." In plain English this means that he is being preserved in dry ice while his family tries to decide whether to go ahead. The seventh, Steven Mandell of New York, was the twenty-four-year-old who had not been caught short by the prematurity of his death. Mandell was the first person to be frozen at a funeral home and stored at a regular cemetery. Once very four months the president of New York's Cryonics Society sees to it that the liquid nitrogen is replenished.

But though believers in Ettinger's theory do die every so often and are frozen, the number is small. Hope, for example, told a Chicago *Daily News* reporter that his original plans for a 2,000-body storage facility had been too optimistic and he was going to build a smaller one. He was particularly chagrined by the poor response to his "Kiddie Kapsules."

"Reactions have been characterized overwhelmingly by caution," remarks Ettinger. He has received several thousand letters, but the tone tends to be passive. People appear ready to wait until cryogenic interment has been generally accepted and is easily obtainable—which may never happen at all. Only twenty-four persons attended the fifth annual LES conference in 1968.

The general indifference astounds Ettinger and his supporters, who had been confident that once the method was described, everyone would seize upon it vigorously, and the rush to the freezer would be on. "But what have you got to lose? You're dead already." They are unable to understand why anyone would throw away any chance at immortality.

Instead what has happened? "In the past year or so, many millions have needlessly been buried," Ettinger wrote in a brochure sent recently to prospective cryonics society members.

What is the reason for the failure of the movement to date? The fact that a frozen dead person is, nonetheless, irrevocably dead? That is the logical reason. But movements no more logical than this one have gained vast numbers of adherents. The missing factor here is the Pied Piper, the leader with personal magnetism that could make people overlook the scientific inadequacies. But cryogenic interment does not have a spellbinder. Instead it has as leader an unassuming middle-aged physics professor, an intellectual and idealist who is inspired rather than inspiring. He does not have the power to compel. By now he seems a little weary, a trifle disheartened by the lack of response.

Nonetheless, the movement is indeed fortunate to have such a man, because his motives are unselfish. It would be all too easy for a plan like this to be promoted by a charlatan. Ettinger does not appear to be crass or mercenary. His is the goal of the zealot—to be the prophet of a movement that will improve mankind's lot. It is significant that he believes not only that people will be revived, but that they will be better, more noble human beings when they are revived because of obtaining freedom from the tyranny of mortality.

His supporters seem equally disinterested in profit. LES coordinators offer their help to the dying. "No coordinator is to receive any salaries, monies, or personal gain because of his position in LES," says their newsletter.

No matter how small the response today, the advocates of freezing believe in the future. The Cryonics Society of New York recently drafted a letter to be sent to Senators and Congressmen. "When the problems involved in trying to make cryogenic interment practical are overcome, it could burst upon the American public with the impact of another 'Sputnik.' . . . If you inform yourself now, you will be . . . able to act in the best interests of your constituents."

In his preface to Ettinger's book, Rostand wrote of a time when "cemeteries will be replaced by dormitories." For Ettinger and his followers, the time is now.

But will anyone ever rise from his capsule-couch in that dormitory? Even those who are most deeply committed are not sure.

"People who are being frozen before the technique is perfected are taking a shot in the dark," admits one of the most ardent of Ettinger's followers. But he does not care.

"The chance is worth it. There's no chance any other way."

Part Five

Cold, the Healer

15

The Freeze That Brings Health

"I feel myself to be the victim of a vicious and causeless joke. I tremble without cease, and without hope of ceasing."

"I am exhausted by the weight of my rigid arm. Every movement is a herculean task requiring an enormous effort of will. And my will fails me as never before."

"Her social, economic, and home life had been so disrupted by the tremor that she sought amputation of the left arm. Her husband had abandoned her because of her affliction. She was unable to get or hold a job."

These words depict the tragic plight of but three of the 1.5 million Americans who are afflicted with Parkinsonism, a disease of the central nervous system. Also known as "the shaking palsy," it claims 50,000 or more new victims a year, most—but by no means all—over the age of fifty. The sufferers are easily identified. Their faces are inexpressive, their voices are monotonous, their posture stooped, and their step shuffling. The thumb moves back and forth over tremulous fingers in a continual pill-rolling movement. In time the ability to work, to walk, to dress and care for themselves is lost. Of all the characteristics, the tremor and muscular rigidity are most troubling to the victims.

Efforts to relieve the unpleasant symptoms have obviously not gone as far as amputation, but they have been both painful and extreme. James Parkinson, who identified and gave his name to the disease in 1816, recommended a most disagreeable treatment: the patient was bled from the upper part of the neck and irritants were placed there to produce a pus-filled discharge. That was all it produced; a cure was not forthcoming. Parkinson's successors subscribed to the theory that a patient who was shaking involuntarily would be benefited by shaking himself voluntarily. Jean Martin Charcot, the French neurologist whose theories influenced Freud, ordered his patients to sit in a moving armchair that he had designed. Other doctors put Parkinson victims on horseback and insisted that they ride for at least two hours a day. The wealthy were dispatched to mountainous regions in the hope that a change of air would bring relief. Many were dosed with chemicals and poisons, such as carbonate of iron, barium chloride, and arsenic. The despairing invalids were ready to try whatever palliative was suggested. Anyone who promised help won followers at once. Forty years ago the hitherto little-known Bulgarian village of Chipka enjoyed a sudden brief burst of notoriety because of Ivan Raeff and his miraculous "Bulgarian belladonna cure." Belladonna had been a standard treatment elsewhere, too, since the late 1800's and had been thoroughly disliked because of its side reactions of palpitation, flushing, and dry mouth. No matter; if Raeff prescribed it, this time it would work. Patients took belladonna along with any other pills he recommended. Doctors were unmoved by the enthusiasm of Raeff and the starry-eyed wonder of the devotees of his method. They analyzed the pills and found them to be made of charcoal, bread dough, sawdust, nutmeg, and calamus root. The Parkinson victims were not so easily convinced that the "cure" was worthless. The medication was only a part of the healing regime anyway. They were required to sleep on the right side only and to take baths in water warmed in nature's way by the sun.

Faith-healer "cures" and sophisticated surgical methods were developed and tried concurrently. Physicians aimed right at the root of the trouble and operated on the part of the brain which they thought ruled tremors and rigidity. But it proved very difficult to locate that spot with sufficient precision to stop only those nerve impulses and no others. One young musician had agreed to the surgery when his left arm became so stiff and trembling that he was unable to perform. After the operation his arm relaxed again, but he never resumed his profession. His personality had changed and he was the sensitive intellectual no more. He lost all interest in music and became a filling-station attendant, careless of his appearance, casual about his earning power, and unfailingly cheerful. Few cases were as dramatic. The most frequent complaint following this surgery was a degree of paralysis and weakness in the affected limb.

In 1940, Dr. H. Russell Meyers turned to a different area of the brain and succeeded in stopping the tremor of the young woman who had sought amputation. She left the hospital, got a job, and was able to support herself and her little boy. Sometime later she called the doctor and expressed annoyance that the tremor returned when she was having an orgasm or was angry or tense. Although her irritation was valid, her position was markedly improved from the time when she was abandoned and unloved. Not all patients had as positive a story to tell. During the next ten years surgery was performed on thirty-eight Parkinson patients, and twenty-five of them improved.

Nonetheless, the uncertainty of relief, the mortality rate of almost sixteen percent, and the technical difficulties of operating led Meyers to conclude: "As of the present the surgical therapy of Parkinsonism must be regarded as in the earliest phases of experimentation."

This "surgical therapy" was soon moved out of the experimental stage by Dr. Irving S. Cooper, a vigorous and attractive young surgeon with extraordinary skill for doing complicated brain operations. By 1952, at the age of thirty, Cooper had already succeeded in surgically halting the tremor of Parkinsonism without producing changes in personality, weakness, or paralysis. He quickly became dissatisfied with the standard method of excising the brain tissue with a scalpel. Instead, he destroyed it with an injection of absolute alcohol. With this technique, he reported, the tremor was relieved in six out of every ten patients, and the rigidity was improved in seven out of ten. The advantage lay in the absence of unfortunate aftereffects; the percentage of patients relieved was no better than that of the past.

The mediocre rate of success clearly was related to the inexact pinpointing of the area of the brain most responsible for the tremor and rigidity. And in 1957 Cooper was convinced that he knew just where it was—in the thalamus, a tiny mass of tissue within the brain.

"The word *talamo* comes from the Greek and its meaning was connubial couch," comments Cooper. "Undoubtedly it was apparent to early investigators that this structure deep within the brain was a hotbed of sensory-motor activity."

If just the right bit of thalamic tissue could be destroyed, the unwanted activities would be disrupted without producing paralysis or changes in personality. Having identified the spot, Cooper began to look for a new way of destroying the tissue that would be safer and more effective than scalpel or alcohol. He found it in cold, such extreme cold that the brain cells could not survive.

Scientists long before Cooper's day had been experimenting on the effects of cold on the central nervous system. S. Openchowski, who was a pioneer in this research, in 1883 placed the shaft of a simple refrigerating apparatus on the cerebral cortex of dogs. He observed that freezing killed the specific brain cells to which cold was applied without causing bleeding or damage to neighboring tissues. Like so many researchers into cold, Openchowski was ignored by his contemporaries; his line of investigation was not picked up again until the late 1940's. Freezing experiments on animal brains were then resumed. By the time Cooper became interested in cold, others had already succeeded in lowering the temperature of human brain tissue to -4°F. Several were working on instruments capable of delivering far greater cold. Nitrogen, which remains in a liquid state until the temperature goes to -346°F., had just been used effectively to treat tiny laryngeal warts in infants, and Cooper selected it as the most suitable for neurosurgery as well.

He designed a wand, or cannula, to carry the nitrogen into the brain and went to the Linde Division of the Union Carbide Corp., and asked them to engineer it for him. This wand, to become known popularly as the "scalpel of ice," is only one-tenth of an inch in diameter, roughly the thickness of a knitting needle. It is insulated, except for the tip that must touch and kill the thalamic tissue. During surgery the liquid nitrogen is fed into the cannula and travels down its length. A mechanical device speeds or slows its flow depending on the degree of cold desired.

Cooper performed his first operations at St. Barnabas Hospital, New York, in the early 1960's and the era of cryosurgery was born. For many, the technique meant new hope. One of the first patients was a sixty-two-year-old lawyer who had shown the initial signs of Parkinsonism three years earlier. Although he continued to practice law, he was frequently embarrassed in court and in his office by the tremor and rigidity of his right arm and leg. He became increasingly depressed, foreseeing a grim future. In 1961 he entered St. Barnabas and was prepared for the startling new procedure.

The man was fully conscious when lifted onto the operating table. He lay as motionless as his tremor would allow while his head was secured in a special holder. A local anesthetic was administered for the opening of the skull and the insertion of the cannula. From then on the operation is painless, as the freezing process makes it impossible for nerve endings to conduct pain. This is why it is feasible for the patient to remain awake, as he must, if he is to guide the surgeon to the proper spot.

Although the general thalamic area is located with roentgenograms taken before and after insertion of the cannula, they are not sufficiently accurate to guarantee that the tip will be exactly on target. No two people are identical in fingerprints, bone marrow, personality, or thalamus. Any differences in this area are infinitesimal, but they can affect the success of the surgery.

Cold, the Healer

Drastic though it sounds, cold has added an element of safety to brain surgery that was never there before. Whereas a cut once made cannot be unmade, freezing is reversible. Destruction is not instantaneous. Ice crystals do not form immediately when temperatures of living cells are rapidly lowered to 5°F. or even -4°F. Instead, the contents of the cells remain liquid briefly in a supercooled state comparable to that observed in the body fluids of cold-climate fish. Even so, although alive, the cells cannot perform their customary functions, and so the surgeon can see what would happen if they were completely frozen. Should the patient fail to improve or should he reveal untoward symptoms, indicating that the tip of the wand is touching the wrong place, the doctor can still remove the cannula, rewarm the cells, and try again until he gets it right.

And so with the probe resting on his brain tissue, the lawyer was asked to relax his shaking arm. The trembling should have stopped, but it had not. As this was not yet the point of no return, the tip was withdrawn, the chilled area of the brain rewarmed, and the probe placed in a slightly different spot. The surgeon watched the arm, and in that instant the shaking stopped.

The next decision involved the amount of tissue to be destroyed. The lesion must stop just short of the point where speech, motor control, or intellect would be affected. The size of the area is determined by the temperature of the tip. When it rests on brain cells, freezing them for three minutes at -40°F., the destruction covers an oval or spherical area with a diameter of six millimeters. When the temperature is dropped to -58°F., the diameter is eight millimeters, and at -148°F., it reaches twelve millimeters. The liquid nitrogen could bring the temperature of the brain tissue down to -320°F. or lower, but such extreme cold is seldom needed. Reactions are highly individual and one patient may require as little as -58°F., while another does best at -112°F. The average lies between -76°F. and -94°F. In the case of the lawyer the temperature was dropped a little at a time, with responses checked at each level, and the -76°F. was found to be right.

Two days after the operation, he was out of bed and five days later he went home. Shortly thereafter he resumed his full legal practice. All that was left to show of the surgery was a one-inch scar. "I'll bet I'm the only man you know with a hole in his head," he remarked to one of his clients.

In the years that followed, the technique was adopted by surgeons in one country after the other. Its originator, Cooper, performed 1,800 operations in a mere four years, claiming success in ninety-three percent, with relapse infrequent. The mortality rate was but 1.3 percent, and side effects, such as speech problems and confusion, were usually transient. Patients flocked to the hospital centers where cryosurgery was performed. Some had the operation twice, as each lesion relieves the tremor and rigidity on one side of the body only. The ordeal of undergoing brain surgery while conscious was no deterrent to men and women desperate for relief from the tremor and rigidity. Not all applicants were taken. Comparatively young people and those whose disease was progressing slowly showed the greatest improvements.

Cryosurgery was hailed as a "miracle cure," although, in point of fact, it was no cure at all. The operation merely removes certain of the symptoms; the patient still has the disease. Many never go back to work anyway.

"Parkinsonism produces a paralysis of the will," explains Dr. Roger Duvoisin, noted neurologist. "The patient complains that he is too tired; he finds one excuse after the other not to act."

Not all investigators agreed that Cooper's method is sound. Dr. John Coe and Dr. Ayub K. Ommaya of the National Institutes of Health used the cryoprobe on ten cats and one patient undergoing brain surgery for cancer. Their findings, described at a symposium in 1963, were the exact opposite of Cooper's. They reported that swelling resulted from supercold, that bleeding followed rewarming, and that it was seldom possible to predict the size and shape of the lesion. "The use of freezing to produce lesions in the central nervous system," they concluded, "offers no advantages and many disadvantages as compared to other methods in clinical use." Four years later, in a personal communication, Coe steadfastly maintained: "We have encountered no particular reason to change our conclusions."

Cooper's sole comment on this counteropinion has been to point to his clinical record of success.

Whatever its limitations, cryosurgery provided Parkinson victims with the first real hope of relief they had ever had. After decades of failure in treating the disease, this initial breakthrough was followed by a second and a third. In the 1960's the key discovery was made that people with Parkinsonism lack dopamine, a substance found in the basal ganglia of the brains of normal people. This led to the new drug, Levo-dihydroxyphenylalanine, known for short as L-Dopa. A selected group of men and women began to receive this drug in 1967, and about three-quarters of them improved.

Not long afterward a doctor prescribed the new antiviral drug, amantadine hydrochloride, to several Parkinson patients ill with influenza. Oddly enough, it relieved not only the flu symptoms, but also the tremor of Parkinsonism.

As L-Dopa is most effective in relieving rigidity, these two drugs were soon being used in tandem.

With the advent of these medications, the peak period for cryosurgery as a treatment for Parkinsonism may come to an end. Cooper himself insists that patients take the two drugs for a trial period and will perform the operation only on those who are not helped or develop side effects from L-Dopa.

Still, far from being abandoned, cryosurgery has gone on to become a recognized surgical method. The technique developed for Parkinsonism has been applied to one condition after another. And its seemingly miraculous "cures" are performed every day.

Cooper's name remains associated with the procedure. His readiness to accept publicity—and the amount of it he receives—has not altogether surprisingly antagonized a number of his colleagues. They would somehow like to cut him down to size. Many other physicians, they point out, have also worked on developing cryosurgical techniques. Those names are unknown, while Cooper appears on television and is acclaimed in newspapers and mass-circulation magazines. He is still comparatively young and his success seems to have been too easy. The statistics and glowing reports of his work are questioned. Yet nothing can really detract from Cooper's accomplishment. His publicity has been a factor in the rapid growth of cryosurgery. Scientists have read of the method and gone on to apply it to their own medical specialities. What might have taken decades took months.

Aside from Parkinsonism, Cooper from the start was using this technique on other diseases characterized by involuntary muscle movements. Dystonia and torticollis can be totally disabling, and unlike Parkinson's disease, often strike children and young adults. No normal life is possible for the victims, even for those who are not bedridden. A girl with torticollis will sit quietly in a chair and every few minutes her head will uncontrollably roll toward her left shoulder, while her chin rotates slightly upward. Another must look forever at the ceiling, with head and neck thrown back. A child can be held by dystonia in an awkward, tortured posture with back bent permanently forward or back. The arms and legs may be deformed and shaken by a tremor.

The victim's plight is so heartbreaking that herculean feats to bring relief are attempted. A man of thirty-three underwent medical treatment with drugs and physiotherapy, and when these failed he was confined in a mental hospital and given electroshock treatments and psychotherapy. His condition continued to get worse until he was totally incapacitated. The new technique of cryosurgery was developed at just this time. The man declared himself ready to try this, too. The operation was performed first on the right side of the thalamus and then fourteen days later on the left. He got up from his bed, and soon thereafter left the hospital and took up a normal life.

Several sites in the thalamus must be frozen in order to block the conduction of all the unwanted nerve impulses producing the symptoms of dystonia and torticollis. As with Parkinsonism, the person being operated on must remain conscious. Patients, particularly young ones, have been able to endure as many as six lesions without ill effects. In fact, one boy who underwent four thalamic operations later went to Yale University and graduated magna cum laude.

"Children appear amazingly mature about accepting cryosurgery on the brain," comments one surgeon.

The operation of one nine-year-old boy was photographed for *Life* magazine. The "before" picture showed him with bent back, knotted right leg, and tremors affecting both hands and both feet. The *Life* photographer looked on while the probe was inserted in the brain, and suddenly the shaking and spasms on the right side ceased. The boy then responded to the surgeon's request that he clench his fist and recite "around the rugged rock the ragged rascal ran" to prove that his speech and mind were not affected. Thirty minutes later, the child sat up, held a glass of water without spilling any, and hugged his parents. No one could be surprised to learn that the article was dramatically entitled "Healing with an Icy Lance," nor that the performing surgeon was Cooper.

The "icy lance," as Cooper is quick to point out, carries no guarantee of relief. "Not all cases in our experience have responded favorably. Some patients in whom the initial response was favorable have demonstrated recurrence in the original or in an altered form some time after surgical intervention." After performing operations on 130 dystonia patients, he concluded that 91 of them had been helped.

Improvements have been shown by patients suffering from a number of other abnormal movement disorders. Although no cure for multiple sclerosis, for example, is known, the cryoprobe sometimes relieves the tremor that can accompany it. In one group of thirty-two multiple sclerosis victims, twenty-seven were helped, but one died. The freezing operation is most likely to succeed, Cooper believes, when done early in the course of the disease.

A young minister with multiple sclerosis was unable to write or hold a cup with his violently trembling hands. His speech was so blurred and tremulous that he would pick up a pen in his mouth as a signal for attention. After a cryo-thalectomy the tremor disappeared. When Cooper heard from him a year later, the minister had again taken up his calling, and was accompanying the hymn singing on the piano.

16

Freedom from Pain

"The *idea* that cold produced insensibility to pain has been floating about for ages. The principle was known, frozen up in the minds of men, but wanting the vivifying influence of the nineteenth century to thaw it into a practical channel," Dr. R. E. Harrison, a British dentist, wrote in his 1858 treatise, comprehensively entitled "What Is Congelation? or the Benumbing Influence of Cold in Producing Insensibility to Pain in Dental Operations Popularly explained with remarks on the introduction of a 'Painless System' in Dental Surgery."

Certainly anyone who has ever clapped an ice bag to his aching head must agree with Harrison's proposition. He was, however, indulging in nineteenth-century chauvinism, as the principle had been "thawed into practical channels" long before. An Egyptian papyrus drawn in about 3500 B.C., known as the Edwin Smith Surgical Papyrus, depicts cold being applied to wounds and infections. Nor was the practice new when the Egyptian scribe carefully drew his hieroglyphics.

The "practical channel" Harrison found consisted of passing a freezing fluid through flexible tubing into a mouthpiece attached to a very fine membrane. This membrane was placed on the gum covering the teeth. When the gum was completely numb, Harrison extracted the tooth. And like other practitioners using cold, he observed that bleeding as well as pain was reduced.

His method frightened some of his patients just as much as the extraction itself. One young girl from the country took a look at the equipment and screamed in terror: "Oh, I won't be *numbed*. I don't *want* numbing." A more sophisticated lady, however, wrote a thank-you note: "Miss _____ presents her compliments to Mr. Harrison, and in expressing her decided approbation of the congelation, begs to assure him, that after experiencing the ease and comfort of that method of extracting teeth. ..."

Toothaches, headaches, muscular aches, bruises ... all are relieved by cold. Compresses, one of the soundest of old wives' remedies, can sometimes relieve misery when modern medicine has failed. Contradictory as it sounds, the only comparable treatment is heat, which may work as well as its opposite. The medical battle over when to use cold and when heat is waged over trivial as well as major ailments. Cold at this point begins to win out, and a number of physicians today follow the concept of "cryokinetics" and treat injuries with cold alone for a fairly long period of time. The most common piece of first-aid advice, however, still is to apply an icepack immediately after an injury has occurred. If the bruise has begun to swell and discolor, turn to heat.

Warmth is soothing, but not anesthetic. For serious injuries, therefore, when pain is intense, cold is the agent employed. Baron Larrey, the surgeon who accompanied Napoleon's Grand Army to Russia, ordered that wounded arms or legs be packed in snow before amputation. The use of cold as an anesthetic was described a few years after that by Dr. James Arnott, a onetime ship's surgeon who was a far more important figure in nineteenth-century cryogenic medicine than was Harrison. Arnott left the sea to become superintendent of the East India Company's Medical Estate of St. Helena, where much of his time was spent on the island's considerable social life. He returned to England in 1835 for a thirty-month furlough and never returned to the carefree existence on St. Helena. As a practicing physician and surgeon in Brighton, he became interested in the pain-killing aspects of cold. When he was about to perform an operation, he would first fill a pig's bladder with water, place it against the affected area, and then drop in ice. After fifteen or twenty minutes the patient had no feeling in that part of the body covered by the bladder. Then Arnott would make the first incision.

Although he was a pioneer in local anesthesia, he did not do his work out of humanitarian impulses. He was an inhuman experimenter, who viewed his patients coldly as if they were guinea pigs on which he could practice his theories. In order to prove that chilling could indeed reduce pain, he gathered a number of doctors around him while he applied the freezing bladder to the pubic area of a young woman and removed a number of very large venereal warts. After showing how painless the operation was, he then waited a bit for the tissues to warm up and removed the last remaining wart without ice. The pain, he was pleased to point out to the observers, was excessive. His research, however heartless, did benefit the sick. He was the first doctor to report on the use of cold to relieve pain in patients with cervical cancer. Arnott scrupulously pointed out that he had not performed any cures.

In the years since Arnott, techniques were developed of carrying cold to places deep within the body and so relieving the agony of cancers and other ills. Then came cryosurgery and with it a whole new approach to the treatment of unremitting pain. The basic technique was the same as for Parkinsonism or dystonia, but instead of destroying those brain cells responsible for involuntary muscle movements, the freezing tip of the probe interrupts the nerve impulses conducting pain. As with Parkinsonism, doctors had been working toward this goal with cruder tools for many years. They excised a portion of the prefrontal lobe of the brain of patients suffering painful terminal illnesses. Lobotomy was then also being used to treat psychotics who had not responded to shock or psychotherapy. Many of those suffering physical pain underwent the same kind of total personality changes observed in lobotomized mental cases.

Cryosurgery, however, permits far more exact tissue destruction than the scalpel. In the 1960's, with freezing an accepted treatment for Parkinsonism, Dr. Melville Roberts and Dr. William M. Chadduck of the University of Virginia School of Medicine decided to insert the tip into the white matter in the frontal lobe of the brain and kill the nerve cells conducting pain and no others. For their first patients, they selected two men and a woman who were in such continual agony that they could not remain at home with their families, despite constant heavy doses of narcotics. The surgery followed the pattern of that for Parkinsonism or dystonia, with the patient remaining awake in order to respond to questions. As with the thalamus, there is a margin for error; the probe can be withdrawn should the individual become irrational or exhibit any physical peculiarities. In each of these first three cases, the patient gradually became euphoric. "I feel the pain, but it doesn't matter," said one. Assured that the probe was in the right place, the doctors lowered the temperature to -121°F. for three minutes. Three lesions were made on each side.

The euphoria lasted long after recovery from the surgery. Anxiety and depression disappeared. These were the only personality changes that occurred—and they were useful ones. Although the patients continued to be aware of the pain, they retained their indifference to it. None went back on drugs. All three returned home and lived with their families in relative comfort until the end.

Localized pain can be relieved by freezing the cancer itself, as the free sensory nerve endings for pain in and around the growth are destroyed. One woman with a cancerous growth on her neck came to Sloan-Kettering Institute for Cancer Research in extreme pain. Even though the cryosurgery performed by Dr. William G. Cahan did not succeed in controlling the malignancy or prolonging her life, it did control her suffering. Women with breast cancers were similarly helped. A lung cancer victim who had been unable to move his arm without intense pain discontinued narcotics and was able to use his arm freely until his death six months later.

The cryoprobe can penetrate cancers located at sites within the body that are hard or even impossible to reach with conventional surgical tools. Certain cancers of the rectum, for example, have been frozen. Even a man of eighty-five endured this type of surgery easily. Pain was relieved, and the frozen mass shrunk in size.

But even if cold can get to almost any cancer, can it ever do more than relieve pain? Can it kill any types of cancer? As of the present time, early in the cryogenic era, no one can answer that question with certainty, and doctors warn against excessive expectations. Still, there are already cases of apparent recovery. The follow-up periods, however, are too short to tell whether the cures will really last.

A large cannula or several small ones used simultaneously are needed to freeze a large tumor. Either the probe is inserted directly into the growth or the nitrogen-chilled tip is touched to one part after another of the surface of the growth. Both of these methods may be utilized on the same cancer.

The degree of cold applied to a malignancy is far more intense than that used to destroy the infinitesimal bits of nervous tissue in the thalamus or frontal lobes. The temperatures must be lowered to between -112°F. and -320.8°F., depending, of course, on the amount of tissue destruction desired. Even at the most frigid levels, the hardy cancer cells must be frozen, thawed, and frozen again several times. The thawing contributes to the death of these tissues. The ice crystals that form within the cells during freezing grow slightly just before they melt and damage the cell membrane. After destruction, the cancer can either be taken out or the dead cells can be left in place. Removal is made easier by the effect of the cold. There is less danger of malignant cells spilling out and spreading through the system than during conventional surgery. The frozen tumor shrinks into a bloodless, solid mass, with a clear separation from neighboring tissues. Although these tissues are invaded during removal, they, too, have been chilled enough to prevent bleeding. Once they thaw, the flow of blood resumes rapidly. The muscle walls of the large arteries are strangely and strongly resistant to the effect of freezing and are not damaged by it. Even the blood within, although frozen, does not clot, but flows again as soon as it is warmed.

The effects of supercold are impossible to predict, and each new use brings new discoveries. When bone tumors are frozen, some of the adjacent bone tissue is frozen, too. Oddly enough, upon rewarming, the tumor cells remain dead; the bone tissue grows again. New bone soon replaces the part that has been killed. This was the experience of a man in extreme pain and with facial paralysis as a result of the spread of a cancer of the external ear into the mastoid bone. Surgeons cut away as much of tumor and bone as they could, and then applied the cryoprobe. The patient has so far remained free of his malignancy.

Certain types of cancers of the mouth, tongue, and skin have responded well to supercold surgery. A cancer on the tongue of an eighty-four-year-old man shrank to the size of a pea and was easily removed after three operations with the freezing probe. A middle-aged man with a severe heart condition developed a cancer of the lip. Standard surgery was ruled out as far too risky. But the cryogenic probe was inserted after only a local anesthetic. The cancer was frozen in six places to a temperature of -292°F. The patient's only complaint was that he had a burning sensation. Within a few days the frozen cells began to slough off. At the end of a month the wound was healed and it was hard to find traces of where it had been.

Despite its experimental nature, many patients volunteer for cryosurgery as an alternative to a threatened drastic excision, such as removal of a cancerous eye. The probe is touched to the tumor and a tiny bit of the frozen tissue is taken out for testing. Should it turn out to be benign, the tumor may be thawed. Should it be malignant, however, the temperature is dropped until the tissues are destroyed. A few cancers have been killed in this manner, although, as with all malignancies, it will be years before there is certainty whether any patient has really been freed of his disease.

The brain tumor can flourish within the tissues of a small child, a man or woman in the prime of life, or an old person. It may be lodged so deep within the brain as to be unreachable by scalpel or X-ray. In such cases cold remains as a last hope. And indeed brain tumors are particularly sensitive to cold. A few years ago, a forty-eight-year-old man entered St. Barnabas Hospital suffering from convulsions and terrible headaches. The tumor within his brain, it was found, was gelatinous and would formerly have been quite impossible to manage. At the touch of the tip of the cryoprobe it froze solid. The tumor tissue stuck to the cannula and was pulled out. Two weeks later the patient left the hospital. Soon thereafter a sixteen-year-old girl with a tumor pressing on the optic nerve was operated on. The tumor was so large that the cannula had to be moved five times. In each location the temperature was dropped to -148°F. for three minutes. The destroyed tissue was left in place. The girl recovered rapidly and retained her vision.

Diseases of the prostate gland occur frequently among elderly men, and surgery is performed both for benign and malignant conditions. Instead of a lengthy surgical procedure, the liquid nitrogen cannula can freeze the entire prostate in about two minutes. In a routine case, a skillful surgeon can insert the wand, freeze the tissues, and withdraw the instrument all in ten minutes. The director of a large hospital walked slowly out of the operating room right after the surgery was performed on him. Within five days he felt perfectly well. The debris of frozen tissue is passed out of the body naturally in just about that time.

After a rather large number of prostate operations had been performed, something happened that may prove to have great significance for the future of cryosurgery. In 1965, a sixty-five-year-old man was treated cryosurgically for prostate cancer at Millard Fillmore Hospital in Buffalo, New York. By the time of the operation the cancer had spread through his system, settling in the lungs as well. This is not uncommon to the disease; cancer cells from the prostate can spill out and travel through the lymphatics or blood. The freezing was uneventful and the man recovered easily, much as previous prostate patients had. But when he came back for a checkup several months later, it was discovered that not only the prostate cancer, but also the cancerous tissues in his lungs were gone. This was then assumed to be a coincidence.

Then three years later it happened again. By this time the surgical technique had been changed slightly, and prostate cancers were being frozen twice, at thirty-day intervals. This double freeze was performed on two patients with prostate cancers which had spread to the lungs, and on another with cancer tissue on the vertebrae. Within three months in each case there was remission of all the cancers. The initial patient, too, was still alive.

Why does it happen? Dr. Richard J. Ablin, Director of Immunology at Fillmore, theorizes that the prostate gland normally produces certain cancer-specific antigens. The immune mechanism of the cancer patient, however, has been damaged in some way so that his body cannot recognize the disseminating malignant cells as foreign and reject them. Perhaps, suggests Ablin, the cryosurgery damages the prostate just enough to cause the release of the necessary antigens into the circulatory system. These go on to form antibodies which destroy the cancerous tissue that was previously accepted.

Some other possible side benefits of cryosurgery are beginning to show up in a few animal experiments. Cancers in rats were killed by freezing and the same type of carcinosarcoma was then reimplanted in each animal. When autopsies were performed, only benign cysts were found at the inoculation sites. The same cancers were implanted in a group of rats that had never had cold-treated growths. The cancers grew and in time killed this control group of animals.

"It is possible that the destruction of malignant cells may leave remnants of the tumor which, although no longer vital, will stimulate auto-immunization against further cancer growth," reports Cooper.

Cold, the Healer

The relatively moderate cold of hypothermia makes the effects of cancer drugs less toxic to healthy tissues; the super-cold of the cryoprobe may make them more toxic to malignant tissue. Researchers are studying whether the drugs do a better job at killing deep-seated and widespread cancers if cryosurgery is performed first. Freezing may produce changes in the membranes of cells in nearby incompletely destroyed tumors which make them more accessible to invasion by chemical agents.

The research into these aspects of cryosurgery is at too preliminary a stage to offer more than working hypotheses.

In a practical sense, cryosurgery has already proved itself repeatedly. A difficulty with conventional surgery on cancers of the liver or kidney, for example, is that these organs are so vascular that hemorrhage is likely to follow. Freezing is safer than excision when blood clots must be removed or heart abnormalities corrected. Any operations performed in the mouth can also cause dangerous bleeding. Cryosurgery, therefore, is being used not only to treat malignant and benign tumors, but also for serious gum infections. In startling contrast to the standard dental techniques, postoperative packing becomes unnecessary after freezing.

The bloodless nature of cryosurgery can sometimes make possible the substitution of a minor operation for a major one. Hysterectomies have been performed to stop the excessive bleeding caused by certain uterine tumors. In some cases as an alternative, freezing may be done for two to ten minutes, depending on the size of the growth. Tumor tissues die, but the uterus remains intact.

Sometimes, a nonmalignant but deadly tumor will develop in the nasal passages. At least three pints of blood pour from the nose during conventional surgery, and occasionally the flow is uncontrollable. A patient died in the operating room recently after losing eight pints. Exposure to liquid nitrogen temperatures, doctors suggest, reduces the tumor to a small bloodless mass that can be more easily removed.

Tonsillectomy, the most common of childhood operations,

is accompanied by the loss of considerable amounts of blood, as any mother who has watched her child return from surgery can attest. Most children can endure this with no lasting ill effects; for adults, however, the danger of hemorrhage is greater and the healing period longer. When the tonsils are frozen instead of being cut out, no blood is lost. In fact, says Dr. Hans von Leden of the Los Angeles Medical Center, most of his grown-up patients have eaten their dinners on the day the cryotonsillectomy was performed. So far, tonsil freezing has been limited to adults and to children with blood disorders, but it may eventually become the common method.

The liquid nitrogen probe can replace the scalpel in tonsillectomy and other routine surgery on patients with leukemia, who cannot afford to lose any blood, and hemophiliacs, who cannot stop bleeding once they start.

In 1960 liquid nitrogen was used for the first time to kill clusters of small wartlike tumors or papillomas on the larynxes of several infants. Although these growths are not cancerous, they make speech and sometimes even breathing difficult. They have always been difficult to remove by traditional means. A child must be taken to the doctor four or five times a year to have the growths snipped off. Liquid nitrogen simplified treatment immeasurably. This early medical success with supercold produced some valuable side effects. The report was read by Cooper, who was then looking for a suitable refrigerant for his cryoprobe.

Warts and other blemishes on the surface of the skin can also be frozen off. This is actually one of the oldest uses for cold. Doctors originally applied plain ice, then cooled air jets, carbon dioxide, and more recently, cotton swabs bathed in liquid oxygen. Today such swabs dipped in liquid nitrogen or sprays are used to deliver a far greater degree of cold. The skin is frozen until it blanches. If necessary, the treatment may be repeated in about three weeks. A stage actor had been unable to get movie or television work because the merciless camera revealed warts on his face. Nine of them were removed in a single session. The growths sloughed off within a few days, leaving no scar for eye or camera to behold.

Acne, the curse of adolescence, can produce scars that ruin a complexion for life. These can be partially obliterated by freezing the skin and then removing the top layer with a rotating brush. Similarly, the scars left by smallpox or a severe case of chicken pox can be frozen away. The most startling feat of surface skin removal was performed recently in response to a frantic plea for help from a man who woke up one morning to find that two nude figures in an obscene position had been tattooed on his arm when he had been drunk the night before.

Dr. Giovanni Doge, noted plastic surgeon at Italy's University of Padua, is now studying the effect of supercold on those injured by its natural opposite, fire. He believes that burned tissue will heal faster and be less scarred if it is frozen.

Cryosurgery has been effective against a number of skin cancers. The probe destroys those malignancies which extend inward some four or five millimeters. The many cancers that go only one and a half to two millimeters beneath the surface can be frozen off more simply, in the same way that warts are handled. When the growths are particularly large a very thin scar may remain.

The extremely common female disorder of cervicitis, an inflammation of the neck of the uterus, is another surface condition that can sometimes be improved rapidly by the application of extreme cold. Some patients are relieved after a single three-minute treatment without anesthesia. The infected tissue sloughs off and the healing is complete within three to five weeks.

For women who should not or do not wish to have children, the cryoprobe might be substituted for the standard operation of tying off the fallopian tubes. The necessary freezing takes a mere two minutes.

Just the opposite has been accomplished, too. "We have been utilizing cryosurgery to treat patients with infertility problems when the infertility seems to be due to a problem of the cervical canal," states Dr. Duane E. Townsend of the Department of Obstetrics and Gynecology at the University of California.

Sexual characteristics can be sadly altered by an overactive pituitary. This gland is no bigger than a pea, yet the hormones it produces stimulate all the other endocrines. Any malfunction, therefore, leads to the most tragic physiological consequences. A dainty girl may be transformed into an almost virile one. The body can grow to gigantic proportions or become acromegalic, a condition in which the hands, feet, and face of the adult are enlarged. Reaching the pituitary in order to destroy or inactivate it is one of the most difficult of operations, neurosurgeons agree. The gland is enclosed in bone and is attached to the base of the brain. Dr. Robert W. Rand at the University of California Medical Center has approached this hard-to-reach gland through the nasal passages. He saws through the bone and makes an opening large enough for the cryoprobe to pass through. Initially he found the pituitary incredibly difficult to freeze even after he had gotten the probe to the right place. Nothing much happened when the tip of the wand was brought down to -94°F. and held against the gland for a full seventeen minutes. It was not until the temperature was dropped to -274°F. and then to -310°F. for fifteen minutes that the tissues were finally destroyed. Since then Rand has successfully treated the pituitaries of many patients. In some cases two probes were used, and each lobe was deactivated separately.

Dramatic though some of these cures have been, pituitary abnormalities are rare. Cryosurgery's present reputation as a miracle healer is based on its success in treating more common disabilities, such as cataracts. Forming an opaque film over the lens of the eye, the cataract is a leading cause of blindness in the old. As Cooper's name is linked with freezing of the thalamus, the name of Dr. Charles Kelman is linked to that of the eye. Cryosurgery is both a young field and a young man's field. Kelman perfected his supercold eye treatment when he was in his early thirties. He likes to point out that he might never have made his discovery at all. After working his way through medical school as a writer of popular songs, Kelman had been tempted to abandon medicine for music.

Even after he had settled on ophthalmology, his particular place in it did not become apparent to him until the day when he started to thumb through a magazine while waiting for his wife to finish dressing. It happened to contain an article about Cooper, which is not really surprising, because articles about Cooper are frequent. The publicity Cooper was receiving regularly had already stimulated doctors in a variety of specialties, and Kelman seized on the idea, too. In order to develop a way of using cold as a substitute for ordinary cataract surgery, he applied to Cooper for permission to work at St. Barnabas.

The need for finding an improved way of extracting cataracts was great. In conventional surgery the casing of the lens can rupture and let the liquid within spill into the eyeball and produce severe inflammation. As Kelman describes it, this standard technique is similar to lifting a bag of water off the floor. If the bag does not break, there is nothing to worry about. But if it does, water gets all over everything. When it comes to cataracts removed at normal temperature, rupture occurs about five percent of the time. This happens rarely, however, when the cataract is partially frozen.

The principle Kelman succeeded in applying ophthalmologically, then, was a very simple physical one: a cold metal sticks to a moist object. And so the cataract sticks to the cryoprobe and comes away from the eye.

After experimenting on rabbits and cats, Kelman performed his first cryoextractions on people in late 1962 and his first paper on the procedure appeared in January of 1963. Kelman's bright hopes of being the first in the world to claim this achievement were dashed when he learned that Dr. Tadeusz Krwawicz in Lublin, Poland, had been freezing cataracts since 1961. What comfort he could derive came from the fact that Krwawicz had used a simple metal probe dipped into a mixture of dry ice and alcohol, and this was difficult to handle and not always reliable. It was left to Kelman to devise a more efficient method for cryoextractions. He began by using Cooper's cryoprobe, but he soon became dissatisfied.

"I found liquid nitrogen hard to manage," he says. "The equipment is bulky and expensive. What I wanted was something any ophthalmologist could keep in his closet and plug in whenever he needed it."

And so Kelman replaced liquid nitrogen with plain water and designed a simple, comparatively inexpensive device that could be plugged into any wall switch. Low temperatures are created by means of the thermoelectric principle known as the Peltier effect: "When a direct current is passed through the junction of two dissimilar semiconducting metals," explains Kelman, "the junction becomes cold and the terminals hot."

The water-cooled cryostylet, as he named the tiny instrument to be applied to the eye, is, like Cooper's cryoprobe, insulated except for its tip, which can reach the temperatures of 24.8°F. to -22°F. required for freezing cataracts. In addition, a heating unit is built into the tip. The surgeon can press a button and immediately thaw any bit of eye tissue, such as the iris or the cornea, that is beginning to stick to the stylet. The instant or two of freezing temperatures does no damage.

The operation, like many other cryogenic procedures, is done without general anesthesia. One might think the nervous strain of being conscious during the eye operation would be intolerable, but as with the Parkinson or dystonia patients, those undergoing it seldom even mention this.

"The patient has complete confidence in the doctor," says Kelman, who exudes cheerful, unshakable confidence. "Why, the relationship with an eye surgeon is as close as that of a woman with her obstetrician."

An injection is given to immobilize the eyeball. A tiny incision is made in the eye, and the cryostylet is introduced and placed against the cataract. It takes just about three seconds for an ice ball to form around the tip. After another couple of seconds, the ice ball has grown enough to include all the tissue that needs to be removed. The cryostylet with the frozen mass sticking to it is then taken out and the little incision is closed. The patient needs to spend only one day in bed, a week in the hospital, and two weeks in a rest home before being fitted with special glasses or contact lenses and returning to a normal, active life.

Although cataracts are generally considered a problem of old age, they are occasionally found in young people, too. They can be congenital, or the result of a severe blow, or of certain drug therapy. Cataract operations on the young are far more difficult, because the spokes, or zonules, holding the lens in the eye are so strong. Kelman still recalls a cataract operation performed on a nine-year-old girl. The cryostylet tip froze the lens and cataract, but when Kelman tried to pull them free, the spokes held firm. It took five minutes for him to break them and remove the ice ball. The cataract remained partially frozen throughout.

As a weapon in the battle against blindness, cold has attacked not only cataracts but also detached retinas. As the name implies, this condition is characterized by the separation of retina and the neighboring choroid layer of the eye. The reasons for the split-off are not known. The space between becomes filled with fluid and vision is impaired. A cure depends upon refastening the two layers together. This can be achieved by irritating the choroid layer until it produces a physiological "glue" strong enough to hold the retina in place. Various methods will achieve this end—heat, light, and chemicals—but there are often undesirable side effects. Cold, which can also induce glue production, appears to be the least toxic of all and works extremely rapidly. Dr. W. S. Banks III of Houston recently reported that he had "spot welded" 520 detached retinas back in place.

With the cryostylet's success in treating detached retinas and cataracts acknowledged, it was soon being tried for other eye ailments as well. The validity of such uses is hotly contested today. Some physicians hail cryosurgery as a cure for glaucoma, a condition in which intense pressure builds up inside the eye. The extreme cold lowers the pressure by decreasing the inflow of liquid. The cryogenic probe is most successful for the older patient who has an advanced case of glaucoma. It may seem odd that an elderly person would be helped most, but the theory, as explained by Dr. Andrew de Roetth, Jr., of Columbia Presbyterian Medical Center, is that the older, less healthy eye secretes less fluid than the younger eye. Whatever additional reduction is brought about by either one or two applications of extreme cold, therefore, is enough to bring relief.

Cryotherapy is coming into use to treat a particularly nasty eye infection, herpetic keratitis. The virus, the same one that causes cold sores on the mouth, can scar the cornea of the eye. The infected part of the eye is frozen to -40°F. and thawed three times in succession. This treatment has been successful for ninety-seven percent of 1,512 patients in the United States, Poland, and Austria, reports Dr. John Bellows of Northwestern University. Most of the eyes regained their luster in about ninety-six hours. Another advocate of this method is Krwawicz, the Polish pioneer in cryosurgery of the eye. He points out that in addition to stopping the infection, freezing sometimes reduces the size of old scars on the cornea.

The enthusiasm of these men is not matched by Kelman, who considers cryotherapy of little use against either herpetic keratitis or glaucoma. "Cryosurgery is only of help in hopeless cases of glaucoma, because it can make a blind eye less painful; it cannot prevent or cure the blindness," he states. "In the matter of herpetic keratitis, it is true that the cryoprobe can pull away the infected cells. But a simple cotton applicator does as well."

Whatever the ultimate decision on freezing for these two conditions, cryosurgery will remain a valuable addition to what one ophthalmologist describes as "our armentarium" against eye disease.

It is being placed in the arsenal of weapons against ear

disabilities, too. Dizziness so extreme that the victim cannot stand up does not look like ear trouble, but it is caused by a disorder of the middle ear. Mild cases of Ménière's disease, as it is known, can be controlled by drugs, but severe ones may respond only to complete removal of the labyrinth of the ear, resulting in total deafness. Again, it was the reports on Cooper's work that led to attempts to substitute probe for scalpel. Dr. Robert J. Wolfson of the Presbyterian-University of Pennsylvania Medical Center redesigned the cryoprobe, adapting it to the ear, and performed experiments on twenty-one monkeys before turning to humans. Although only four of his first fifteen patients were completely cured, Wolfson remained optimistic, attributing the high record of failure to faulty technique.

"The basic principle seems sound," he wrote. "It is anticipated that further laboratory investigation and clinical experience will solve the remaining problems and lead us to an effective and safe operation."

And it was not long before he was proven right. Two years later he was able to report that twenty-seven out of thirty-three patients had been either completely cured of vertigo or greatly improved.

What does the future hold for supercold temperatures in medicine? Concluding a report on his use of cold in treating tumors, cancer specialist William Cahan gives the following appraisal: "Further speculation as to the possible applications of cryosurgery is almost limitless."

Part Six

Cold, Food's Keeper

17

"To Cap the Jubilation, Dishes of Ice Cream"

"Indeed, I could not but smile to see several of them cooling their mouths with lumps of ice, which they had just before been burning with salts and peppers," Joseph Addison informed the readers of the gossipy *Tatler* in March of 1709.

The lumps of ice Addison was describing so amusingly were part of an elaborate ice cream dish with "pyramids of candied sweetmeats . . . hid in an artificial kind of frost . . . and great quantities of cream beaten up into snow."

In Addison's day ice cream was still a rare and exotic dish for the very rich, although thousands of years had passed since it had first been prepared. No one can trace this dish to its exact origin. Water ices made with fruit pulps antedate frozen cream and may actually have been the very first processed frozen food. Nero, always in search of a food to excite his jaded palate, is credited with the invention of a primitive sherbet or water ice made by adding fruit pulp, juice, and honey to snow. But Nero could not possibly have been the originator of this refreshing dessert. Marco Polo centuries later returned from Asia with a sherbet recipe that had been used there for thousands of years. The dish became popular in Italy almost at once among members of the aristocracy, many of whom shared the Roman Nero's love of luxury. As ice was beyond the reach of the citizenry, sherbet remained a food for royalty for the next four hundred years. Recipes for cakes and soups as well as "starters" for yeast breads were for centuries included in the dowries of brides of humble folk. But there was nothing humble about sherbet. Legend has it that Catherine de Medici took the recipe with her to France when she went there to be the bride of Henry II.

As with the entire history of ice cream, there is no knowledge of exactly when and how cooks turned from water to milk or cream. It had certainly happened by the seventeenth century, as records tell that it was eaten with relish by King Charles I of England. He was much envied for possessing the services of the French chef who perfected it. Charles ordered the cook, whose name has become garbled over the centuries as De Mirco, De Mireo, De Mirro, or De Marco, to keep the recipe forever secret. He promised to pay five hundred pounds a year for life, a fortune for those times, in return for silence. The sum was apparently not enough, because the secret was soon leaked. Some believe that another aristocrat outbid his ruler for the ice cream recipe. Whether for this or some other treason, the unlucky chef was beheaded in 1649.

Within the next few years ice cream recipes were passed from hand to hand and the dessert began to appear on dinner tables in the New World as well as the Old. "We had a dessert no less Curious; among the Rarities of which it was Compos'd, was some fine Ice Cream, which, with the Strawberries and Milk, eat Most Deliciously," reported a guest following a dinner party at the governor's palace in Maryland in 1700.

In Vienna, Ludwig van Beethoven was so impressed with the general enthusiasm for ice cream that he wrote to one of his friends: "The Viennese are afraid that it will soon be impossible to have any ice creams, for as the winter is mild, ice is rare."

Toward the end of the eighteenth century an Italian who had moved to France prepared a new ice cream dish. He placed soft, creamy, very sweet ice cream in a fluted paper cup and covered it with powdered almonds. His name, as any dessert fancier could guess, was Tortoni.

The most famous American ice cream lover was George Washington, and his Martha kept two pewter ice cream pots handy. Ice cream was believed to turn out better when made in a pot of pewter rather than tin or zinc. Washington's successors shared his fondness for ice cream and Dolly Madison decided to serve it at the inaugural ball. Her servants spent hours beating the mixture by hand and then shaking the pot up and down in a pan of salt and ice.

The hand-cranked freezer came as a great improvement on this and all other earlier methods. Many people, particularly from rural areas, can still remember turning the handle of the freezer on a hot summer day. The freezer retained its popularity for many years—even among commercial manufacturers. And at home it was quite as common as an electric blender or mixer is today. Some freezers are still in use, and not only among old-fashioned or simple folk. People who take ice cream seriously insist that nothing is as good as the hand-cranked variety. A freezer in the home today has become a form of reverse snobbery.

The principle of the hand-cranked freezer is very simple. A container holding the ice cream ingredients is placed in the midst of a salt and ice mixture. As the handle turns, the container is briskly shaken. One might think that such a primitive technique would antedate George Washington, or even Nero, but the ice cream manufacturers' trade association, which looks into such matters, puts the date at 1846. The brilliant inventor was a woman, Nancy Johnson. A head for business did not go along with her mechanical ability and Miss Johnson never bothered to patent her invention. Perhaps she, too, thought the idea so obvious that someone else must have thought of it before. And so another inventor, a Mr. Young (at least his first name is forgotten, no matter how much business sense he had), did take out a patent in 1848.

But it is quite possible that Miss Johnson was right about being anticipated. "It is simply a rotary churn applied to the purpose of refrigeration," went an article that appeared in the British *Mechanics Magazine* in 1844, two years before her "discovery." "We have ourselves seen two quarts and a half of ice cream manufactured . . . in less than four minutes."

The "it" that performed this feat is the ice machine designed by Thomas Masters and described in his *Ice Book*, published in London that same year. "Art has, however, not rested content with providing the luxuries and preparing the necessaries of humanity," marveled Masters. "It has dared to imitate nature in the production of its most wonderful phenomena, and *ice*, once the sole produce of her mighty laboratory has been made by the skill and enterprise of her subject—man."

Turning to more practical matters, he describes his freezing mixtures, which include not only the classic old-fashioned ice with salt, but also the more modern technique of freezing without ice, but with a refrigerant such as ammonia. Acids work well, he adds, but probably have "destructive effects on the garments of servants."

Even today when one ice cream manufacturer boasts 200 flavors and another 128, the recipes given by Masters can compete. There is Nesselrode (with two wineglasses of brandy), custard, mille-fruit, ratifia (fruit kernel liqueur), ginger, Howqua's tea, cinnamon, brown bread (which includes a slice of bread browned in the oven plus a glass of maraschino per quart), currant, and apricot. Should the color of the ice cream be pallid and uninteresting, Masters suggests the addition of one ounce of cochineal and one ounce salts of wormword. Water ices are not forgotten—barberry, melon, punch. To make the latter, to one and a half pints lemon water, ice add one glass of white rum, one of champagne, one of pale brandy, and half a glass of warm jelly. Those who fear the effects of this dessert may substitute fruit nectar for the wine and the rum, but the brandy, Masters insists, is a must.

This punch could not only intoxicate, but also refresh the palate, a characteristic of all sherbets and water ices. Nero undoubtedly so stimulated his flagging appetite during the banquets that included a dizzying number of delicacies. Sherbet and water ice filled a similar function during the latter part of the nineteenth century when massive nine-course dinners were the fare of the wealthy. Although the words are often used interchangeably, water ice and sherbet are not the same. Sherbet contains some milk or milk solids which makes it smoother, yet chewier than water ice. One or the other was clearly needed by those who proceeded through such meals as this which was served at the Waldorf-Astoria Hotel on the night of February 11, 1899. After beginning with an oyster cocktail and green turtle soup, guests toyed with a basket of lobsters and columbine of chicken before moving with gusto to roast mountain sheep with puree of chestnuts and brussels sprouts and asparagus with cream sauce. At this point came the break for a dish of sherbet, and then on to terrapin, duck, orange and grapefruit salad, fresh strawberries and raspberries, vanilla mousse, bonbons, more fruits, and coffee. All this was accompanied by sherry, white wine, champagne, burgundy, port wine, and liqueurs. It was an era when tightly laced corsets were required to make up for all excesses at the table. No one thought of dieting.

While sherbet was being relegated to an almost medicinal place on the menu, ice creams were growing ever more glorious. Ice cream became a raw material for the artist hidden in every cook. One gentleman had his coat of arms—an imaginary one presented by a fraudulent genealogist—embossed in ice cream. Others served ice cream molded into the form of a heart, swan, cupid, bouquet of flowers, or cameo portrait.

Ice cream variants undreamed of even by Masters or the French chefs of the Astors and Vanderbilts were developed. Accounts of ice cream history do not agree on the name of the inventor of the ice cream soda or the ice cream cone. The story that is most frequently told begins on a hot day in the summer of 1879 in the Detroit ice cream parlor of Fred Sanders. Customers came in as usual to request what was known as "soda" in those days—a mixture of cream, fruit juice, and carbonated water. One day when Sanders went to pour the cream into the bubbling juice, he observed from the smell that it was sour. The customer was waiting impatiently, so Sanders looked around for a cream substitute and had an inspiration. He dropped a spoonful of ice cream into the soda.

The ice cream cone is usually traced to the Louisiana Purchase Exposition in St. Louis in 1904, but as cones had been made in Manchester, England, and imported to the United States for some years prior to that, it seems likely that someone must long before have had the fancy of adding a spoonful of ice cream.

The next ice cream step forward came in 1921 with the invention of the Eskimo Pie by C. Nelson of Waukon, Iowa. The original Eskimo Pie was a rectangular piece of chocolate-covered vanilla ice cream, which was hard to handle. Only those who could eat very fast could get through a pie without dripping ice cream. Anyone could pick the Eskimo-Pie-eaters out of a group of children just by looking at their clothes. This problem was alleviated, though by no means conquered, by the addition of a wooden stick to create the ice cream pop.

With the Eskimo Pie and ice cream pop came the vendor on foot, on bicycle, on a truck. He peddled his wares, as he still does, through city streets and country lanes, in ball parks, amusement parks, and on street corners. The ice cream in the more-or-less insulated container is kept cool with steaming slabs of dry ice. While this is one of the best of refrigerants, it has one drawback. So much heat is released by the carbon dioxide in the process of transformation from solid to a vapor state that it can give a very bad burn to anyone who touches it while reaching for the ice cream.

The Popsicle is surely one of the most popular novelties carried in the vendor's box. The story of its invention is presented by ice cream makers as an example of serendipity, almost like the chance discovery of penicillin. This tale begins on a winter's day in 1926. It happened that a man named Epperson who ran a concession at an amusement park in Oakland, California, went on a visit to friends in New Jersey. One night he became thirsty long after dinner, and so he prepared himself a lemonade and took it up to his room. He was giving the drink a final stir when the telephone rang, so he put the glass on the windowsill and went to answer. By the time he got off the phone, he had forgotten all about the lemonade. It remained on the sill all night with the stirring spoon still in it. The night was cold and by morning the lemonade was frozen solid. Epperson held the glass upside down under the cold water tap in the bathroom and the lemonade slipped out in a solid block with the spoon still in it. "This is an Epsicle!" the man cried out, seeking immortality. But he was cheated of it when the name was changed to Popsicle.

Since then there has been a never-ending flow of novelties —sandwiches, prepackaged sundaes, parfaits, cake rolls, ice cream cakes, cakes on a stick, two-flavor Popsicles, prepackaged cones, ice cream Popsicles coated with coconut or burnt almond. When the bell of the ice cream truck is heard, children stop whatever they are doing and run.

Flavors rival Masters' in ingenuity and outdo him in number. From hickory nut to peanut brittle to peppermint stick, gooseberry, brandy, rum raisin, passion fruit, banana, quince, mint chocolate chip, butterscotch ripple, and blueberry—the count seems endless. But no matter how many flavors are offered about half of all ice cream eaten is vanilla, with chocolate second choice. Orange is by far the most popular sherbet, and pineapple ranks next. In water ice, it is orange again, but lime is the second here. Of the novelty items, the chocolate-covered ice cream pop on a stick is the overwhelming favorite.

Most ice cream is bought in supermarkets in the form of pints, quarts, half gallons, or packs containing half a dozen or more novelties.

In other parts of the world novelty items make up a larger portion of sales than they do here. Step out of the Vatican, the Louvre, or the Tate Gallery and an ice cream vendor will be standing there eagerly waiting for business. Ice cream or sherbet cones, the "lollie" or English Popsicle, the ice cream sandwich are obtainable almost everywhere. The housewife in Europe, on the other hand, is less likely than her American counterpart to pick up a package of ice cream at the market and take it home. If she can afford it, she may order a fancy

ice cream cake or log with an ice cream center and an elabo-
rately swirled frozen whipped-cream topping for a dinner
party. But this is hardly the same thing. The difference in ice
cream habits is a result of the difference in refrigeration. The
large home refrigerator with the freezer top became common
in the U. S. long before it appeared, except in homes of the
very rich, in other parts of the world. The deep-freeze with
its fantastic storage capacity that practically demands the
purchase of a few gallons of cherry vanilla, pistachio, or fudge
ripple is also more widely used in the U. S. than elsewhere.
In some areas refrigerators are still a luxury. And even where
they are not, people have grown accustomed to buying ice
cream from a vendor, in an ice cream parlor, or in a restaurant, and eating it on the spot. Eventually the habit of postponed consumption will probably be gained, as supermarkets
and refrigeration spread to every part of the world. Ice cream
can be kept in a refrigerator freezer for two to three weeks
and in a home freezer for two months.

An American ice cream maker recently discussed the possibility of doing business in a rural area of Greece. A col-
league who had made a similar attempt urged him to sell
frozen custard or soft ice cream instead of regular ice cream.
These can be made from a mix just before serving. The need
for a good refrigeration system for storage purposes is mini-
mized, as the mix can be held at a temperature of 30°F. to
40°F. Ice cream requires a freezer maintained at between zero
and -20°F.

Anyone with fond memories of the good old days may
assume that fresh sweet cream is a basic ingredient, at least
for the quality ice creams. With today's refrigeration that is
no longer necessarily so. The cream used has in many in-
stances been taken from the cow a summer or more earlier
and been processed by heating and then freezing and storage
at a temperature of zero degrees or less. Plastic, or concentrated, cream with eighty percent fat, or butter itself, can also
be sources of butterfat. The ice cream mix contains in addition whole or condensed milk or skim milk, and/or nonfat

dry milk solids. On the average, eighty to eighty-five percent of ice cream consists of such cream and milk solids.

As for the rest, sweeteners make up the largest part by volume, from fifteen to eighteen percent of the total. Too much sugar is as bad as too little, because sugar lowers the freezing point of ice cream. This means that it takes longer to freeze and then requires a colder storage temperature. A little corn syrup is usually used in addition to the cane or beet sugar. It makes the ice cream firmer and chewier, but if too much is included there is an unnaturally sweet taste.

The flavoring materials are only a small portion of the ice cream mix, but the finished product stands or falls on their excellence. Vanilla, the world favorite, resisted mass production for hundreds of years. It was first recognized as a flavor by the Indians of Mexico. This was rather an accomplishment, as neither flower nor fruit of the beautiful orchid *Vanilla planifolia* has any aroma to give a hint of the flavor within. Vanilla's rise to its present popularity began in the sixteenth century when Spaniard Hernando Cortez set out to conquer Mexico. The ill-fated Aztec ruler Montezuma invited Cortez to his court, and in an effort to please, offered a cup of "xocolatl." The drink was made of cacao beans, or "chocólatl," and "thilxochitl." Because the latter was the harder of the two to pronounce, the Spaniards said "vainilla," meaning "little scabbard," which describes the shape of the bean pod. As everyone knows, Montezuma's courtesy availed him nothing in the end.

Vanilla planifolia was transported to Europe, and to its possessions, but would not bear fruit. The failure was attributed by the superstitious to Montezuma's curse. The curse was eventually proved to be sexual in nature. The plant could be pollinated by a species of bee that lived only in Mexico. Once this was understood, the hand of man was substituted for the leg or antenna of the bee. Following this discovery in 1836 vanilla plants were grown in a number of warm, humid countries, notably Madagascar, and vanilla ceased to be exclusively for the rich.

Purists, though they are rare today, insist upon using the pod itself as a base for ice cream, scalding it with heavy cream. Ice cream manufacturers at best use either vanilla extract or powdered vanilla. Certain types of powder do not dissolve entirely, but leave black specks in the cream. Many gourmets, therefore, will eat only ice cream in which these appear, assuming that all others are made with synthetics. This is unfair, as some powders do not leave specks, and they are filtered out of natural vanilla extract. More often than not, though, the suspicions are all too true. Vanilla is costly. It is still hard to produce, requiring curing and drying for six months or more before powdering or extracting can begin. And so the natural is frequently reinforced with synthetic vanillin, obtained from waste woodpulp liquor and other sources.

If one speaks to ice cream manufacturers one gets the impression that only natural flavors are used. Yet companies that produce synthetics count the ice cream industry as an excellent market. Apparently, as in the old vaudeville song, it is always "somebody else not me" who in this case applies artificial flavoring.

The other portion of the Aztec drink, the "chocólatl," was also carried back to Europe by the Spaniards. They improved its naturally bitter flavor by adding sugar to it. Chocolate became fashionable as a drink long before it found its way into ice cream. In fact, chocolate houses grew up at just about the same time as coffee houses in London, Amsterdam, and other major cities. The English made a contribution to chocolate enjoyment that has proven nearly as significant as the Spaniards' sugar: they added milk. The chocolate flavor comes from the seeds of the cacao plant, which, like vanilla, must go through a long period of preparation. At one point in the process the cocoa butter melts to form chocolate liquor. Blends of this liquor with the finished cocoa powder are used by most ice cream manufacturers today. The strong taste of the cocoa is brought out by the high fat content of the liquor. Chocolate ice cream needs more sugar than vanilla does; as the Spaniards observed, the bitterness of the cocoa is hard to overcome.

From other tropical lands come the nuts—Brazils, filberts, peanuts, pecans, almonds, pistachios, walnuts, cashews—that find their way into burnt almond, butter pecan, pistachio, black walnut, peanut brittle, and other ice creams. The nuts are roasted and then buttered and salted, because in this state they absorb less moisture.

For every fruit, there is an ice cream version. Strawberry is the favorite of all fruit ice creams. Fresh fruit plucked at the peak of its season gives the very best flavor to strawberry, raspberry, or other fruit ice cream. Unfortunately, the season is too short to satisfy the year-round demand for the dessert, so most is made with frozen, freeze-dried, or canned fruits. Their flavor is enhanced by the addition of concentrated fruit juices and/or synthetics.

The ideal synthetic flavor is a chemical reproduction of the actual compounds that exist in the natural fruit. A long time ago chemists observed that the amyl esters smell like bananas, and that methyl anthranilate smells like grape. Therefore, they combined the former with vanillin and citrus oils and came up with a banana flavor; the latter was the base for artificial grape. Years later chemical analysis revealed that amyl esters really exist in bananas and methyl anthranilate in grapes.

A complete laboratory breakdown of the natural fruit reveals the chemical compounds present. Nearly one hundred different chemicals have been discovered in coffee, and twenty-nine in apple, for example. These chemicals are then combined in the laboratory. Sometimes the result is an all-but-perfect reproduction, but in other cases it is not. The identified compounds are duplicated and put together and the end product still does not taste right. Perhaps even the most modern laboratory equipment is not powerful enough to detect every trace chemical. Or perhaps the chemist has not combined them in the exact manner in which they were in nature.

Smell, which gave away the key to banana flavor, is not always a good clue. A chemical that smells like rancid butter may in the end produce a strawberry flavor, and one that resembles a cheap violet perfume is essential in making a good raspberry.

Oddly enough, some good imitation flavors do not contain any of the chemicals found in the real fruit. A number of artificial peach and strawberry flavors bear no chemical resemblance to the real thing, but taste and smell similar.

Occasionally one natural product is substituted for another that is scarce, costly, or hard to use. A maple-type flavor can be derived from the seed of the foenugreek plant, which grows freely in India, Iran, Saudi Arabia, and Greece. Although it does not taste exactly like maple, it has been used so widely that many people think it is maple. When they eat something made with real maple flavor or a true reproduction, they think that is the imitation.

Some of the most popular flavors do not taste anything like the natural, nor are they supposed to. Cherries, for example, have a rather bland flavor. The pleasure of eating them lies in the sensation obtained by biting into the cherry, letting the sweet juice flow into the mouth, enjoying the faint aroma. Take away the texture and very little is left. The accurate imitations of cherry are uninteresting and weak. What is commonly known as cherry flavor is actually an imitation of maraschino cherries. These are cherries which have been soaked in maraschino liqueur, or to go a step farther, in a liquid that is a chemical imitation of the liqueur.

But if perfect imitations can be made, why are all imitations scorned by gourmets? Part of the prejudice is a survival from the days when artificial flavors were indeed crude. Part of the prejudice, but not all. A good deal is quite justified. There are vast numbers of synthetic versions of each flavor. One of the largest firms making flavors has developed several thousand formulas for cherry alone. Each is a little different from the others, depending upon the use for which it is intended, and the price the user wishes to pay. The cheaper the synthetic the less like the natural it will be. And of course the cheaper ones are used most often. Once a manufacturer decides to make a quality product, he may well share the prejudice of the consumer and turn to the natural flavor.

Just as the presence of natural vanilla is "proved" by the presence of black specks, so the real fruit is proved by the little bits that remain in the ice cream. Most people today are convinced that "they don't put as many strawberries in strawberry ice cream or cherries in cherry vanilla as they used to." But then, what is ever as good as it was in the good old days?

A tabloid newspaper recently ran an exposé of ice cream of all things. This revealed such devastating facts as that ice cream often contains seaweed. Why this should be so terrible is hard to imagine, as people in many parts of the world eat seaweed, but it was made to sound on a par with eating sawdust (which has also been done under hardship conditions). The implication was that large fronds of gelatinous brownish-green weed were put in the ice cream in place of strawberry bits or fudge ripples. The truth is that the chemical sodium alginate, obtained from kelp, or Irish moss (carrageen), taken from another weed, *Chondrus crispus,* may be used in small quantities as stabilizers. They give the ice cream more body, a smoother texture, and improved ability to endure the sudden shock of being taken from freezer into summer heat. Otherwise, coarse, unattractive ice crystals will form. When seaweed is not used as a stabilizer, a gum or gel usually is. The gum may very well come from cotton, which, despite cottonseed oil, has the connotation of being inedible.

No matter which stabilizer is used, it cannot protect ice cream after melting. Should the liquid ice cream be frozen again, it will be icy, rather than creamy, because large crystals form in refreezing.

An emulsifier is another unattractive-sounding ice cream component. It is added to the mix before either pasteurizing or freezing. Emulsifiers are used more widely than in the past, because of the popularity of novelties. The ice cream becomes stiffer and drier, and is thus better able to take and hold a shape throughout the molding and wrapping process. There is also an extra touch of smoothness. The air cells within the ice cream are smaller than otherwise, and this gives the eater the impression of very rich ice cream.

When dried or frozen egg yolks are added, the end result is known variously as frozen custard, French ice cream, French custard, or egg nog ice cream.

A number of the firms that make quality ice cream report that they use nothing but dairy products, sugar, and flavorings, eliminating even the stabilizers.

The different combinations of the standard ice cream ingredients do not begin to exhaust the infinite variety of frozen desserts. Some ice creams are made with synthetic sweeteners and intended for diabetics or dieters. In addition, there has been a spurt in the consumption of ice milk, both by those who diet to lose weight and those who are switching from foods that are high in the saturated fats that raise the cholesterol level of the blood. Production of ice milk increased by twenty-five percent between 1964 and 1968, a period notable for the heavy publicity given the probable relationship of a high cholesterol blood level to heart disease. As cream, butter, and eggs are all cholesterol-raising foods, this has been particularly irksome to the dairy industry. It has been attempting to counter the endless flow of anticholesterol medical studies with publicity of its own, and by sponsoring research to discount the cholesterol theory.

Ice milk cannot contain more than two to seven percent of milkfat, and usually has five percent or less, compared to ten to fourteen percent for inexpensive ice cream, ten to sixteen percent for frozen custard and French ice cream, and twenty to twenty-two percent for the premium. The legal requirements for milkfat vary among the states but tend to be within these ranges. Should the fat content be below the legal limit, the product cannot be called ice cream. Hence ice milk.

This is as good, or better, a choice for the calorie counter as sherbet, which has traditionally been selected as a dessert by people on diets. It is true that the fat content of sherbet is minimal, but the amount of sugar used is apt to be twice as great as in ice cream. While some brands of sherbet equal ice cream in calories, or are slightly lower, the majority are, surprisingly, higher. A typical sherbet, according to Pennsylvania State University's College of Agriculture, runs to 586 calories per pint, only slightly less than ice cream's 615, and considerably more than ice milk's 450.

Aside from its dietary advantages, ice milk makes particularly good milk shakes and soft ice cream. Most of the soft-serve ice cream sold at roadside stands is really ice milk. It tastes even colder than ice cream, so that a child licking an ice milk cone gets an immediate sensation of refreshment. Ice milk is cheaper to produce than ice cream, so the cones may be bigger.

While ice milk is made of whole milk, mellorine, another frozen dessert, is not. Instead of butterfat, mellorine contains a vegetable fat. It is considerably lower in calories than ice cream but, as produced by most manufacturers today, is not as low in cholesterol as it might be. Most mellorine is made with coconut oil, which is one of the very few vegetable fats high in cholesterol-raising saturated fats. Some mellorines are actually made with meat fat, which has no advantage over butterfat in terms of cholesterol. Research is now going on into methods of producing mellorine with peanut oil, a neutral vegetable oil, neither raising nor lowering blood cholesterol, and with safflower seed oil or soybean oil, which are high in polyunsaturated fats and do lower the blood cholesterol. The problem with using soybean oil so far has been that its flavor seeps in and detracts from the otherwise ice-cream-like taste of mellorine. Ways of avoiding this are being studied.

Most mellorines made today contain milk solids. There is a new, milk-free version that was originally developed in order to increase the frozen dessert consumption of Orthodox Jews who follow the strict kosher dietary laws. According to these laws, milk products such as ice cream may not be served at the same meal as meat. This naturally limits the number of times ice cream will be the dessert. A mellorine without milk solids would be "parve," or permissible, at any time, regardless of whether meat or dairy products are on the menu as well.

A bitter fight against mellorine with or without milk solids is being so vigorously waged by dairy farmers that sales are still prohibited in many states. Industry members remember how long they succeeded in holding off the sale of nondairy oleomargarine in some states, and they hope to repeat their success.

Despite all restrictions, mellorine production outstripped either of those old reliables, sherbet and water ice, through much of the 1960's. In 1968, for example, 50,670,000 gallons of mellorine were produced, compared to 47,685,000 for sherbet and 44,565,000 for water ice.

But mellorine, sherbet, water ice, and ice milk—with 256,-050,000 gallons that year—are but drops in the bucket, compared to ice cream production and sales. In 1859, 4,000 gallons of ice cream were produced in the United States. This was only eight years after the first ice cream business had been opened in Baltimore by Jacob Fussell. By 1889 the figure had risen to 851,000 gallons. In the course of the next twenty years, output leaped over the million mark and went on to top 5 million by the end of the century. The year of the great stock market crash, 1929, was not accompanied by a decline in ice cream consumption and production reached nearly 260 million gallons. By the end of World War II it was up to more than 471 million. Even this looks like little today when production runs to better than 780 million.

The ice cream industry gives wide publicity to a one-billion-gallons-plus figure for production. This is not an exaggeration, but an overall total, with ice milk, sherbet, water ice, and mellorine added in. The average American consumes more than fifteen quarts of ice cream a year and another seven of ice milk, sherbet, and other frozen desserts.

The production climb has been dependent upon advances in freezing techniques, as well as a growing population of ice-cream-eaters. A billion gallons with a hand-cranked freezer would be impossible. One long-lived Iowa manufacturer can still remember "on the fourth of July, 1890, we shipped out 300 gallons of ice cream—all frozen by hand." It was possible even before then to use more sophisticated means, and some commercial manufacturers did so. Electric motors rather than manpower made the freezer handle go around. In 1902 the batch freezer was invented. In terms of efficiency, it was a great step forward, and it is still used by some small manufacturers. The ice cream is frozen a batch at a time, a process that takes from four to ten minutes.

The batch freezer has been all but superseded by the continuous freezer, which does the job in seconds.

The preparation of the mix is identical whichever freezing method is used. It must be pasteurized by heating to 175°F. for twenty-five seconds, and then homogenized, in order to break down the fat globules. The mix, which is still hot up to this point, is cooled to a temperature of between 30°F. to 40°F. In the batch freezer, the ice cream is partly frozen and then the refrigerant is cut off and the thickened mix is whipped and taken out. When the continuous freezer is used, the mix, together with a measured amount of air, is pumped into one end of the freezer, and whipped by dashers. The tube containing the mix is surrounded by a refrigerant. As soon as the mix touches the frigid side of the tube, it starts to freeze.

The ice cream made by the continuous method is extremely smooth, because it is frozen so rapidly that the ice crystals formed are very small. It is colder than batch ice cream, coming out of the freezer after a minute at between 21°F. and 24°F. More than half of its water content is frozen.

Even so the ice cream is still soft and must be sent into a hardening room or tunnel where the temperature is between zero degrees Fahrenheit and -30°F. Cold air is blown over the ice cream and in four and a half to five hours it reaches the desired temperature of -25°F. Men who work in the ice cream cold room are dressed as if about to set off on a polar field trip, and indeed conditions are not too different. Arctic clothing complete with helmet is needed. No more than fifteen minutes at a time are spent in the hardening room. The men then go out for another fifteen minutes to warm up.

Bulk ice cream, three-flavor bricks, dixie cups, pops, and other novelties are all handled by machine.

"Mechanization makes it possible for us to produce 25,000 gallons a day," comments the manager of one of the largest ice cream companies in the United States.

Within the ice cream plant, there are huge cans of frozen fruits and enormous tanks, some containing as much as 3,000 gallons of the flavors. Then there are other tanks for freshly brewed coffee and roasted nuts, and, of course, the most basic raw materials, the cream, condensed milk, and other ice cream mix ingredients. Manufacturers have switched from the pewter popular in Washington's day to stainless steel. The mix goes to the blending room, where sugar is added. From there it passes through the final stages of preparation before being pumped into a pipeline which carries it through a flavor tank, where it is automatically mixed with stainless steel rods. As with all modern factories, machines have largely replaced human hands. Only one man is needed to check that everything is going as it should. The pipelines then take the liquid ice cream directly to the freezer.

A few people are present at this point to direct the ice cream to its proper machine destination. There are many places where it might go. It may move on a conveyor belt until it reaches a spot where a half-gallon box is waiting, and then drop in. When filled, the box is closed and sealed and the conveyor line rushes on. Forty half-gallon containers can be filled in a minute. A separate pipeline lays ribbons of rich chocolate neatly through the vanilla ice cream for the flavor specialty fudge ripple. Elsewhere chunks of vanilla, chocolate, and strawberry drop exactly next to one another to form a brick. This is automatically cut to size and separated with paper. Then the conveyor belt brings the box the bricks are to occupy. Human hands are involved only in the very final packing. Some ice cream must go to the fast-spinning cup machinery and drop into the requisite spaces. When one cup is full, it moves on, and another takes its place; then the tops go on. One hundred and sixty cups can be filled in a minute. Another batch of ice cream travels to the pop device. It falls into a pop-shaped mold, a stick is dropped in, and the pop is lifted briefly, and then dunked automatically in melted chocolate. The pop is lifted up again to dry, and at last placed on a paper wrapper which closes around it firmly.

Still, ice cream, for so long a hand-tooled product, will never be as perfect a candidate for the assemblyline as the automobile. In the course of a single afternoon, a visitor to an ice cream plant can observe some sticks tipping too far into the melted chocolate and getting a thick build-up around the stick, and others not going in far enough to cover all the ice cream.

However made, ice cream's popularity has never faltered since the days of Washington. His fellow general Anthony Wayne described how he and his subordinate officers returned from a western campaign and waited "only long enough to wash away travel stains" before sitting down to a dinner of venison, beef, mutton, duck, raccoon, opossum, mince and apple pies, plum cake, and floating island. This might seem to be enough for any soldier no matter how hungry, but there was more to come.

Then, said Wayne, "to cap the jubilation, dishes of ice cream, a dainty which the Army had not seen since it left the East."

18

Of Nero, TV Dinners, and the Iceman

During the great days of the Inca empire of Peru the rulers ordered relays of runners to travel to and from the sea carrying fish. When one runner became tired, he would be replaced by a fresh one, and in this way between 100 and 150 miles could be covered in a day. Borne at such speed, the fish would arrive at the palace of the emperor without having spoiled in the humid tropical air.

That anyone would go to such lengths to get good fish seems strange to people today when fleets of refrigerated ships and trucks bring fish from the seas, rivers, and lakes of the world. And this fish is as far from decay as on the day it was caught, whether that was one or 600 days earlier.

Even for their own period of history—500-odd years ago —the Incas' roundabout method was curiously old-fashioned. Long before they ruled Peru it had become known that cold could preserve food for long enough to carry it from sea to emperor's table. And a variety of ways of obtaining cold in warm climates had been worked out. Along with those observations went another: ice could add a delightful and refreshing quality to certain foods and drinks.

These discoveries have been attributed to practically every historical figure of note. One source names the great Greek physician Hippocrates, who lived in the fifth century B.C.; another says that Alexander the Great a century later was the first to enjoy cold drinks. Everyone agrees that the Roman emperor Nero, known for the excessive luxury and extravagance of his court, insisted upon having ice in his drinks. He let nothing stand in the way of his desire. In a sense a predecessor of the Inca ruler, he sent runners selected for their speed to the mountains with orders to carry back containers filled with ice and snow.

Obtaining the ice was only the first problem to be solved; keeping it from melting before it could be used was much more difficult. Alexander the Great is said to have employed a simple method that with variations has been—and occasionally still is—used all over the world. He had his men dig deep trenches in the ground, place ice within, and cover it over with branches.

Food as well as ice will last for a long time if kept beneath the ground. The cellar has been the main storehouse for perishables since ancient times. There are kept the bottles and cans of peaches and tomatoes, the racks of wine, the bins of potatoes and onions. A summer or two ago a traveler was driving through a small, desperately poor village in Greece. As he slowly steered his way around the ruts in the dirt road, he noticed an old woman pulling up a bucket from a well and taking a loosely wrapped packet out of it. He put his head out and asked her what she was doing. She told him that she always put her cheese in the well. Deep within, chilled by the nearby water, the cheese remained fresh and soft. This primitive technique is used each summer by picnickers in more affluent countries, too. Bottles of wine, beer, or soda are buried in the damp sand near the water's edge. They will remain cool for hours, no matter how hot the day.

Antiochus of Syria in the third century B.C. had as strong a desire for a cold drink as any modern picnicker. Two boys in his court were regularly employed to fill porous jugs with water and then to keep on wetting the sides. This cooled the liquid within. In similar vein, people who live in areas where refrigeration is uncommon save perishables by trickling water over the porous walls of a storeroom during the hottest part of the day.

In pioneer times in America, as in many other countries, a farmer first made sure that a cold water stream was on the property before deciding to settle there. He would then build a springhouse over the water, which could flow through troughs within. Containers of butter, milk, and cream would be set in these troughs to be cooled by the water.

But even a springhouse was no substitute for ice. In regions where the winter is cold, it was the custom to collect and carry the ice to a special house for storage. Some of the chunks would remain frozen through the spring and into the summer.

Enterprising businessmen built commercial icehouses in the cities. These were filled with blocks of natural ice taken from the ponds and rivers in the surrounding countryside and then sold like any other commodity. The risk was greater, for what other shop can have its entire inventory turned into water? The price, however, included a sizable percentage for loss by melting.

During the early years of the nineteenth century the expanding British fishing industry was in great need of ice. Some was exported from America and from Norway. It was packed for the journey with layers of sawdust to serve as insulation.

Shipping ice to a country with ice of its own seemed singularly inefficient and wasteful to Englishman Samuel Hewitt. The cost of ice was such that small fishing ships went without. Hewitt decided to set up a massive ice-collecting business in Essex County on the north bank of the Thames. Many fishing vessels took off from this area on trips that usually lasted a week or two, quite long enough for some of the fish to spoil and the rest to lose its delicate flavor and begin to smell. Forming a firm, Hewitt of Barking, Hewitt announced that he would pay between ten and fifteen shillings for a cartload of ice, the difference depending on quality. With this incentive, several thousand men, women, and even children went to work gathering ice. Some was collected from nearby marshland which was frozen over from autumn on. As this quantity was insufficient, local farmers were induced to flood their fields. Some men were hired to serve as watchers so that the ice on fields or on ponds would not be damaged by the boots of careless children or the runners of skates. All who would use ice for pleasure not profit were relentlessly chased away.

The ice was cut into blocks and then piled in an icehouse buried beneath the ground. The walls were eight feet thick, according to accounts of the time, and 10,000 tons of ice could be stored there at one time. Nonetheless, ice continued to be so precious that fishermen rationed it and tossed such common varieties as haddock overboard or left them in an unrefrigerated box. For some years the ice was used only in the part of the hold where the choicest fish was being stored, or was laid outside of the fish boxes. The English long believed that putting ice directly on top of fish provided too great a shock to the tissues and would cause as much damage as heat.

By the 1890's, however, this belief had lost favor and it was common practice to preserve herring by salting and covering it with ice chips. This method was given the odd name of "klondyking," possibly because of the gold rush in the Klondike of the Yukon, which was going on concurrently.

The use of such primitive methods might lead one to assume that nothing better was available. Actually, an ice-making machine had been invented as early as 1775 and the first patent was taken out in 1824. That patent holder was named Vallence. Despite this easily documented fact, credit for the first patent (and discovery) is more often given to an American, Jacob Perkins, and the date is put at 1834.

The early machines contained a refrigerant such as ammonia and operated on the simple principle that heat is absorbed when a liquid changes into a gas.

For many years the use of refrigerators was limited to industries dealing in perishable foods on land and, to a lesser extent, at sea. In 1877 a Frenchman, Tellier, was able for the first time to carry meat from Buenos Aires to Rouen in France in a journey that lasted 110 days. One of his countrymen repeated this feat soon afterward and kept a record of the temperature at which the meat was maintained—5°F.

Cold, Food's Keeper

With fear of spoiling reduced, in 1886 more than 30,000 sheep carcasses were loaded on board a single ship at the Falkland Islands and carried to England. Eventually some fishing ships were to carry such excellent freezing equipment that they could stay at sea for half a year.

While the number of mechanical refrigerators increased steadily throughout the nineteenth and early twentieth centuries, they were not adopted for general home use even in the wealthiest and most highly industrialized countries. Many people can still remember when the iceman with his open truck or cart was a familiar sight in the streets of any town or city. He carried a heavy chunk of ice into the house of each of his customers and deposited it in the icebox.

But the iceman is gone. The American Ice Company recently announced that it had changed its name and was concentrating henceforth on its cold-storage warehouse business. Most people who heard of this were surprised that it had not been done long before.

Other ice purveyors, retired now, look back to the days of their pride. They tell of the time in 1914 when Martha, the last passenger pigeon on this earth, perished in Cincinnati at the age of twenty-nine. The scientists who had been waiting for her demise had ordered a 300-pound chunk of ice in advance. The body was frozen into the ice and shipped to Washington to be prepared for immortality. It sits to this day on a branch in a glass case in Washington's Smithsonian Institution.

The preservative powers of ice, to be sure, have been applied more often to food than to pigeons. In the days when Martha and her companions were still alive, the possession of an icebox and the purchase of a regular supply of ice did not save the housewife from the time-consuming task of marketing every day. The home icebox was small, and, of course, unless kept in a freezing unit, ice melts. Milk, butter, ice cream, and meat could not be stored for long. Yet the mere fact of having ice in the home at all was considered a luxury.

It is comparatively recent for iced or out-of-season foods to be consumed by any but the very rich.

In time refrigerators entered the home—almost every home in the U.S. Indeed any family, except the most desperately poverty-stricken, owned one. By 1969, the trade association for the home appliance industry was able to report that refrigerators were in more than 61 million homes.

Milk and cream, fresh meats and poultry, vegetables and fruits are stored for days, sometimes weeks on end. No longer is it necessary, like Nero, to send to the mountains for ice, or to follow the example of the poor of a century or two ago and sweep snow from the streets for personal use. Instead, a never-ending supply of ice cubes flows from the freezing unit of the refrigerator.

In fact, ice has become so plentiful that doctors recently discovered a new strange appetite perversion or pica. Certain individuals consume one or more trays of ice cubes a day. Although the aberration could be described very simply as ice hunger, it has been given the medical name of pagophagia, from the Greek *pagos*, meaning frost or ice, and *phagein*, to eat. This type of perversion more often involves eating dirt than ice. The basic cause of pagophagia appears to be an iron deficiency, but why that leads an individual to ice cubes instead of iron-rich foods cannot be explained.

To a more moderate extent, the desire for ice cubes is shared by all Americans. If a man in London, Istanbul, or Dakar asks for ice water or Scotch on the rocks, the natives assume that he comes from the U. S. A taste for iced drinks is a part of the foreign stereotype of the American.

Over the years refrigerators became larger; so did the freezing compartments. Instead of holding ice cube trays only, they were gradually expanded so as to hold large quantities of foods. Eventually huge freezers were installed in more than one-fourth of all homes wired for electricity. All this was in keeping with the growth of a new industry, frozen foods.

Until the advent of sophisticated freezing methods, foods

could be frozen in polar areas only. The Eskimos for generations froze caribou and later ate it raw.

Members of an American Antarctic expedition one day entered a hut that had been abandoned forty years earlier by Ernest Shackleton's party and looked around for something to eat. They expected that any food they found would still be edible. Had not Rear Admiral Richard E. Byrd warmed up and finished off a portion of roast beef and a slice of bread he had left on his plate four and a half years earlier? In Shackleton's larder the men came upon a jar of curried rabbit. Not daunted by this exotic dish, they heated it and found it just as wholesome as it could possibly have been on the day it was first prepared.

Such a meal is no longer really startling to Americans, accustomed as they are to the frozen TV dinner. A typical home refrigerator contains meals that are no more American than Shackleton's curried rabbit—egg foo young, enchiladas, sauerbraten. Each of these meals was prepared long—though not quite forty years—before being warmed and eaten.

The berry plants have long since been buried beneath the snow, the winter wind whistles over the cornfields, and the branches of the peach trees are bare. Yet the strawberry, the ear of corn, the peach are still offering their flavor and aroma, altered only a little from their summer succulence.

Who invented commercially frozen foods? Most people give credit to Clarence Birdseye, who attained this immortality by making his a brand name. Foods, however, were frozen long before Birdseye's time. A search of patent records shows that an Englishman named H. Benjamin registered a method for freezing food by dipping it in ice and salt brine in 1842.

Birdseye's discovery, though, was based on observing nature, not on reading about Benjamin's. In 1915 he took a trip to Labrador. On a day when the temperature was well below zero and the winds were howling, he saw that the natives were putting meat and fish out of doors. It froze almost instantly. When he asked what was to be done with the meat or fish, the natives told him that they planned to do nothing more until they needed some. They would take the food into the house weeks or even months later and then thaw and cook it. The result was perfectly wholesome and tasty, they added, far better than the dried, salted, or canned meats and fish that were the alternatives.

What nature provided for the natives of Labrador, Birdseye sought to achieve in the food-processing plant. It did not take him long to discover that free water in food solidifies at temperatures between 20°F. and 28°F., lower than the freezing point of water. For complete freezing, the food must be brought down to zero. He also observed that the faster the freezing, the better the quality of the end product, whether it is meat, fish, fruit, or vegetable. Slow freezing brings a risk of deterioration. Even if this does not occur, large ice crystals form and damage the flavor and consistency.

Birdseye worked out a process involving a quick-freezing principle and in 1929 sold it to the Postum Company (later General Foods). Whatever the name of the company, Birdseye was the name by which its frozen foods were to be known from then on. There were other frozen food pioneers, among them Dr. Frank App of Seabrook Farms, but they have remained unknown to the general public.

The era of frozen food began with a line of twenty-seven different items, including peas, spinach, haddock, and raspberries. From this modest introduction the frozen food industry moved on to its present eminence. Nowadays more than 14 billion pounds of frozen foods—and this does not include ice cream—are produced every year. And of all varieties packed, none is consumed in greater quantities than the lowly potato—French fried, mashed, hash-browned, boiled, stuffed and baked, formed into balls, into patties, into pancakes. Purchases are so heavy that they average to more than seven and a half pounds per person per year. Next to potatoes come peas; these were in that first line of frozen foods, and they have retained their popularity ever since. Strawberries are the favorite of fruits, with 34 million pounds eaten annually. The desire for seafood has not waned since the days of the Incas, and better than 430 million pounds are packed in a typical year. Frozen meat products total about 600 million pounds. This is as nothing in comparison with poultry, however, which accounts for more than 2 billion pounds of the frozen food total. Orange juice concentrate has become such a staple that many children would be completely at a loss if shown an orange juice squeezer and asked to identify it. About 128 million gallons of concentrate—multiplied by three when reconstituted—are turned out every year.

Lima beans, corn, blueberries, peaches, chicken, flounder, beef, and most other vegetables, fruits, poultry, fish, and meats can be purchased alone or in a variety of combinations. A look in the frozen food cabinet of any supermarket will show the shopper how peas have been joined with carrots, with butter sauce, onions, mushrooms. The fish filet has been ground, extended, crumbed, rolled, and fried into sticks, cakes, or balls. There are blintzes, pizzas, chili, macaroni with cheese, stuffed turkey, veal rolatine, hamburger patties, "pigs in a blanket," eggplant parmigiana, rock cornish game hen, fried chicken, pork chops, devilled crabs, partly cooked sausages, pancakes, stuffed cabbage, lobster Newburg, French toast, spinach soufflé, shrimp with cocktail sauce, chopped liver, whipped toppings. Next to orange juice, lemonade, and punches are the cream of shrimp soup, lobster bisque, daiquiri and whiskey sour mixes. Then come the stacks upon stacks of the convenience food of our time—the TV dinner, complete with meat loaf, chicken, roast loin of pork, fried shrimp, pot roast, gravies, muffins, stewed fruit, brownies, potatoes or green peas or both, occasionally soup. The illusion of home-baking is produced with brown-and-serve, partially pre-cooked, biscuits, muffins, croissants, and pastries. And if this seems too tedious, the fully baked product is frozen—coffee cake, cheese cake, éclair, pie, layer cake, corn bread, bagel, strudel, turnover, and Parker House roll.

Some come in boxes and some in cans, others in pouches or on aluminum trays. They are heated in the oven or on top of the stove in a small amount of water. The boilable pouches are dropped intact into a pot of boiling water. Fruits and cakes have but to be taken out of the freezer and left to defrost in refrigerator or on the kitchen table. And should this be too time-consuming, some fruits are packed in a pouch and can be thawed in a matter of minutes by being immersed in warm water.

Complete entrees in packages or pouches were a failure at first, for reasons no market researcher has ever been able to fathom. In the early 1960's most frozen food companies abandoned them altogether, having lost a combined $30 to $40 million. No sooner were they gone than they were back, and became a most popular item.

Frozen foods are frequently served in all innocence as fresh ones. Some loaves of bread that are bought in the market may be soft, fragrant, and fresh in taste; nonetheless, they are old in actuality. A good deal of bread is held in frozen storage and then defrosted and distributed as a fresh product.

The success of all frozen foods is due at least in part to the large increase in the number of working women, many of them mothers, in the last few years. A return at 5:30 P.M. from a day in the office does not require the family to live on nothing but hamburgers and chops. Instead, chicken tetrazini or beef goulash can appear on the table, accompanied by wild and white rice pilaf and artichoke hearts, and topped off with coconut custard pie. There is no chopping, cutting, folding, or whipping. All that has been done in advance. No stop at butcher or baker need be made on the way home. Everything is in the house already, purchased the previous Saturday.

A meeting of dieticians was held at a hospital in Jacksonville, Florida, a few years ago. The two dieticians who were in charge of the major banquet arrived at the hospital at 4:15 in the afternoon. They found a small "old tired hospital kitchen" and a frantic administrator, fearing for his reputation. By six o'clock, when hundreds of dieticians sat down to dinner, thirteen different dishes were ready for them. How had two men prepared so much so fast? Frozen foods, of course.

There was a time when someone in a home—the housewife, her mother, the cook—had to know how to prepare all of the dishes served. A family of Scandinavian origin living in the Midwest was hardly likely to consume chop suey or spaghetti with meat sauce, except in a restaurant. Today these are as apt to appear on the table as any Nordic dish—ready-made, to be sure, not custom-tailored. A good cook is now, as always, valued, but the most unskilled bride or bachelor can manage to present meat loaf, fried chicken, or turkey on the first try. With "boil-in-the-bag" entrees and vegetables, she need not even watch the clock. The gravy on the turkey slice will not dry out. Nor must he butter the string beans or cream the spinach; all that has been done by knowledgeable hands in the processing plant. And for the special little candlelight dinner that will melt the heart of a companion, one can purchase out-of-the-ordinary dishes cooked in small quantities, frozen, and sold in gourmet shops. There is frozen quiche lorraine, bite-size mocha éclair puffs, chocolate, strawberry, and coffee mousse. Prices are high, to be sure, but are still cheaper than hiring a chef and easier than learning to cook.

As the owner of a large restaurant remarked the other day: "If a chef doesn't show up, it isn't pandemonium. Someone else can do the job—maybe even the dishwasher."

How often does this happen? The editor of a city newspaper sent a reporter to make a survey. He discovered that frozen foods were being used in some of the country's most fashionable and expensive gourmet restaurants. In addition, several lower-priced chains have in the last few years without fanfare changed from fresh to frozen entrees.

A food industry spokesman accepts this casually: "The chefs are probably annoyed."

And what of the consumer? Although all are agreed as to the convenience of frozen food, its excellence is challenged repeatedly. During the Johnson administration a food coordinator from Texas was summoned to the White House to organize the kitchens and save on the cost of food. Upon learning of some of the planned economies, the chef resigned. "I think it is very lousy to have frozen foods in the President's house," he informed *The New York Times,* so heated that he lost his customary refinement of speech.

On the other hand, frozen foods can improve the caliber and add to the variety of meals served in institutions and schools; these are rarely noted for gourmet touches. A new trend is to have lunches for schoolchildren prepared in a central kitchen, frozen, and then carried by refrigerated truck to the schools in a district. All that each school then needs in the way of cooking equipment is a warming oven. In England a similar "food factory" plan has also already been launched. A central hospital kitchen will cook 50,000 meals weekly for patients at three hospitals in the area. As a start, the Darenth Park Hospital is preparing 5,000 meals a week, fast-freezing them, and having them transported to a psychiatric hospital a mile and a half away.

It is infinitely more difficult to maintain high quality for full meals than for the individual parts. A good case can be made for frozen fruits and vegetables. No one, not even the frozen food packer, claims that a frozen peach is as good as a fresh one plucked at the moment of ripeness and eaten at once. But this happens rather seldom. Much fresh fruit is packed while still a bit green, and it must ripen in the warehouse or on the way to market. It may remain underripe and hard, or conversely be overripe, brown-flecked, and mushy. The fruit or vegetable to be frozen is picked at its peak of perfection. A new type of farmer, geared to growing crops for freezing, drives around the fields in a car equipped with an intercom system. Radio contact is maintained with a central office. Should the farmer report in at midnight that peas or corn have ripened, pickers are summoned and rushed to the crops. "We live with the fields," says one of the observers. "Once we give the signal, everything moves like clockwork."

Crops intended for the fresh vegetable bin, rather than the frozen food processor, are maintained in cold storage while waiting for their turn to go to market. The temperature requirement varies from one species to another. The ideal for grapes is 31°F. to 32°F., for Bartlett pears, 29°F. to 31°F., cucumbers, 45°F. to 50°F., coconuts, 32°F. to 35°F., and lemons, 55°F. to 58°F. If the temperature is lower, cold injury will result; on the other hand, two or three degrees more warmth causes the fruits to ripen too rapidly. Crops with different temperature demands cannot be held together. Should potatoes and apples be stored at 40°F., the apples will absorb the earthy taste and odor from the potatoes. When the warehouse is cooled to 32°F., no odor will be absorbed and the apples will be in good condition, but the potatoes will become unpleasantly sweet. Even when maintained at the ideal temperature and humidity, crops cannot be stored indefinitely. They must be brought to market, canned, or frozen within a time limit that varies from crop to crop. Sweet cherries can be held for only ten days to two weeks even at 31°F. to 32°F., while cranberries will keep for three months or so at 36°F. to 40°F.

Some crops are so perishable that they must be chilled before going into cold storage. Corn, for example, may deteriorate in a few days, unless plunged into ice water immediately after picking. Peas are often packed in crushed ice to prevent loss of sugar content.

That vegetables, fruits, meat, and fish need ice and refrigeration is not surprising; but cold is also an essential element in the preparation of foods that would seem to need none of it. The International Institute of Refrigeration, which maintains headquarters in France, notes that soda is superior if cooled before being carbonated. The carbon dioxide gas is more completely absorbed at low temperatures, and what is more, the fizz does not go out so fast when can or bottle is opened. Beer, the group notes, should also be cooled during manufacture.

It is not easy to maintain the identical flavor from one batch to the next of beer, blue-type cheeses, pickles, and sauerkraut. The micro-organisms that ferment and produce the desired taste sometimes develop mutations, and wild strains may creep in. This danger could be avoided if the desired microbe were frozen, and a small quantity defrosted each time it were needed.

Once food has been processed or frozen, the problem arises of maintaining it in good condition until used or brought to a freezer. One of New York's best-known caterers describes glowingly how a dinner for 250 was prepared by two chefs and an army of assistants in the city and then carried by truck 175 miles to a debut party in Newport, Rhode Island. The breast of chicken supreme stuffed with wild rice, and the tomatoes and string beans amandine were protected from the June warmth with "mountains of dry ice." The chilling powers of the solid carbon dioxide were applied the following day for a diplomats' dinner that started with a whole Canadian salmon in aspic and ended with a ring mold of vanilla ice cream and pineapple ice filled with fresh peaches and strawberries.

Large-scale food movement takes place in refrigerated trucks, ships, and railroad cars. In their frigid holds food is carried from slaughterhouse, fishing port, farm, dairy, frozen food processor, and ice cream factory to refrigerated warehouse and store. Refrigeration at sea has produced some freak accidents. A steward on board a freighter was locked into a meat freezer for two and a half hours. As a result of the freezing, he suffered brain damage. Another side effect was impotence, and although he was already the father of eleven children, this was not a disability he or his wife took lightly. In the end he was awarded $10,000 in damages. A new policy instituted by some big shippers will reduce the likelihood of a man's being overlooked for that long. Wives are allowed to accompany their husbands on the voyages.

For long-distance operations some large distributors both at sea and on land have turned to the liquid gas that has proven most valuable in many fields of cryogenics—nitrogen. For truck transport the liquid nitrogen is stored in a tank and is released automatically whenever the temperature rises. The door of a truck is opened and closed many times as it goes from one chain store, institution, or restaurant to the next. At each stop some of the food is removed, while the rest is exposed to the outside air. The liquid nitrogen is so efficient a coolant that within thirty seconds after the door is closed again, the temperature has been returned to its desired low. The nitrogen atmosphere preserves fresh fruits and vegetables as well as frozen ones. Lacking oxygen, they cannot oxidize or decay.

And what happens at home? At a normal refrigerator temperature of 45°F., most perishables will keep for three or four days, and at 40°F., a bit longer. Although the food-spoiling bacteria are not killed at these temperatures, their growth is arrested and they become unable to produce toxins. If they go directly from refrigerator to stove, they will not be restored to active life at all. Both the heat of cooking and the cold of refrigeration preclude microbial metabolic activities. Should meat or a casserole or creamed dish be left out on the kitchen table or warmed to a temperature below 140°F., growth will resume and spoilage can occur. Many people remember that in their grandparents' homes smoked meats were kept at room temperature for long periods of time without becoming contaminated. In those days when refrigerators were uncommon, ham had a higher salt content to prevent bacterial growth. Today, according to Dr. Richard V. Lechowich, a food scientist with Michigan State University, the salt content of ham is only two percent compared to eight percent in the past, and ham has become a rather frequent source of summer food poisoning. Leftovers of all foods should be put back in the refrigerator as quickly as possible. The widely held belief that food will turn sour or lose its flavor unless allowed to cool slowly on the kitchen table before being refrigerated is an old wives' tale. It is no more sound than the old theory that ice could not be put directly on fish, and it is considerably more dangerous.

Longer-term storage requires the temperatures of 0°F. or lower, which can be obtained only in a freezer. Most housewives are not sure just how long frozen foods can be stored.

A good rule of thumb, say experts, is to keep frozen food for no more than one year at zero degree temperatures. Some foods can be kept for more time than this; others, such as fatty fish, ground hamburger, and sausage, for somewhat less. The Department of Agriculture recommends a temperature of -10°F. for vegetables to be kept for more than six months. Proper wrapping extends the period of storage for all food. While the prudent will not take the chance of eating food kept beyond the recommended storage time, it does not necessarily become contaminated.

"The main changes that occur are in quality," declares Leonard S. Finn, Director of Technical Services of the National Association of Frozen Food Packers. "The food may lose some of its nutrients."

Even canned goods do not retain them indefinitely at room temperature, frozen food manufacturers make haste to declare. A number of cans of processed baby food were tested for vitamin B_1 content. Some cans from that lot were then stored at 25°F., and others at 85°F. The cool baby food had more of the vitamin content at the end of six months than the warm.

Flavor may also change slightly as time passes. "Very minor chemical changes can take place in food stored in a freezer, and these may affect the taste," points out Joseph H. Colquitt, Secretary of the National Association of Refrigerated Warehouses.

When frozen food is warmed and then chilled again one or more times between processor and consumer, the flavor, smell, and quality all change for the worse, observed the National Research Council of Canada. Frost accumulates within the package during each fluctuation in temperature and this affects the texture. More important, bacteria may grow during the warm spells. Laboratory tests can tell if frozen fish, for example, has been thawed and refrozen on its trip to the consumer. One enzyme is known to become particularly active in fish that has been thawed. This information is of rather little help to the housewife, however, who can hardly perform a chemical analysis on all packages in the supermarket freezer.

The bulk of frozen food today is cooled by the method of blast (or continuous) freezing that has not changed very much in thirty years. When a cake, to take one example, is to be frozen, it is placed on a conveyor belt and moved through a huge blast freezer where the temperature is held down to between -30°F. and -40°F. In about two hours the cake is frozen and is carried on to a storage freezer. One of the major producers of frozen baked goods boasts that the main storage freezer is larger than a football field and can hold 7,800,000 frozen cakes, cookies, pieces of Danish pastry, croissants, dinner and sweet rolls at one time.

As Birdseye observed in the dawn of the frozen food era, the speedier the freezing at the outset, the better the results. Liquid nitrogen can freeze virtually any product more efficiently than conventional refrigerants do. Birdseye had tried to freeze foods with liquid nitrogen in the 1920's, but the cost was so high that he gave it up. Eventually the process was revived and improved. For a time the pear or perch was immersed directly in the liquid nitrogen. Some foods, however, cracked or peeled as a result of the shock. Then a new technique was developed in which the food is sprayed with atomized liquid nitrogen. Processes involving nitrogen are too expensive to supersede blast or continuous freezing completely, but the liquid gas is being used for a growing number of products.

About 1,500 pounds of fish can be frozen in liquid nitrogen in an hour. The scallop or filet of sole is precooled to -50°F. in gaseous nitrogen. This keeps the surface from cracking. It is then taken down to the -320°F. of the liquid gas. This method, known as flash freezing, does work "as quick as a flash." Fish are frozen in about eight minutes, and some other foods in even less time. A whipped-cream layer cake or a brownie, for example, is ready in five or six minutes, and apple strudel and pecan coffee cake take only one or two, providing an aluminum pan is used.

Many frozen cakes and pies are sold in such pans. The complaint is sometimes heard that the pan, which is not really needed by the housewife, raises the price of the cake. The pan does serve a practical purpose, however. Cake freezes faster than when placed on a paper board. This results in a saving of liquid nitrogen, which may—or may not—be reflected in a lowering of the final price.

For many years certain foods were known as unfreezable. Frozen whole mushrooms, tomato slices, avocados, bananas, whole strawberries, and melons bore little resemblance to the fresh product. They become mushy and shapeless when defrosted. Although conventionally frozen strawberries, for example, are popular, they are really more like a sauce than a fruit. The problem is that foods like this contain a lot of water. As a result, ice crystals form under standard freezing methods and damage the cells. Liquid nitrogen, however, works so quickly that the cell structure remains intact.

Because of the cost of nitrogen, some producers use a combination method. They first spray a turkey, for instance, with liquid nitrogen, which helps to keep the skin particularly attractive. Then the turkey goes into a regular blast freezer and is frozen all the way through.

Freon, one of the standard refrigerator coolants, can actually freeze the food it will later chill. Although its liquid temperatures range from -21°F. to -30°F., not even close to nitrogen's frigidity, it vaporizes so rapidly that it works nearly as well. Freon can absorb heat from the food within seconds. A product can be immersed or sprayed with freon without suffering quite the shock that nitrogen gives. Its greatest advantage over nitrogen, processors point out, is price.

Not only freon and liquid nitrogen, but any kind of refrigeration is scarce in many tropical underdeveloped areas of the world. Even moderate cooling—storage at 59°F. to 68°F. —is not always obtainable.

"While people are starving, food is being wasted. It spoils due to lack of refrigeration while being moved from sea or farm to the cities. And in the cities it is wasted, too," comments Colquitt.

The International Institute of Refrigeration points out that the situation is made infinitely worse by the severe climate in these countries. A crop will flourish one year and be wiped out the next. In addition, the food that is highest in protein —meat, fish, eggs—is most perishable. With the cost of producing power a major drawback to refrigeration, the IIR urges consideration of solar energy. That at least is plentiful in many underdeveloped areas.

On the other side of the globe, nature has not yet been altogether superseded by mechanical refrigeration. At Grise Fiord, 700 miles north of the Arctic Circle, lies the most northerly Eskimo settlement. A family there lives in a government-built frame house warmed by an oil heater. Even so the men still go out each day to hunt the polar bear or seal. During the winter they keep these meats, particularly the seal that is the dietary staple, in an unheated storehouse. When summer comes and the Arctic sun burns high in the sky, the hunter and his wife dig a pit deep in the ground and fill it with ice. The seal meat is lowered into the pit. It will be hauled up from time to time and a chunk hacked off for use. While her counterpart in temperate climates is defrosting beefsteak and chicken, the Eskimo housewife thaws a seal roast and morsel of blubber and then pops them into the oven to cook until they are succulent and tender.

19

Space Food

Shortly after the lunar module set down on the moon, mission commander Neil A. Armstrong and Colonel Edwin E. Aldrin, Jr., had a light meal of bacon squares, peaches, sugar cookie cubes, coffee, and pineapple-grapefruit drink. Most of this food that they consumed before depressurizing the cabin, opening the hatch, and climbing down the ladder to take man's first steps on the moon had been produced by means of cold.

Three days earlier, while the Apollo 11 command ship was hurtling toward the moon, Mission Control in Houston received the following radio message: "My compliments to the chef. That salmon salad is outstanding."

Such accolades are accorded to the space and moon menus because of freeze-drying. This most modern of food preparation methods is a direct descendant of an ancient technique known to primitive peoples the world over. Two or even three thousand years ago the natives in the Andes highlands of South America dried potatoes and then prepared *chuñu.* Inhabitants of the Near East have for centuries dried dates, figs, apricots, and grapes so as to have a ready supply to carry when traveling by camel caravan or as a reserve for seasons of scarcity. In Africa the sun that may someday be used to provide refrigeration has been used for generations to dry foods. Biltong, for example, long thin strips of dried lean meat, has been standard fare for natives and foreign hunters. Scientists attempting to reconstruct the eleventh-century voyages of the Vikings believe that dried meat and fruits were among the supplies that sustained them on their way. The American Indians dried buffalo and beef, sometimes known as jerk or jerky, in the sun.

During any time of war or famine, dried foods have come into prominence. Shipments of dried potatoes and carrots went to British troops engaged against the Russians in the Crimea. During the Civil War, rations included a peculiar kind of dried sausage padded with peas, along with vegetables, soup mixes, apples, and peaches. In World War I, dehydrated potatoes, onions, carrots, turnips, and meats were stocked by British and French quartermaster corps. With the outbreak of World War II, food dehydration plants sprang up in the United States and Europe. A new generation of soldiers came to know and be nourished by, but not always to like, dried foods. They complained that many were tasteless, shriveled, and unattractive.

Dried foods are still widely used, particularly raisins, apricots, skim milk, and potato (flakes). But by and large, they have lost ground to products in which drying has been linked with freezing. The simplest of these processes is dehydrofreezing, in which food is first partially dried and is then frozen. This method works particularly well for sliced apples. According to bakers, such apples make very good pie filling.

The method that is beginning to have a real impact on our eating habits is just the reverse of dehydrofreezing. In freeze-drying, food is first frozen and then dried. This process was adopted in the laboratory before it reached the kitchen. Even freeze-dried food, however, is not as new as the advertisements for freeze-dried coffee would have one believe ("Now, an entirely new process . . ."). Such claims ignore the fact that mother's milk was freeze-dried in the mid-1930's and oysters were treated in similar fashion in 1936 by a party of men making a trip to the far north. There the shellfish were reconstituted with milk.

The Japanese have in wartime managed freeze-drying with no equipment at all. During the early years of World War II they found it necessary to preserve cooked rice, the dietary staple, so that the troops could take it along on the march. To this end, the mess officers spread the rice out to freeze at night in the open. The moisture was then sublimated in the radiant sunlight the next day. Before meals the rice was cooked as usual in a little water, which restored the desired consistency.

Although shrimp, chicken, and some other foods were freeze-dried in the 1950's, the industry did not make its spurt until the 1960's. While the Japanese technique might lead one to suppose that freeze-drying is simple, it has not been found easy to make a good freeze-dried product. The method employed is complex: the food is first frozen and then placed on trays in a vacuum cabinet which is cooled to -40°F. before the vacuum pump is turned on. Then as the pressure falls, the ice within the food begins to sublimate and the resultant vapor is drawn out through a tube. The process is speeded by heat applied through plates or coils until the trays are at a temperature of 200°F. to 300°F., which warms the food on them to 140°F. The heat must be applied slowly and cautiously or the food will burn. Yet the temperature must become high enough to get all the way through each product. The outside of peach or beefsteak dries first, and therein lies the problem. The cooled outer shell becomes an insulator shielding the cells around the inner core from the heat. Getting the inside as dry as the outside can take a good thirty-five hours. This is rare, fortunately; on the average, between ninety-eight and ninety-nine percent of the moisture can be removed from food in eight hours, with some products dry in only three.

How many foods have been freeze-dried? The ever-lengthening list includes chicken, beef, mushrooms, asparagus, eggs, orange juice, beef stew, meat loaf, shrimp creole, chicken à la king, melon balls, cottage cheese, Swiss steak, chives, pineapple wedges, banana slices, wintergreen, tarragon, omelet with mushrooms, goulash, roe, oysters, celery, tomato paste, scampi, ground beef, milk shakes, celery extract, coffee, tea. Freeze-dried ingredients are found in many soups, stews, and chilis. A food processor asked his family to serve as a test panel for a freeze-dried shrimp salad containing celery, egg, pimento, and onions. The dish was greeted with as much enthusiasm as the salmon on Apollo 11. Of all freeze-dried foods, none has won popular acceptance so quickly as freeze-dried coffee. It is made from freshly percolated coffee that is flash-frozen and then dried. Freeze-dried strawberries, peaches, bananas, and blueberries are added to dry breakfast cereals. A few enterprising businessmen are freeze-drying beer and wine. One, even more daring, is offering freeze-dried squid. Europeans are applying the process to leeks, and natives of the tropics are drying papaya, mangos, and passion fruit.

Freeze-drying could bring us an ice cream that does not require refrigeration, strange as that seems, and a great deal of research is going on now. Unrefrigerated ice cream possesses obvious advantages for people in underdeveloped areas, for explorers, for campers. Astronauts might enjoy an ice cream sundae while en route to Mars. Freeze-dried ice cream may also be used as a filling for candies and cookies. The ice cream center can be freeze-dried into bite-sized pieces and coated with chocolate, caramel, nuts, or biscuits. To obtain the delicious ice cream flavor, one bites into the candy and the saliva reconstitutes the cream. Astronauts have been doing this very thing for a variety of staple foods.

An attempt to coordinate freeze-dried ice cream with other foods has already been made. One food processor applied ice cream as a coating for a breakfast cereal. The ice cream flavors offered were chocolate, vanilla, and orange. The cereal tasted like an ice cream cone. The addition of milk brought the ice cream to life. When word of this innovation got out, the editor of an ice cream industry newspaper went to look for the new product, eager to give it a try. But by the time he reached the market that had stocked it, he learned that the ice-creamy flakes were gone. They had been a total failure and had been withdrawn almost at once. Still, as most people would not eat ice cream cones for breakfast anyway, this can hardly be considered a fair test for the freeze-dried version.

Not all foods are suitable for freeze-drying. One key to a good end product is a high melting point, as the food must not melt during the drying part of the process. Poultry, beef, shellfish, and other high-protein foods freeze-dry successfully, as do foods, such as potatoes, which are high in starch. On the other hand, those that are rich in sugar or fats, such as pork, do not. Exceptions are avocado and cream cheese, which turn out very well. Foods with a high water content can be freeze-dried, but the result is a bit startling in appearance. Tomato, watermelon, cucumber, or lettuce are recognized as much by shape and texture as by flavor, and this is irrevocably lost in the processing. As a result, processors prefer to freeze-dry and then reconstitute a fish cake rather than apply their efforts to a whole fish, or to handle chicken à la king, not a whole chicken. The loss of shape may occasionally be an advantage, however, as in the case of squid.

When it comes to flavor, even the manufacturers concede that it is not up to that of the fresh or even frozen product.

"With each step in processing you lose some of the qualities of the original," explains Leonard Finn of the National Association of Frozen Food Packers. "In freeze-drying you start with a frozen product that has already lost some of the qualities it had when fresh, and you go on to do something else to it that removes a few more."

Along with the water inevitably go some of the volatile constituents of flavor or aroma. The cell structure is changed sufficiently to rearrange some of the salts.

In the early days of freeze-drying, a dozen or fifteen years ago, a processor remarked to a friend about to go into the business: "The first thing you have to learn about freeze-drying is how to apologize for your product diplomatically."

Since then there have been considerable improvements and no one is apologizing for freeze-dried coffee, shrimp, chicken noodle and mushroom soup, sausage, creamed chicken, ham, and a number of other products that turn out well. On the whole, though, a series of taste tests performed by the Department of Agriculture's Marketing Economics Division reveals that most people prefer fresh or frozen to freeze-dried. Not one of thirty-three foods tested was classified as "very good"; nor was any rated "very poor." One panel of tasters declared that freeze-dried steaks had the peculiar disadvantage of being "dry, yet oozing juice." Swiss steak was described as "stringy" and "fibrous."

Freeze-dried foods cannot fairly be compared with frozen or fresh, but rather with dried, asserts Kermit Bird, USDA Agricultural Economist and one of the nation's experts on freeze-drying. In comparison with regular dried foods, the freeze-dried are superior. Many men who ate dried scrambled eggs while in the Army during World War II swore never to touch dried eggs again. The eggs had a strange, glassy look and a custardy taste and texture. The method used in those days, however, did not involve freezing, and the surviving prejudice is unjustified today.

No one really expects freeze-dried foods to replace most of the staples in the family larder. Freeze-drying is a costly process and the prices of the foods, therefore, are high. Only those that are either truly a convenience or are superior to other prepared foods stand a chance. Freeze-dried coffee, for example, is higher in price than instant, but a good many women today are buying it anyway because they prefer the flavor.

An advantage of freeze-dried over fresh and frozen foods is that they do not need refrigeration but can stand on a shelf at a room temperature of 70°F. for about two years. Such extended shelf life is possible only with air-tight, moisture-proof, lightproof packaging, and this adds to the price. A European research concern has observed that if oxygen gets into the package, freeze-dried carrots and spinach develop an off-flavor in only two or three months. Foods high in unsaturated fats become rancid easily, because the fats oxidize in air even without water. In order to avoid all this, many freeze-dried foods are either vacuum or nitrogen packed. Fruits and berries are particularly hard to store for long, regardless of packaging; they are high in sugar and melt unless kept cool.

The preservation time for any freeze-dried food is greatly increased by lowering the air temperature around it. Bird notes that each drop of 18°F. doubles the shelf life. A product could thus last for a year when the temperature is 88°F., two years at 70°F., and four years at 52°F. Even this temperature can be easily achieved in winter without refrigeration equipment.

Ease of storage and lightness in weight give freeze-dried food its two greatest advantages. Take a hundred pounds of frozen cooked beef and remove the water. What is left weighs a mere forty-two pounds. The same hundred pounds of mushrooms dries out to a fragile eleven pounds. This lightness of weight is obviously a boon to the camper, hosteler, picnicker, hiker, and hunter on safari. A good quantity of food, and varied food at that, can be carried in a knapsack on the back.

It is also perfectly feasible to air-lift large amounts of freeze-dried foods and then drop them by parachute over famine or disaster areas.

As this kind of food can be transported in unrefrigerated trucks, the Army has become the largest single buyer. Freeze-dried products, such as eggs and chicken, are included in the combat rations, the "Quick Serve," and "Meal Ready to Eat," developed by the Quartermaster Corps. These are superior in flavor to the field rations of old. The Army is also buying beef, pork chops, and uncooked fish squares, and is serving them in the regular mess halls at stateside bases.

In order to study underwater life, scientists and crew remain submerged in submarines for long periods of time. The commander of a recent 1,500-mile voyage beneath the Gulf Stream refused to allow any cooking. "This atmosphere is going to stick with us for thirty days, so why contaminate it any more than we can help," he declared firmly. In the past only a Captain Bligh could have made such a demand, as the only way to avoid cooking contamination would have been to limit the diet to hardtack, tepid juices, and dried apricots. The crew of today enjoys a wide variety of meats, vegetables, and fruits. Freeze-dried foods can be reconstituted with hot or cold water stored at the start of the trip in heavily insulated tanks.

The most significant consumption of freeze-dried foods today takes place neither on land or beneath the sea, but rather in outer space. The quantities involved are minimal, the importance incalculable. At the dawn of the space age the most that could be said for the meals was that they were nourishing and proved that men could eat when in a weightless condition. Freeze-dried chicken and gravy and pot roast appeared for the first time on the spacecraft menus of a 1963 Project Mercury flight. During the later Mercury flights bite-sized compressed and dehydrated foods were also tested. The complaint came back from outer space that "the cookies crumbled" and that tiny bits were floating about the cabin. An edible coating from then on covered the cubes and controlled the crumbs. These food cubes were rehydrated in the simplest possible way—with the saliva in the astronaut's mouth.

As plans for the more ambitious Gemini program were being formulated in 1964, experts at the U. S. Army Laboratories at Natick, Massachusetts, were asked by the National Aeronautics and Space Administration to develop guides for preparation of food for space flights. It had to be "lightweight, highly nutritious, and resemble the color, flavor, and texture of freshly prepared food." Just as important, it had to be able to endure a temperature range from about 20°F. to 135°F., extreme changes in pressure and gravity, humidity variations of thirty to ninety percent, weightlessness, and an atmosphere composed of oxygen. Freeze-dried food comes the closest to fitting all these requirements.

The scientists worked on two different ways of presenting freeze-dried foods. Some, such as sandwiches, fruit cake, beef pot roast with gravy, were compressed into cubes that could be rehydrated with saliva. Others were formed into bars, each the size of a single serving. A germicide tablet was attached to each package. If an astronaut were not hungry enough to eat the entire bar at one time, he could simply add the tablet and it would keep the remainder of the food from spoiling until it was wanted again. Luncheon meat cans, of the twelve-ounce size, are found to be exceedingly good molds for forming the logs which are later sawed into bars and freeze-dried.

Green beans and carrots in cream sauce were among the first foods tested. The idea here was that the white sauce would make it particularly easy to rehydrate the vegetables and would also add needed calories. Both vegetables were a failure, as they rapidly developed a rancid taste. This did not happen, however, to cream-style corn (in this case canned corn was frozen, adding yet another process). Green peas held together with pregelatinized starch were also adopted for space use. The peas were crushed to speed rehydration.

Bars and cubes of the selected foods are vacuum-packed into four-ply laminated plastic containers. The bag for the bar includes a folded-over eating tube, as well as an arrangement for the introduction of water from an outside source. The water is obtained as a by-product of fuel cell operation. Dinners for the Apollo missions, the series that followed Gemini, were improved by the addition of equipment to provide cold water to reconstitute the applesauce and tunafish salad, and hot water for the potato soup and chicken and gravy. This was for command ships only. The men on the lunar module had to make do with cold water only. Before a meal the astronaut inserts a water dispenser that resembles a child's water pistol and injects the requisite amount into the container. He must then knead the bag for about three minutes to mix all the ingredients. When the food becomes edible again, the astronaut cuts the tab separating the eating tube from the container and squeezes the food into his mouth.

By the time Apollo 10 went up in May of 1969 a new type of package, the "spoon bowl," had been developed and added to the larder. After rehydration the food packed in this way can be eaten with a spoon. The astronauts aboard Apollo 10 were the first to take up foil-wrapped "wet pack" rations of regular, undehydrated food. While all space travelers naturally prefer to eat ordinary dishes, weight limitations are such that the bulk of the food carried on long missions must be freeze-dried.

As Thomas J. Kelly of Grumman Aerospace Corporation, chief designer of the lunar module, has explained: "For every pound you take from orbit to the lunar surface, you must have three and one-quarter pounds of propellant aboard." The weight problem will be even more acute for longer visits to the moon, Mars, and the other planets.

Before setting off on a space journey, the men select their own menus. All the foods and beverages for each meal chosen are placed in an aluminum wrapping with a colored tab to show who the meal is for. In addition, there is a pantry holding such earthly favorites as hot dogs for between-meal snacks.

Just what does an astronaut eat as he journeys through space? On the Apollo 7 mission, Major Donn F. Eisele elected to begin his day with freeze-dried sausage patties, apple cereal cubes, and cocoa. A luncheon menu for Walter Cunningham consisted of corn chowder, barbecued beef bites, cinnamon toast, chocolate pudding, and orange-grapefruit drink. At that same time, Captain Walter M. Schirra, Jr., was having chicken salad, gingerbread, and grapefruit drink. The men reported that they could not finish all the food they had brought. It was too filling, they said, and too sweet.

Deciding on earth what one will want to eat in space is difficult in any event. When Lieutenant Colonel L. Gordon Cooper, Jr., and Lieutenant Commander Charles Conrad, Jr., prepared for their eight-day Gemini 5 mission in August of 1965, they declared that they would have none of the bars of freeze-dried foods. Adding water and kneading the bags seemed too much trouble. They would take only the bite-sized cubes that they could reconstitute in their mouths. The dismay of space agency officials was such that the astronauts relented. That turned out to be just as well. Once in orbit and beyond reach of supplements or changes for their diets, they lost their taste for the cubes. Most were returned to earth in the storage compartment of the capsule. The freeze-dried bars, fortunately, pleased the men and they ate all they had carried out into space.

Part Seven

Cold and Its Unlimited Horizons

✳

20

Can Life Begin on a Cold Planet?

In how many worlds has life begun? And what form has it taken? Perhaps on one planet or another, even as on earth, several types of living things may have emerged, only to die of heat, cold, solar radiation, and the noxious gases of a primordial atmosphere. Until at last one form of life developed able to adapt to its world. In the earth's 4.6 billion or so years, the triumphant organic life has been based on carbon compounds containing the key molecule DNA (deoxyribonucleic acid), which carries the characteristics of life from one generation to the next.

These living compounds were the end result of a period of chemical evolution that may have lasted a billion and a half years. The sun's light or the sparks from an electric storm at some moment in prehistory probably provided the energy that formed the large molecules containing DNA. These compounds continued to evolve farther and certainly by 3.2 billion years ago they had reached the stage of the bacteria-like particles that have been found in shale in Swaziland.

Space scientists are engaged in a study of how life began here on earth, in order to discover principles that could be applied to other planets. Even though chemical elements and compounds of an earthly type can be identified elsewhere in the solar system, there is no certainty that the development of such compounds must inevitably lead to the formation of life. They could reach a molecular dead end.

Many stars, besides our sun, must have planet systems capable of supporting life. Some astronomers believe that roughly five percent of the stars relatively near our own could have habitable planets.

The likelihood of life appears greatest on planets something like earth associated with a star somewhat like our sun. Stars have been classified according to spectrum, color, and temperature, ranging from blue and bluish white, through white, yellowish white, yellow, orange, red, and very red, and in temperature from 90,000°F. to 3,600°F. Our sun is in Class G, a yellow star with a surface temperature of 10,800°F. And perhaps other stars that are yellowish white, yellow, or orange may be the source of heat and light to planets like earth. The sun is a luminous star, and so we might expect life on satellites of other luminous stars. There is but one star in our solar system, which leads to the assumption that binary and multiple star systems are rather unlikely to spawn life-bearing planets. Some stars may have planets that travel about them in an eccentric orbit; the possibility of life then is sharply reduced. Planetary orbits are elliptical, rather than circular, and on an eccentric orbit, a planet could journey for a time through an area either too hot or too cold for any form of life to endure. Still, there are so many millions of stars that it is possible that somewhere in this universe, near stars totally unlike our sun, life might have evolved—possibly to a high level.

Which of the nearby star systems is most likely to include planets with life on them? Astronomers rule out the nearest neighbor, Alpha Centauri, which is 24 trillion miles away. It is a triple star, giving rise to eccentric planetary orbits. In the past decade two planets, each roughly the size of Jupiter, have been discovered orbiting Barnard's Star, 30 trillion miles from our sun. Perhaps a whole family of planets, including one like earth, remains to be discerned by more powerful telescopes. Barnard's Star, though, is smaller than the sun, orange red, and considerably cooler at 8,000°F. There is a chance, even a "reasonable" one, to quote astronomers, that a fairly high order of living things has evolved on planets revolving around the more distant Eridani or Ceti. Eridani is 10.8 light years away (a light year is 5,800,000,000,000 miles) and Ceti 11.8. Comparatively near, as distances go among the stars, they are far beyond man's reach in the terms of current technology. For the present the search for extraterrestrial life is concentrated on this solar system.

Although traveling around a hot star, most of the planets in our solar system are cold. The temperature of the most famous of all comets, Halley's, which flashes across the sky every seventy-six years, has also been described by scientist B.J. Luyet, writing in *Cryobiology*, as varying between -333.4° and -351.4°F. during sixty years of its period. Its orbit carries it to a zone where its temperature can move above the freezing point for just a few months. The nucleus is in all probability made up of particles, gases, and ice frozen together. On only three planets—Mercury, Venus, and Earth —is the average surface temperature above the freezing point of water. Even Mars averages out to a lower figure. The large Jovian planets are colder by far. Luyet puts Jupiter's surface at a chilling -229°F., and Saturn's at -238°F. Uranus is even colder at -256F., while Neptune is estimated at -264°F. Pluto is so far away that valid calculations are not considered possible, although a figure of -450°F. has been suggested.

Jupiter is five times as far from the sun as the earth and should logically have a surface reading of -274°F. Some astronomers explain the higher temperature generally attributed to this planet as the result of radioactivity in the interior. Some regions may be considerably warmer than the frigid average and life might conceivably emerge there.

It is odd that the shady places on Jupiter are hotter than the sunny. This phenomenon was first observed by Dr. Robert L. Wildey in 1962 when he was at the Mount Wilson and Palomar observatories. Jupiter has twelve moons, the four largest of which were discovered by Galileo. When these Galilean satellites pass between Jupiter and the sun, the shadows produced by the eclipses are 50 to 100 degrees warmer than the rest of the sunlit planet. The hot shadows, or Wildey Effect, are, nonetheless, colder than a hundred degrees below zero Fahrenheit.

Cold does not necessarily doom all living things. The blood

that is frozen in liquid nitrogen when thawed will course through human veins and arteries. The sperm can be taken from its freezer and yet beget normal, healthy babies. Defrost the encephalitis virus after years in the cell bank and it will go to the brain and produce its dread illness. Small cactuses planted in soil frozen to -320°F. cease all active growth; their seeds, however, will bring forth new life if they are thawed and put in the ground. Cells have been immersed in liquid helium, colder by far than nitrogen, and have been restored to active life again. But the fact that cells survive at temperatures approaching absolute zero does not of itself prove that they could have evolved in low temperatures in the first place. They survive by going into a state of dormancy. Evolution is dependent upon chemical reactions between molecules or within cells. It has always been assumed as a matter of course that all reactions are slowed if not stopped by even moderate cold.

In 1965, however, Dr. Norman H. Grant and Dr. Harvey E. Alburn, in the course of low-temperature research at the Wyeth Laboratories in Radnor, Pennsylvania, made a surprising observation. Some biochemical reactions were taking place more rapidly in ice than in water. Ascorbic acid (vitamin C), for example, oxidized at greater speed at 12.2°F. than at 33.8°F. In the opinion of the scientists, the ice structure may have served as a catalyst.

"These findings have possible implications in . . . consideration of the origin of life on earth and elsewhere," they suggest.

Another common belief has it that life could not begin in the absence of liquid water on the ground or water vapor in the air. An environment in which water existed only as frost or ice was considered barren. If, however, important reactions can indeed take place in that frost or ice, as the Grant and Alburn findings indicate, then life could possibly evolve on a frozen planet.

Should any moisture rise from ice to atmosphere, the likelihood of the continuance of life is greatly enhanced. In those places on earth where no liquid water flows, forms have evolved that are capable of making use of vapor. Fungi can absorb moisture from the air. In this way lichen, the combined fungus-alga plant, ekes out a bare existence on dry rock surfaces. And in the laboratory at least, seeds of higher plants have succeeded in germinating with vapor as their only source of moisture. In one experiment all the seeds of winter rye and celosia, an herb belonging to the amaranth family, sprouted in vapor alone, as did eighty-five percent of the turnip seeds and sixty-three percent of the flowering portulaca.

Those planets and satellites which have water, whatever its form, are obviously the likeliest to be possessed of living things. Lacking both atmosphere and oceans, the moon is not a probable haven for organisms. During the two-week night the thermometer falls to -250°F. or possibly -280°F., rising to 250°F. at high noon. If life should have evolved during an earlier, friendlier period, it must have found a protected place far below the surface to rest. It is cold there, but not much colder than the deep-freeze in which earthly microbes can survive in a dormant state. Tiny amounts of carbon and chemicals associated with life's origin have been detected in below-surface moon soil collected by men on Apollo 12. But scientists caution that these may come from meteorites, earthly contamination, or error. They await future missions and more and deeper moon soil.

What of the search for life elsewhere in our solar system? Dr. Willard F. Libby, Nobel-Prize-winning chemist, has declared that higher forms of life "are entirely conceivable," albeit unlikely on Mars, Venus, Saturn, and Jupiter. These would most likely be organisms that could survive below the planetary surface, where they would be sheltered from the temperature extremes and from the unfiltered rays of the sun. Nor would all necessarily be dormant. Here on earth, in areas where conditions would seem to make normal life impossible, bacteria have evolved that are capable of living without air. While it might seem that on other planets no form of nourishment would be present to sustain similar microbes, there might very well be organic matter in subterranean rocks and soil. Such substances do exist in the universe; they have been found in meteorites.

Temperatures on Venus are particularly inimical to life. The surface heat of the equatorial regions has been estimated variously between 800° and 932°F.; yet scientists do not dismiss the possibility of Venerean life in latitudes or altitudes away from that heat. The chief gas in the atmosphere is carbon dioxide, with some nitrogen and traces of hydrogen fluoride and hydrogen chloride. The planet is wrapped in layer upon layer of clouds, with the nearest ones believed to be made up of brightly colored mercuric compounds. The temperature drops between one layer of cloud and the next. Twenty-two miles away from the planet the measurement is already down to 270°F.; nine miles farther, it is a comparatively livable 100°F. At an additional twelve and a half miles up, large white clouds are drifting through the Venerean atmosphere. They look something like the high cirrus clouds of our earth. Some scientists speculate that the appearance of moisture is deceiving and the clouds are in truth made up of volcanic dust. Others, however, believe that the clouds are as they seem and contain ice crystals. The temperature is no more than -30°F. and some simple forms of life might be floating there.

Now Libby is going one step farther and suggesting that life may exist on the planet Venus itself. He postulates that liquid water may be present. Before the data of the recent series of unmanned probes were reevaluated, equatorial surface temperatures were thought to be 518°F. Under those conditions, Libby had theorized that the poles might be cold enough for icecaps to form. At the rim where the hot winds from the equator would touch the ice, small oceans and freshwater lakes would form. The revised information, however, indicates temperatures so high as to make any ice at all improbable. Should winds carry this heat poleward, whatever ice was forming would melt instantly. But at the atmospheric pressure believed to exist on Venus, water does not boil until it reaches a temperature of 512.6°F. And to Libby this does not seem an unlikely temperature for the polar regions. Oceans then become a possibility. If they do exist, the composition of the water must be different from that on earth. The chemicals identified as being present in the atmosphere would probably cause acid-filled water. Steam would rise from the seas, condense, and drop back as rain, and thus maintain the water level. Rain would fall nowhere else on the planet; the air over the equatorial deserts is far too hot. Libby suggests that in order to produce the 0.5 percent moisture content of the atmosphere over the equator reported by the Soviet Venera-4 probe, the seas must be 9 or 10 kilometers deep, compared to 2.8 for earthly oceans, and have an average temperature of possibly 149°F.

Could plankton of some sort live in the hot acid seas, or microbes on the dry desert shores? It is improbable, yet, to Libby at least, not utterly impossible. A component of the earth's troposphere that is produced by plant life has been found in the Venerean troposphere. Could it, too, be the result of plant life on Venus? Only future probes will tell.

However poor the possibilities of finding living things on Venus specifically, there is no question that life can spring up under the most adverse conditions. Take away favorable temperatures, a supply of water, sufficient oxygen—and even then there is life. Astronomers suggest that somewhere in the universe planetary atmospheres might contain pure nitric oxide and hydrogen sulfide. Molds in a laboratory experiment died of these gases, but bacteria thrived. The microscope revealed their active growth and reproduction. Could more highly developed organisms, like the bacteria, be relieved of their dependence on the type of air found on earth?

Consider the flowers of our earthly gardens—the marigold, the lovely little alyssum, the brilliantly colored zinnia, ageratum, the leafy green fern, and mint. Then turn to the vegetables and cereal grains that make up a good part of our earthly diet—the lettuce, tomato, cucumber, bean, turnip, broccoli, rye, corn, and rice. Take any of these plants out of its native air and into an atmosphere of five percent oxygen or less and only three percent carbon dioxide. Even then it will survive for days. Practically all the seeds of the cucumber and rye plants and at least half of the lettuce, cabbage, bean, coleus (mint), tomato, and dianthus (carnation family) germinate in this starved atmosphere and put forth sizable seedlings.

"Ordinary plants do not necessarily require air in order to thrive," says Dr. Sanford M. Siegel of the University of Hawaii.

Seeds of bean, sweet pea, onion, tomato, and rye have sprouted in air containing nitrogen oxides, formerly believed to be lethal. Winter rye grains, for that matter, can germinate in the presence not only of nitrous oxide, but also carbon monoxide and hydrogen, and can be grown in deuterium oxide, or heavy water, provided that the atmospheric pressure is low enough, as on a planet like Mars. Cucumber seedlings can live in iron oxide.

Move plants into a different type of hostile atmosphere— to a chamber in which an unnatural, unearthly air has been prepared, made up of about 0.1 percent oxygen, 97 percent nitrogen, 3 percent carbon dioxide, and a mere trace of water vapor, and even here they will go on living, although not reproducing. A cactuslike shrub survived for ten months. These experiments were begun before the Mariner IV flight and the air the plants were exposed to was known as "Martian." Then the information sent back to earth by the probe revealed that carbon dioxide, rather than nitrogen, was the chief atmospheric ingredient. The work was not abandoned on that count. The ability of plants to live in a variety of gases remains the significant part of the experiment. And perhaps a nitrogen-filled atmosphere exists over some other planet, if not in this, then in some other solar system.

On many planets organic life would have to face not only oxygen starvation but extreme cold as well. It would be natural to assume that those which can survive the former would be killed by the latter anyway. In the course of his laboratory work with living things under unlivable conditions, Siegel made a strange discovery: when the temperatures are below freezing, plants can more easily endure oxygen deprivation. The reverse of this is true, too: when the atmosphere around them is reduced in oxygen, plants can more easily endure freezing.

Cucumbers are not particularly cold-resistant, yet a seedling cooled to -14°F. survived undamaged in a box containing only two percent oxygen and ninety-eight percent argon. A control specimen grown in air was subjected to the same treatment; it died. Whenever the temperature is lower than 60°F., cucumber seeds do better in an argon atmosphere with a mere 0.0005 percent of oxygen than they do in air. A larger percentage germinate. Cucumber and mustard seeds will sprout in a hydrogen atmosphere, so long as the temperature is held between 45° and 48°F. Should the room be warmer, they are inactivated.

Desert plants have been grown in closed jars, some containing air, and others a mock extraterrestrial atmosphere of 0.09 percent oxygen, 0.24 percent carbon dioxide, 1.39 percent argon, and 98.28 percent nitrogen. All were placed out of doors during winter months when daytime temperatures varied from 29° to 46°F. and the nighttime range was between 10° and 32°F. At the end of three months, most of the plants grown in earthly air were dead or severely damaged. Those in the planetary atmosphere were green and growing.

The finding that two (or more) unfavorable conditions are not necessarily worse than one increases the hope of finding life on exceedingly hostile planets. "Organisms that are able to resist one set of unfavorable factors are also able to resist some totally unrelated stresses," observes Siegel.

There are forms of life that can endure freezing, low oxygen, and a high level of radiation. The sturdy reindeer moss is an excellent example of such an organism. The essentials for life are wrested out of the dry rocky soil of the Arctic and the thin air of the mountaintop. Should the temperature drop to -30°F., it will still continue growing, though a little more slowly. It is just as viable in heavy water as in water. Nor does radiation kill or maim the moss. The performance of its life functions is not interrupted by exposure to 4,000 times as much ultraviolet radiation as falls here on earth. Gamma radiation at 1,000 times the amount that would kill a man does very little damage. Perhaps the moss could even survive the heavy radiation striking Mars.

The moss, or the similarly hardy lichen, are the most advanced forms of life astronauts can expect to encounter on other planets of our solar system. But the discovery that seed plants, too, can live without earthly air, warmth, or much water encourages hopes that perhaps someday it will be possible to start agriculture on another planet. This would make it much easier to colonize Mars, for example. Plants selected for hardiness would be exported from earth and replaced from time to time when they fail to reproduce or die out. Corn and a variety of other vegetables radioactive with radiocarbon have been grown successfully in experimental enclosed farms.

Certain animals, too, can almost match the ability of plants to carry out their metabolic functions lacking most of the factors normally believed essential. The protozoan *Colpoda* lives in a synthetic extraterrestrial atmosphere, and the paramecium is not changed in any way when deprived of oxygen, maintained at low atmospheric pressure, and exposed to the heavy G forces of acceleration.

Nematodes, or roundworms, can manage in an argon atmosphere for more than a week at a time. Their resistance to adversity is such that they can also withstand temperatures below the freezing level. Perhaps on a dry, eroded planet, any tiny amount of liquid water would be as salty as the Dead Sea on earth. The nematode can manage in salt as well as fresh water.

The mealworm, which eventually metamorphoses into the common black beetle, would not seem a good candidate for extraterrestrial existence. It can stand neither extreme cold nor a shortage of oxygen. But when the two factors, each fatal in itself, are combined, the mealworm can take them very well. This is the same type of adaptability displayed by the cucumber seedling. Put the worm into a chamber with less than 0.1 percent of oxygen and if the temperature is low enough, it will live.

A few animals can actually produce young in unearthly atmospheres. The brine shrimp, *Artemia salina,* was kept in an extraterrestrial chamber; living larva hatched from its eggs.

The common red-eared turtle, *Pseudemys scripta-elegans,* has been subjected to conditions similar to those that existed when its ancestors walked the earth in the days before recorded history. It has changed rather little over the millennia; possibly because the species' prehistoric adaptations to all-but-lethal conditions have served it well ever since. Ultraviolet radiation does the turtle no harm, even when it sticks its head outside the shell and extends its neck. The shell, its most easily apparent adaptation, is like a warm house which shelters the turtle from temperature extremes. Turtles have been chilled to -22°F. for fifteen minutes and then thawed. They got up and walked away. If cold is prolonged, the animal will respond by going into a state of dormancy akin to hibernation. The turtle can stretch out a small amount of air by holding it in a space beneath the carapace that serves as a portable oxygen tank. In the low atmospheric pressure of a planet like Mars, which is comparable to that of earth at altitudes of 100,000 to 150,000 feet, turtles can go for months with only two percent of oxygen.

To be sure, no one imagines that any life forms as complex as the turtle could have evolved on Mars. Scientists have long ago abandoned the idea first presented in 1877 by Italian astronomer Giovanni Virginio Schiaparelli that the *canali* proved that intelligent Martian beings were irrigating their dry desert soil.

Nonetheless, Mars has long been considered a planet enough like our earth to support at least some simple forms of life. In the summer of 1969 the data provided by the unmanned probes, Mariner 6 and Mariner 7, began to shake the belief that Mars is earthlike. Television pictures showed a crater-torn terrain, more like that of the moon than earth, and an area of ridges and valleys jumbled together chaotically in a manner that bears no resemblance to any other place.

Still, some similarities to earth do remain to challenge the imagination. At both north and south poles of Mars white caps can clearly be seen. They have been enticing man for generations. When it is spring in one hemisphere, the white cap shrinks and a wave of darkening spreads from the fringes and moves toward and across the equator at a rate of twenty-eight miles a day for a period of about 130 days, stopping at a latitude where the temperature never rises above the freezing point. By the end of this time the polar cap has shrunk to a fraction of its winter size. In the fall the dark recedes and the cap grows again.

The most obvious explanation for this phenomenon has been that the caps are of ice, and that as they melt in the spring, plants begin to grow in the moisture. The color changes, then, are caused by growth, maturity, and death of vegetation.

This appealing theory has come under steadily mounting attack. The more that is discovered about Mars, the less likely it seems. Once it was learned that the atmosphere of Mars was heavily laden with carbon dioxide, astronomers began to suggest that solid carbon dioxide, or dry ice, was a more logical polar covering than water ice. The infrared temperature measurements made by Mariner 7 seem to back up this discouraging view. The average reading is too low to have been made by water ice but is close to the freezing point of carbon dioxide in the extremely low atmospheric pressure of Mars. Still, as the temperature is a little higher in some places—particularly around the edges of the polar cap—a possibility remains that a very small quantity of water ice is mixed in with the dry ice. While proof must wait for the results of future probes and manned flights, Mars appears to be much more hostile to life than was believed just a year or two ago.

There are explanations for the seasonal changes around the poles that do not involve either water or life. The color sweep across the planet could result from variations in the irradiation of the chemical compounds of the soil. Or perhaps winds of spring carry differently colored soils from one area to the next, and then the fall winds send them back. Some astronomers aver that the darkening is caused by the melting of ice from the polar caps but point out that this is no proof of vegetation. Instead, as the ground alternately freezes and thaws in the course of a Martian day and night, there is an infinitesimal heaving of the soil. Micro-hills rise, giving the optical illusion of darkening.

Data from the Mariner probes have been interpreted to mean that there are also some clouds of dry ice hanging over the polar areas. This is not a bad sign, however. Should there be life—a hope that dims but does not die—the clouds would provide some protection against the bombardment of ultraviolet rays from the sun.

Yet water cannot be altogether ruled off the red planet. Some water ice crystals have been detected in the air, probably in a fog, indicating that at least a little water is on the surface or in the atmosphere. These crystals hang in a thin haze over the warmer latitudes where temperatures have been measured as either a hospitable 54° or 73°F. Were there even one cubic mile of liquid water, not quite sufficient to fill a large lake, it might, nonetheless, be enough to support life, particularly if evolution took place earlier in the history of the planet, at a time when there were some oceans. All planets are believed to go through roughly the same kind of primitive stage. At some time in their history Venus, Jupiter, Pluto, and the rest may have had oceans and atmosphere comparable to those of the primeval earth.

Still today large quantities of water might remain, trapped in the form of ice, beneath the cold Martian surface. Such a layer of soil would not be too different from the permafrost that lies beneath about one-fifth of the earth's land surface, principally in the Arctic regions. On earth this permafrost may be as much as 1,300 feet thick, or as little as five or ten. The upper portion usually melts in the polar summer, while the lower remains frozen. On Mars the periods of warmth are too short to get through any significant amount of permafrost. Yet somewhere deep beneath the soil of Mars, some volcanic activity might be taking place. The warmth would rise upward, melting the permafrost and creating warm liquid pools. Beside these pools oases might spring up. Lichens, mosses, viruses, and bacteria would flourish in the Martian desert, much as date palms do in the deserts of the earth. Blobs that look like huge convective cloud systems or thunderheads have appeared in some photographs of Mars. They may in reality be nothing of the kind, but theoretically at least, they could be formed by water vapor released upward by hot springs.

To determine the likelihood of permafrost on Mars, NASA scientists constructed "Mars" in a box. The frigid night temperatures were achieved with liquid nitrogen and the warmth of noon was produced with infrared lamps. At the north pole every night the thermometer dropped to -158°F. At the equator in the box, as on the red planet itself, the temperatures varied from -94°F. at night to a warm and pleasant 86°F. at high noon. The ground consisted of an eleven-inch layer of "Martian" soil of limonite (an iron ore) and sand. The temperature beneath the soil was -58°F. and did not present the fluctuations of the surface. And in that cold soil the scientists found the layer of permafrost they were seeking. It was deeper at the equator and came up to the surface at the pole.

A thin creeping whiteness can sometimes be detected in the late afternoon in certain areas of Mars. Perhaps this is the hoarfrost forming on the high ground as the sunlight fades. The following day the frost may melt in the noontime sun. Then vegetation could absorb the moisture of the melting hoarfrost, and grow by day and rest by night. Or perhaps it is not like this at all.

On earth, where the seasons blend slowly into one another, living things can become acclimated to heat or to cold. The climatic zones are clearly enough defined, so that tropical creatures adjust to heat only and polar animals to cold alone. On Mars any living organism would have to be capable of adjusting to both, and at incredible speed as well. The adaptation that made life pleasant at two o'clock would bring death at eight. In addition to the temperature adaptation, the metabolism of Martian organisms would need regulators to make possible the use of the brief noonday warmth for growth and reproduction and of the nighttime cold for dormancy.

The possibility of such boundless viability has been studied on earth. Many different species of bacteria and fungi have been subjected to laboratory conditions that mimic the brutal freeze-thaw cycle of the Martian day and night. Vials of microbes were thus frozen in dry ice and then thawed. After four and a half hours of warmth, they were chilled again. Some died, but a surprisingly large number endured the temperature variations. Two common bacteria, for example, reproduced so vigorously during the mild temperatures of the "Martian" noon that at the end of four days there were 4,000 times as many of them as at the beginning.

Higher forms of life are surprisingly resistant to temperature swings, although of not quite the same severity. For seven consecutive days winter rye grains were frozen to -22°F. for sixteen hours, then thawed to 68°F. for eight hours, and then frozen and thawed again. They succeeded in germinating. One out of ten flowering rock garden plant seeds sprouted after three and four days in which they alternated between 19.4°F. for sixteen hours and 73.4°F. for eight hours.

Two stag beetles were placed in an extraterrestrial simulation chamber. After eleven hours at -4°F., the beetles were warmed to 77°F. One collapsed and could not be revived; the other, however, returned to normal within a few hours. As Charles Darwin has observed, some members of a species are far better equipped for survival than their seemingly identical fellows. In this way evolution proceeded on earth, and possibly elsewhere.

Man judges the probability of evolution and life in terrestrial terms that he can understand. The experiments performed here keep alive hope of ultimately finding signs of life, past, present, or future, on our neighbors in the solar system. What of the planets farther from our sun? Unlike the carbon-dioxide-rich atmospheres of Mars and Venus, those of the Jovian planets are heavy with ammonia and methane. Until recently these gases were believed to be poisonous. A change in attitude is based on a new understanding of the origin of life on earth. The search for life elsewhere involves a search for conditions similar to those that once existed here. What gases swirled about the ancient earth?

In the opinion of some scientists, the earth's original atmosphere, rich in the noble gases, was lost in a period before the creation of organic molecules. What is commonly called the primary atmosphere is really secondary. And it was in that atmosphere, when the earth was wreathed in mists of ammonia, methane, and hydrogen, that life first evolved. This primordial atmosphere, too, is gone. But elsewhere in the universe, these gases remain. Ammonia molecules have been identified as part of the dust clouds in the interstellar space that lies toward the center of our galaxy. The fabled rings of Saturn appear to consist of large quantities of ammonia ice.

The atmosphere of Jupiter today may not be unlike that of the primordial earth. Perhaps, just as happened on this planet, an electric discharge or flash of light is providing, or has already provided, the energy necessary for organic molecules to be formed there.

How far could organic evolution go in that atmosphere? Exobiologists have placed molds and bacteria in pure ammonia and these have grown. A *Penicillium* mold, related to the ones that make penicillin, died when exposed to air high in nitrogen and carbon dioxide. The same type of fungus was able to live in ammonia. The hypothetical Jovian atmosphere containing methane as well has been reproduced in the laboratory, and molds and bacteria have survived there, too. Samples of the soil in the chamber filled with this primordial atmosphere were analyzed from time to time. One day a strange umbrella-shaped organism was found. Only 1/5,000 of an inch in size, it looks like no other microbe on the earth today. It does, however, bear a strong resemblance to a two-billion-year-old fossil discovered recently in a Canadian quartz rock deposit.

Many of the most familiar microbes of the modern world reveal an atavistic ability to grow and reproduce in an ammonia-rich atmosphere. Some higher plants can survive, too, though they cannot bear fruit. A number of healthy plants were placed in a simulated Jovian chamber to serve as food for micro-organisms. The dim light in this chamber was such as might fall on a planet distant from our sun. In the space of two months, a large number of bacteria and fungi, some unidentifiable, had battened onto these plants, despite the rigors of an alien atmosphere.

Should the time ever come, as most people believe that it must, when man will land on Jupiter, he will almost surely find himself in a world that bears little resemblance to the one he left. Perhaps, as the late British geneticist J. B. S. Haldane once speculated, the planet will be covered with oceans. But these Jovian seas will not contain the brine in which life on earth began. Instead, on the shores, the astronaut will hear the gentle lapping of ripples, the thunderous roar of waves of liquid ammonia. Within the ocean's ammoniac depths, ices and salts are in solution, and far below the surface are the rocks of ice. As he looks toward the horizon, he may see clouds of ammonia vapor and methane where ocean meets sky.

On the primeval earth a water-based life developed. Evolution may not follow that pattern on Jupiter. Perhaps it does not need to. Some scientists are not convinced that water in any state—whether frozen, liquid, or gaseous—is irrevocably linked to organic evolution.

Some living things have survived in an artificially created

world almost totally devoid of water. A good number of fungi and bacteria can cling to life in laboratory chambers where the moisture content of the air is reduced to one percent. A few can better that record; they will grow and reproduce with less than four-tenths of one percent of moisture around them. A thorny cactus plant was placed in a synthetic desert so dry that the vapor content could not be measured with instruments. In the morning a laboratory technician noticed something that looked like tiny bits of cotton hanging on the cactus. As no cotton could possibly have invaded the chamber, the mysterious substance was scraped off the plant and studied under the microscope. The cotton was unveiled as the common mold *Mucor*. It was not only alive in the dry environment; it was reproducing.

Turning to the properties of liquid water, Dr. Sanford Siegel and Karen Roberts reported, "none of them seems to involve a functional uniqueness that would preclude life without that property." They went on to observe that enzyme action could go on in a variety of waterless media, such as formic acid.

Both organic and inorganic chemical reactions can take place in liquid ammonia. In a world so cold that this is the only fluid, a form of ammonia-based life might evolve.

But even if this happened, would we ever know it? When the spaceships land on Jupiter at last and the astronauts step out onto that frigid world, will they recognize that what they are seeing is alive?

21

Human Hibernators

How long is the journey to another solar system? When 100,000 years have passed, a spaceship would just be approaching Alpha Centauri, the star that is the sun's nearest neighbor. The passengers will not find a resting place in that solar system, as any planet orbiting would in all probability be hostile to life. And so the ship will hurtle on for perhaps another 100,000 years or longer to find a friendlier planet revolving around a more distant star. The man who steps out of the spaceship at last would be a distant descendant of those who started out, with no memory of the earth on which his kind was spawned.

Even when space journeys are limited to our solar system, the problem of what to do about time will before long present a critical problem. Man's voyages become more ambitious. According to a recent estimate by Dr. Thomas O. Paine, director of NASA, a trip to Mars allowing ninety days in the vicinity of the planet and a return passing close to Venus would take about two years. Unmanned probes to the Jovian planets may in time be followed by manned spacecraft. Space stations will be put into orbit around the earth. Even though the staff members will alternate with others from earth, celestial tours of duty will of necessity be long.

At the station or on board a spaceship will be men with all the normal human needs and desires. The purely physical requirements of food, water, and air could theoretically be satisfied with a self-regenerating life support system. It might be based on algae, the primitive plants that can provide food and oxygen, while absorbing carbon dioxide and wastes in a never-ending cycle. Algae would be particularly valuable in allowing a margin for error. In case of a technical failure, a spaceship and its crew could wait in orbit indefinitely until rescued. Should the astronauts need to extend explorations beyond the scheduled time, they could do so. Although it is highly nutritious and can be flavored in a variety of ways, a diet of algae and nothing else for months and years would be unpleasant. Other foods, therefore, would be needed, too.

NASA scientists are working out the logistics for carrying sufficient food, oxygen, and other essentials, leaving algae aside. Captain Abraham T. K. Cockett and Captain Cecil C. Beehler of the U. S. Air Force Medical Corps have calculated that each crew member must breathe in 1.13 pounds of oxygen every day. He will then exhale approximately two pounds of carbon dioxide. If that is to be neutralized chemically, an equal quantity of lithium hydroxide will be needed. The absolute minimum amount of water is two liters a man, and three would be better. The astronaut will eat 1.14 pounds of dehydrated and freeze-dried food. (This is less than the 1.3 to 1.4 pounds per man allotted by NASA for the shorter flights.) Even with the more modest calculations, a three-man crew would use up about 8,000 pounds of basic supplies in a reasonably brief space trip of eight and a half months. And this does not count in the weight of extra clothing, medical supplies, instruction manuals, and other necessities—let alone the technical and scientific instruments. Additional weight would have to be allowed for equipment to sterilize and recycle solid and liquid human wastes, to clear water vapor as well as carbon dioxide from the air, and to keep the cabin temperature constant.

Although such exact figuring might make it seem that scientists know how a long space voyage, such as the one projected for Mars, will affect the crewmen, this is not possible. It is all guesswork now. Only after six months of living in space would any long-term physiological problems develop. Dr. Charles E. Berry, medical director of the Manned

Spacecraft Center in Houston, points out that the body goes through an almost complete cellular change in that period.

In addition to dealing with physiological needs, which are fairly clear-cut, efforts must be made to anticipate and solve psychological problems, which are not. With enough food to eat, water to drink, and oxygen to breathe, the astronauts will still find it hard to get through the many days and nights of a journey. They will be trapped week after week in a small capsule, with no escape from their surroundings or from one another. No moment of privacy will be granted. The physical discomfort of the life cannot fail to become irksome when the first exhilaration wears off. Space calisthenics cannot make up for hours of unnatural inactivity. The suits are bulky, the food at best dull. A man can shave in space, brush his teeth with edible paste, and wash himself with specially prepared wet washcloths and dry ones, but never relax in a bath or be invigorated with a shower. On earth, however hard the day, it ends in bed. On a space journey his hours of rest from duty may be adequate, but the astronaut is denied the comfort of thick mattress, smooth sheets, and soft blankets. Sex, in this womanless microcosm, becomes an increasing problem.

What effect will the long confinement have on each man's relationships with his fellows? For surely he cannot on a long trip travel alone. Men tested one at a time in a space cabin simulator became confused and had hallucinatory experiences not too different from those induced by LSD or marijuana. They have been irritable, hostile, and depressed. It is likely that for any prolonged trip, a three-man crew is the absolute minimum, and some projections have been worked out around five- to fifteen-man groups. The three-man crew most frequently suggested provides an extra astronaut in case one of the others becomes ill, disabled, or dies. One man can remain in the spacecraft while the other two set off in a module to explore another planet or take photographs close to its surface. There is a danger, however, that two of the men might gang up on the third and make him the target of their hostility. Or perhaps all three of them might release their anger on the space officials giving orders from the ground, and this could interfere with the mission. Subordinates, in the enforced informality of the cabin, may also refuse to acknowledge the direction of the craft's designated commander.

The longest studies of confinement show apathy rather than aggressiveness to be the main problem. In the U. S. S. R., A. V. Lebedinskiy conducted an experiment that lasted 120 days. The men functioned in a reasonably normal manner for the better part of two months. Then they began to complain of being tired and unable to sleep. Their efficiency dropped and they lost interest in their work. This apathetic attitude and weakness lasted for quite some time after their return to a normal life.

There is reason to hope that this would not occur in space, where the men would be buoyed up by a sense of mission. The question is how long that feeling would last. Astronauts on short space journeys endure discomfort relatively easily, because their extremely high motivation carries them through. But as the days stretch out into months and years, the most highly motivated and dedicated man may flag.

The closest earthly analogy to space travel lies in the Antarctic. Particularly in the early era of exploration, an expedition wintering over on the cold continent was faced with discomfort and privation comparable to those of space. There was the misery of extreme cold, the confinement in narrow quarters, the same unchanging group of companions, the never-ending darkness, the crudeness of the facilities, the poor food, the limited opportunities for amusement, the impossibility of a normal sex life. The only escape from the confinement involved taking a dangerous field trip over crevasse-broken ice. This might be compared to the walk in space or on the moon or planetary surface.

In the Antarctic, as in space, there has been a great sense of excitement and discovery. During the early heroic age of exploration, expedition members strained themselves to the utmost, ready to face death for the reward of being first to set foot where no one had, of seeing vistas never seen before, of making a major contribution to knowledge, and coming home a national hero. Yet psychiatric problems have plagued most Antarctic expeditions. These go far beyond the general irritability, feuds, and arguments, common to all groups living in cold or confinement. Problems have not disappeared, even though men are ruled out in advance for Antarctic, as for space, duty, if they are considered at all unstable. Only those who appear particularly healthy mentally are accepted. It is apparently impossible to predict who will collapse under the strain.

One bitter winter's night a meteorologist went out ostensibly to check on his equipment, wandered away, and eventually died of the cold. Upon hearing of this, an experienced polar explorer expressed doubt that the misfortune was accidental. Having seen many emotional breakdowns, he considers it more likely that the act was done deliberately out of deep depression.

As described by Norwegian explorer C. E. Borchgrevinck in 1899: "During the gradual shortening of the days we experienced great depression as if watching ourselves grow old." When all daylight has faded, a peculiar gloom seizes men.

A young geologist recently spent a night in a stalled truck waiting for help. When it came, all he could talk about was the "ice forest with giant sequoia trees" that he thought was all around him.

In the Antarctic when a man breaks down he can be sent home by plane. The astronaut must remain where he is no matter how long the journey, and so some way must be found of removing him from all the pressures.

For the past few years experts in the U. S. and the U. S. S. R., the two countries that are most deeply involved in space travel, have been considering a method that would make the trip seem shorter and pleasanter to the astronaut and less hazardous to him physically, while at the same time lightening the weight of the spacecraft. They would have the astronaut imitate the animal who in time of hunger and stress absents himself physiologically by going into a state of hibernation. Like the marmot waiting out the winter curled up in his hole, the astronaut would wait out the months of travel to Jupiter or Neptune. Were there a three-man crew, one man at a time would be chilled into a state of dormancy. The others would perform the necessary duties and arouse him when his turn came up.

No longer would the trip seem endless. Days, weeks, and months would slip by while he lay unaware. Boredom, restlessness, and the emotional strain of confinement would be relieved. The astronaut would awaken refreshed again, ready to accept his crewmates, the capsule environment, uncomfortable suit, and rehydrated food. He would bring new enthusiasm to the work assigned him and be able to encourage the other awake astronaut who by then might be bored and irritated with the crew member just going into hibernation. When psychological pressures would build up dangerously for one individual or another, he could be allotted additional time of dormancy.

The hibernating human, like the hibernating animal, would be free of the demands of his body. The dormant animal requires no food or water, and hardly any oxygen, nor would the astronaut. The heart pumps sluggishly, and the blood moves slowly through arteries and veins. The astronaut's chest is almost unmoving, rising and falling seldom and imperceptibly with his infrequent, shallow breaths. Taking in little, the hibernator gives out little. There will be no, or minimal, amounts of body wastes requiring sterilization and recycling, and only small quantities of carbon dioxide to be neutralized.

Thousands of pounds of food, oxygen, water, and chemicals can be saved, making it easier and safer to launch the craft. The smaller the inventory of supplies, the more comfortable life in the spacecraft will be for the awake crewmen. An area that would otherwise hold food packages could be left free for the men to move around in and perhaps to store books and magazines for their amusement. The absolute minimum space for any flight that lasts 300 days or more has been calculated at 200 to 250 cubic feet per man. Between 350 and 400 feet is acceptable and 600 to 700 is good. As the hibernating crew member requires no more space than his sleeping body occupies, his fellow astronauts will have the use of the footage he would have needed for all his activities.

Let us assume that through some misadventure the oxygen, water, and food are running low and the spacecraft still has some months to travel before reentering the earth's gravitational pull. Disaster could be staved off by the simple expedient of sending two men at a time into hibernation. Thus the use of essentials will be spaced out to last until splashdown.

A catastrophic loss of oxygen could occur while the craft was 60 million miles or more away from earth. What if a meteorite were to strike a ship and knock a hole in it? This is by no means beyond the realm of possibility. A small meteorite is believed to have struck the unmanned spacecraft Mariner 7 as it approached Mars, apparently puncturing a tank of compressed gas. A Martian or Saturnian rock might rip the spacesuit of an explorer. Oxygen would spill out and be lost in space. A fire might start in the space capsule and, if all other efforts to quench it fail, be put out by filling the cabin with carbon dioxide or an inert gas. Oxygen equipment, however well designed, could break down under stresses not anticipated. A technical mishap might prolong a trip beyond the limits of the oxygen provided. What would this do to the astronauts? Without oxygen, it does not take long for consciousness to be lost and brain damage to occur. Reducing the body's need for oxygen immediately by chilling it to dormancy could mean the difference between life and death.

In the course of space travel the astronaut's body is forced to endure one insult after the other. He goes from extreme heat to excessive cold, from gravity to weightlessness, to heavy bombardments of radiation, to changes in atmospheric pressure, to a constant shift in G (acceleration of gravity) forces. He is guarded externally by the well-engineered space capsule and the carefully designed suit. Internally he might be helped by hibernation.

A strange incident with no equal in medical history can illustrate what hibernation might be able to achieve. At eight o'clock on the morning of June 4, 1969, a jet airplane landed in Madrid after a nine-hour flight from Cuba. A few minutes later the unconscious body of a young man, dressed only in a light shirt, pants, and one shoe, fell out. Upon regaining consciousness in the hospital, the stowaway said that he had climbed into the plane in Havana, wishing to escape his country. During the flight the temperature fell to -40°F. The wheel pod in which he lay hidden held hardly any oxygen and was unpressurized. His survival is so inexplicable in any normal medical way that the Spanish doctors immediately suggested that he had experienced "a superhuman fatigue, a temperature that meant practical hibernation." The suggestion is fantastic, because human beings are not natural hibernators and need help to go into that state. Yet unless conditions in the hideaway were for some reason not as desperate as is believed, it is hard to find another explanation for the young Cuban's surviving a variety of stresses, any one of which should have brought death within minutes.

During periods of descent, men within a spacecraft are subjected to high G forces. The Apollo 10 spaceship reached a speed of 24,750 miles per hour, for example, as it reentered the earth's upper atmosphere and came under the strong influence of gravity. While all astronauts to date have stood acceleration very well, future space flights could involve exposure to much higher G forces. When chilled, experimental animals have survived 2,300 Gs for a period of a quarter of an hour. The astronaut of tomorrow might benefit from going into hibernation just before a tremendous acceleration of gravity is anticipated.

Radiation presents a great danger to space travelers. The cooled body, however, can take the exposure to gamma, cosmic, and other rays much better than the warm one. A large number of mice have withstood irradiation when they were chilled to 41°F. Astronauts might thus be guarded by cooling just before entering the Van Allen Belt, or when solar flares are releasing great quantities of radiation.

Brief periods of hibernation might be used in emergencies or as medical treatment. Short-term hibernation is, after all, hypothermia, a recognized medical technique on earth. Special temperature controls on a spacesuit could make it work like the cooling blanket or mattress in a hospital. A drug to control shivering would be included in the space medical kit. The Russians have apparently been thinking along similar lines. They have tested an "automatic device for inducing reversible and controlled hypothermia which can be utilized during space flights." Dogs have been maintained by this means for 120 hours at temperatures ranging from 71.6° to 77°F.

Chilling can protect the brain from swelling and bleeding following a head injury that might befall an astronaut walking, digging, and performing experiments on terrain completely different from the earth he left. His companion astronaut could help him back to the module and return him to the command ship, where he would be placed under hypothermia until danger of brain damage was passed.

Cooling the body can also reduce the risk of traumatic or bacteremic shock that may follow injury or infection. In space, an astronaut may become ill as a result of earthly germs that somehow slipped through the sterilization procedure, possibly incubating in the body of a fellow crew member. He might also be exposed to extraterrestrial pathogens to which he has no natural resistance. Should an astronaut be infected by a Jovian germ, for example, hypothermia could keep him alive while doctors and exobiologists decided on a course of treatment.

Decompression sickness, or the bends, is customarily associated with deep-sea diving, rather than high-altitude flying. The conditions of the two, however, are not totally unalike. Tremendous differences in atmospheric pressure exist not only between the deep sea and the surface, but also between the pressurized module and space, the moon, or planet. A spacecraft might become depressurized or repressurized at the wrong time through some unforeseen misadventure. Like the diver rising to the surface too quickly, the astronaut returning from a space walk or trip to the surface of a planet might be unable to make the gradual change planned and go from one kind of atmospheric pressure to another too soon for his body to adjust.

In research performed by physiologist P. V. Byeloshyts'-kyy at the Ukrainian Academy of Sciences, white rats were subjected to decompression stress. Only six out of twenty rats maintained at normal temperatures lived through this experience, compared to fifteen of the twenty rats that had been cooled to 69.8°F.

After completing a series of experiments exposing animals to a variety of space dangers, Byeloshyts'kyy commented that the protective role of hypothermia "is a matter beyond doubt."

Prolonged human hibernation, if it ever comes, will be a result of space research. But the method might ultimately be used on earth as well. If the population expands beyond the ability of the earth to feed it, dormancy might in some tragic future be a last hope for the desperate. Each year a given percentage of people would take its turn at sleeping and thus relieving the tired land of the necessity of providing it with food. The number would be increased at times when crops fail or a natural or man-made catastrophe devastates the land. The shortage of food then is quite as great as that faced in the polar winter by hibernating animals. With the bulk of the population dormant during the disaster, there would be enough food to nourish those who must remain awake to replant the fields and start the factories going again. The hibernators would awake from their winter sleep to find a new spring of plenty.

Unfortunately, as practiced today, both Soviet and American researchers have observed, prolonged hypothermia is a danger of itself. Even under the most ideal conditions—in a modern, well-equipped hospital with a staff trained in its use —hypothermia remains an emergency medical treatment. It is most often applied for relatively brief periods, as during or immediately after surgery. Techniques of extending the time of safety are yet to be developed.

Man must learn how to mimic the animals that can easily stand lengthy periods of dormancy. Not only the ground squirrel, chipmunk, and marmot, but even creatures like polar bears, which are not true hibernators, have evolved in ways that make it possible for them to go into "carnivorean lethargy," as Raymond J. Hock of the Northrop Space Laboratories has termed it. Could man be made a hibernator after millions of years of evolution have produced a normally inflexible temperature regulator? Instead of a hibernating mechanism, he has been given the intelligence to clothe, feed, and shelter himself, no matter how intolerable conditions around him.

How can he overcome his heredity and force himself into hibernation? And if he did, what would be the result? No one can answer even so simple a question as what would happen to his digestive processes during months of chilled inactivity. They must slow to a virtual standstill. Animals can take this very well. The bear, for example, does not defecate during the period he spends in the den, even when it lasts for some six and a half months. Evacuation is made physically impossible by a fecal plug, mostly of vegetable matter, stopping up the rectum.

Hibernators, both true and partial, hold their urine, too, for however long they sleep. After awakening from a hibernation of four months, a grizzly bear did not rush to urinate, but retained the accumulated urine for another two days. And in the first voiding, he released less than five and a half ounces.

Could man's digestive and excretory functions be interrupted for so long, and then resume? What would happen to the micro-organisms that inhabit the gut and are essential to human health?

The hibernating animal never loses his sensibility and can be quickly aroused from his winter slumber. His nervous system is soon restored to its former state. But more complex brain function may not be able to endure so long a period of inactivity. Would all intelligence, memory, and traits of personality be retained? Or would some knowledge, skills, talents, and beliefs be forgotten?

What would happen to the hibernating man's biological time clock—the rhythm whereby he instinctively feels the need to sleep at night and wake by day? Human beings, animals, plants—all respond to a daily time scheme set by the revolution of the earth around the sun. It is hard to break that rhythm. At one time astronauts were being trained to a sixteen-hour schedule, with eight hours of sleep and eight of duty. The adjustment proved too hard. The body clings to its habits. Many think of themselves as night people because they enjoy the social hours that follow work. The number who are truly attuned to a night-waking schedule is small. One hears of an old belief that natives in regions where light is continuous in one season and darkness the next sleep little in summer and make up for it when winter comes. As anyone who has traveled to the Arctic Circle knows, this is untrue. In winter, as in Robert Louis Stevenson's child's poem, they "get up at night" each morning, and in summer "go to bed by day" each evening. The daily activity patterns of Arctic wolves and foxes, too, are little changed by the seasons, according to Dr. G. Edgar Folk, Jr., physiologist at the University of Iowa and an expert on Arctic animals.

The time clock of the hibernating animal is unaltered. He returns to his former physiological rhythm when he awakes. In the case of the partial hibernator, such as the black bear, the timing is not altogether absent even during the time he is lying rolled in a ball in the den. The bear has a relatively fast heartbeat for about thirty minutes of each day. Inside the den there is no clue as to whether there is night outside or day. For that matter, were he outside the den, there would be unbroken darkness. Only the internal clock can tell the animal when it is day. And indeed the period of higher metabolism occurs every day at noon. Would man be similarly true to his inner rhythm, or would he change and return to his home planet out of step with other earthly organisms?

Although many dread eventualities exist, hope remains high that it will somehow, someday, prove possible to make man a hibernator. Perhaps scientists will find ways for man to mimic the hibernator physiologically. The earthly practice of placing a person into hypothermia by merely chilling and giving a drug to control the shivering process, while applicable to emergency medical treatment in space, is totally inadequate for hibernation of long duration. That involves inaugurating the whole range of physiological changes that take place in hibernating animals. This must probably be induced by some sort of drug. There is no drug today able to bring prolonged and harmless hibernation; no one has even succeeded in drawing up specifications for it. Increased understanding of hibernation in animals and of the effects of cold on man are needed. But this is coming, and perhaps the miracle hibernation pill will not be far behind. The astronaut would swallow the pill and slip easily into hibernation.

The concept that age takes a holiday in space is remarkably ubiquitous. When greeting the astronauts returning from the first journey to the moon, President Richard M. Nixon joked that they had become younger. That was a trip of but a few days, and hardly significant even to those who believe in this theory and hold that people who make longer journeys beyond the earth will be truly set free from the inexorable march of time. They may travel for ten years or fifty and return, still young, to wives and children grown frighteningly old. There is no scientific basis for this romantic fantasy. Aging occurs because of changes in heart and lungs, brain, glands, and all the other organs, cells and tissues that make up a living being. On the spacecraft, as on earth, each breath, each heartbeat, each movement will carry the astronaut one bit nearer the grave. Man's body in interplanetary space, on Mars, or Pluto will still be subject to the tyranny of earthly time.

But what if he were placed in a state of hibernation? The

hibernating bat lives for more than twenty years, while the nonhibernating shrew has a brief span of fourteen to seventeen months. The two animals are roughly the same size. Is hibernation responsible for the difference in longevity? It seems likely.

During the weeks and months of hibernation, all the body processes are slowed. The system takes what amounts to a physiological vacation. Biological time just barely passes. Perhaps the astronaut chilled into dormancy as he travels through the vast loneliness of space will arise from his long cold sleep to find that his earthly life has been prolonged.

Index and Bibliography

✳

✳

Bibliography

Ablin, R.J.; Soanes, Ward A.; and Gonder, Maurice J., "Immunologic Studies of the Prostate." *International Surgery*, July, 1969.

Agricultural Research Service, "Damage and Recovery in Deciduous Orchard Trees from Major Freezes." U. S. Department of Agriculture, July, 1959.

————, *Plant Hardiness Zone Map*. U.S. National Arboretum and American Horticultural Society, rev. 1965.

————, "The Search for Hardier Fruits and Nuts." U.S. Department of Agriculture, January, 1964.

Albin, Maurice S.; White, Robert J.; Locke, George S.; Massopust, Leo C., Jr.; and Kretchmer, Henry E., "Localized Spinal Cord Hypothermia." *Anesthesia and Analgesia*, January–February, 1967.

American Medical Association House of Delegates, "Statement on Heart Transplantation." *Journal of the American Medical Association*, March 3, 1969.

American Medical Association Judicial Council, "Ethical Guidelines for Organ Transplantation." *Journal of the American Medical Association*, August 5, 1968.

Antarctic Journal of the United States (and *Antarctic Report*). National Science Foundation and U.S. Naval Support Force, Antarctica, 1965–1969.

Asahina, Eizo, and Aoki, Kiyoshi, "Survival of Intact Insects Immersed in Liquid Oxygen without Any Antifreeze Agent." *Nature*, August 2, 1958.

Ashwood-Smith, M.J., "Blood and Bone Marrow Preservation." *Cryobiology, a Conference, Federation Proceedings*, March-April, 1965.

Bach, Fritz H., "Bone-Marrow Transplantation in a Patient with the Wiskott-Aldrich Syndrome." *Lancet*, December 28, 1968.

Barnard, Christiaan N., "A Human Cardiac Transplant: An Interim Report of A Successful Operation Performed at Groote Schuur Hospital, Capetown." *South African Medical Journal*, December 30, 1967.

Bass, David E., *Temperature Regulation in Man*. Quartermaster Research and Engineering Command, U.S. Army.

Bell, Corydon, *The Wonder of Snow.* New York, Hill & Wang, 1957.

Belsey, R.H.R., et al., "Profound Hypothermia in Cardiac Surgery." *Journal of Thoracic and Cardiovascular Surgery,* October, 1968.

Bering, Edgar A., Jr., "Effect of Body Temperature Change on Cerebral Oxygen Consumption of the Intact Monkey." *American Journal of Physiology,* March, 1961.

Bernhard, W.F.; Harvey, R.J.; La Farge, G.; Norman, J.C.; Robinson, T.; and van Someren, L., "An Investigation of Induced Chronic Hyperthermia and in Vivo Heat Dissipation." *Journal of Thoracic & Cardiovascular Surgery,* November, 1966.

Bigelow, W.C., "Methods for Inducing Hypothermia." *Annals, New York Academy of Sciences,* 1959.

Bilder, Richard B., "Control of Criminal Conduct in Antarctica." *Virginia Law Review,* March, 1966.

Bird, H. Marcus, "James Arnott, M.D.—A Pioneer in Refrigeration Analgesia." *Anesthesia,* January, 1949.

Bird, Kermit, "An Appraisal of Some Food Processing Methods of the Future." 7th International Congress of Nutrition, August 9, 1966

———, "Developing and Testing New Foods and Fibers." *The Marketing and Transportation Situation,* November, 1964.

———, "Selected Writings on Freeze-Drying of Foods." U.S. Department of Agriculture, January, 1964.

Black-Schaffer, B.; Hensley, G.T.; and Simson, L.R., "Protection of the Adult Mouse against 1800 G Acceleration by Hypothermic Immersion." *Aerospace Medicine,* December, 1961.

Blair, Emil, *Clinical Hypothermia.* New York, McGraw-Hill, 1964.

———, *Hypothermia.* Hagerstown, Maryland, Lewis-Walters Practice of Surgery, 1966.

———, Wise, Arthur, and Mackay, Albert G., "Gram-negative Bacteremic Shock." *Journal of the American Medical Association,* January 13, 1969.

Boyle, Robert, *New Experiments and Observations Touching Cold.* Printed for Richard Davis, Bookseller in Oxford, London, 1683.

Brettschneider, Lawrence; Daloze, Pierre M.; Huguet, Claude; Porter, Kenneth A.; Groth, Carl G.; Kashiwagi, Nobura; Hutchison, David E.; and Starzl, Thomas E., "The Use of Combined Preservation Techniques for Extended Storage of Orthotopic Liver Homografts." *Surgery, Gynecology, Obstetrics,* 12:263, 1968.

Brooks, C.E.P., *Climate in Everyday Life.* New York, Philosophical Library, 1951.

Budd, G.M., and Warhaft, N., "Acclimatisation to Cold." *Lancet,* October 22, 1966.

Burns, M.E., "Cryobiology as Viewed by the Microbiologist." *Cryobiology,* September–October, 1964.

Busby, Douglas E., "Space Clinical Medicine." *Space Life Sciences,* Holland, August, 1968.

Buskirk, E.R., and Bass, D.E., "Climate and Exercise." Technical Report EP-61, Quartermaster Research and Engineering Center, U.S. Army, July, 1957.

Byeloshyts'kyy, P.V., "Possibilities and Prospects in the Use of Hypothermia in the Exploration of Space." *Fiziologichichny zhurnal,* Vol. 13, No. 4, Ukrainian SSR, 1967.

Byrd, Richard Evelyn, "All-out Assault on Antarctica." *National Geographic,* August, 1956.

————, *Discovery.* New York, G.P. Putnam's Sons, 1935.

Cahan, William, G., "Cryosurgery of Malignant and Benign Tumors." *Cryobiology, a Conference, Federation Proceedings,* March-April, 1965.

Chatfield, Paul O., "Hypothermia and Its Effects on the Sensory and Peripheral Motor Systems." *Annals, New York Academy of Sciences,* April 13, 1960.

Chippaux, C., "Application of Artificial Hibernation to War Surgery in Indo-China." *International Record of Medicine,* June, 1954.

Cockett, Abraham T.K., and Beehler, Cecil C., "Total Body Hypothermia for Prolonged Space Travel." *Aerospace Medicine,* June, 1963.

Coe, John, and Ommaya, Ayub K., "Evaluation of Focal Lesions of the Central Nervous System Produced by Extreme Cold." *Symposium on Local Cooling in the Nervous System,* Baltimore, Maryland, November 18, 1963, revised, May 18, 1964.

Coffman, Franklin A., "Survival of Usable Stands of Fall-Sown Oats in Different Geographic Areas." Agricultural Research Service, U.S. Department of Agriculture, August, 1965.

Coltman, Charles A., "Pagophagia and Iron Lack." *Journal of the American Medical Association,* January 20, 1969.

Cooper, Irving S., "Clinical and Physiologic Implications of Thalamic Surgery for Dystonia and Torticollis." *Bulletin of the New York Academy of Medicine,* August, 1965.

————, "Cryobiology as Viewed by the Surgeon." *Cryobiology,* Vol. 1, No. 1, 1964.

————, "Cryogenic Cooling and Freezing of the Basal Ganglia." *First International Symposium Stereocephalotomy,* Philadelphia, 1961.

————, "A Cryogenic Method for Physiologic Inhibition and Production of Lesions in the Brain." *Journal of Neurosurgery,* Vol. XIX, No. 10, 1962.

————, "Cryogenic Surgery." *New England Journal of Medicine,* April 4, 1963.

————, "Cryogenic Surgery of the Basal Ganglia." *Journal of the American Medical Association*, August 18, 1962.

————, "Cryogenic Surgery for Cancer." *Cryobiology, a Conference, Federation Proceedings*, March-April, 1965.

————, "Cryogenic Surgery in the Geriatric Patient." *Journal of the American Geriatrics Society*, September, 1964.

————, "Effect of Thalamic Lesions upon Torticollis." *New England Journal of Medicine*, May 7, 1964.

————, "Relief of Intension Tremor of Multiple Sclerosis by Thalamic Surgery." *Journal of the American Medical Association*, March 6, 1967.

————, "Surgical Treatment of Parkinsonism." *Annual Review of Medicine*, Vol. 16, 1965.

————, and Lee, Arnold St. J., "Cryostatic Congelation: A System for Producing a Limited Controlled Region of Cooling or Freezing of Biologic Tissues." *Journal of Nervous and Mental Disease*, September, 1961.

————, and ————, "Cryothalectomy—Hypothermic Congelation: A Technical Advance in Basal Ganglia Surgery, a preliminary report." *Journal of the American Geriatrics Society*, August, 1961.

————, and Stellar, Stanley, "Cryogenic Freezing of Brain Tumors for Excision or Destruction in Situ." *Journal of Neurosurgery*, Vol. XX, No. 11, 1963.

Coriell, Lewis L.; Greene, Arthur; and Silver, Ruth K., "Historical Development of Cell and Tissue Culture Freezing." *Cryobiology*, September-October, 1964.

Cornish, C.B., and Scott, P.J., "Freeze-Dried Aortic Valve Heterografts in Aural Surgery." *Lancet*, July 9, 1966.

Crary, A.P., "Antarctica, the International Laboratory." *Bulletin of the Atomic Scientist*, January, 1964.

Cutting, Charles L., *Fish Saving*, New York, Philosophical Library, 1956.

Daly, Olive W., and Siegel, Sanford M., "Effects of Oxygen on the Millipede, *Spirabolus.*" *Abstracts, 6th International Congress of Biochemists*, 1964.

————; Davis, Gwendolon; and Siegel, Sanford M., "General and Comparative Biology of Experimental Atmospheres and Other Stress Conditions: Experiments with the Turtle, *Pseudemys scripta-elegans.*" *Aerospace Medicine*, April, 1965.

Dansgaard, W.; Johnson, S.J.; Møller, J., and Langway, C.C., Jr., "One Thousand Years of Climatic Record from Camp Century on the Greenland Ice Sheet." *Science*, October 17, 1969.

Davis, T.R.A., "Thermogenic Factors During Cooling and in the

Stabilized Hypothermic State." *Annals, New York Academy of Sciences,* April 13, 1960.

DeRoetth, Andrew, Jr., "Cryosurgery for the Treatment of Glaucoma." *American Journal of Ophthalmology,* March, 1966.

Deryagin, B.V., "The Equivocal Standard." *Saturday Review,* September 6, 1969.

DeVries, Arthur L., and Wohlschlag, Donald E., "Diving Depths of the Weddell Seal." *Science,* July 17, 1954.

——, and ——, "Freezing Resistance in Some Antarctic Fishes." *Science,* March 7, 1969.

Donn, William L., and Ewing, Maurice, "A Theory of Ice Ages, III." *Science,* June 24, 1966.

Douglas, R. Gordon; Lindgren, Keith M.; and Couch, Robert B., "Exposure to Cold Environment and Rhinovirus Common Cold, Failure to Demonstrate Effect." *New England Journal of Medicine,* October 3, 1968.

Drescher, James W., "Environmental Influences on Initiation and Maintenance of Hibernation in the Arctic Ground Squirrel, *Citellus undulatus." Ecology,* 48 (6), 962–66.

Duncan, F. Martin, *Wonders of Migration.* London, Sampson Low, Marston & Co., 1946.

Dyson, James L., *The World of Ice.* New York, Knopf, 1962.

Eklund, Carl R., and Beckman, Joan, *Antarctica.* New York, Holt, Rinehart & Winston, 1963.

Emiliani, Cesare, "Ancient Temperatures." *Scientific American,* April, 1957.

Emmings, Fred G., "Cryotherapy in Oral Surgery." Paper presented at the 109th Annual Scientific Session, American Dental Association, 1968.

——; Koepf, Sheldon W.; and Gage, Andrew A., "Cryotherapy for Benign Lesions of the Oral Cavity." *Journal of Oral Surgery,* July, 1967.

Ettinger, Robert C.W., *The Prospect of Immortality.* New York, Doubleday, 1964.

Evans, Alfred S.; D'Allessio, Donn A.; Espiritu-Campos, Lourdes; and Dick, Elliot C., "Acute Respiratory Disease in University of the Philippines and University of Wisconsin Students: A Comparative Study." *Bulletin of the World Health Organization,* 36:397–407.

Ewing, Maurice, and Donn, William L., "A Theory of Ice Ages." *Science,* June 15, 1956.

——, and ——, "A Theory of Ice Ages, II," *Science,* May 16, 1958.

Eye Bank for Sight Restoration, *Manual-Recommended Proce-*

dure for Eye-Bank Receiving Laboratories. 1964.

Farrand, William R., "Frozen Mammoths and Modern Geology." *Science,* March 17, 1961.

Fellner, Carl H., and Marshall, John R., "Twelve Kidney Donors." *Journal of the American Medical Association,* December 16, 1968.

Fisher, Frank R., ed., "Man Living in the Arctic." *Proceedings of a Conference,* National Academy of Sciences, 1961.

Fisher, K.J., and Greiner, M.D., "Acute Lethal Catatonia Treated by Hypothermia." *Canadian Medical Association Journal,* March 19, 1960.

Flosdorf, Earl W., *Freeze-Drying.* New York, Reinhold, 1949.

Folk, G. Edgar, Jr., "Physiological Observations of Subarctic Bears under Winter Den Conditions," in *Mammalian Hibernation,* K. Fisher and F. South, eds. Edinburgh, Oliver and Boyd.

———; Folk, Mary A.; and Brewer, Max C., "The Day-Night (Circadian) Physiological Rhythms of Large Arctic Carnivores in Natural Continuous Light (Summer) and Continuous Darkness (Winter)." Fourth International Biometeorological Congress.

———; ———; Simmonds, Richard C.; and Brewer, Max C., "A Two-Year Study of Winter Lethargy in Subarctic Bears." *Bull. Ecol. Soc. Amer.* December, 1966.

———; Simmonds, Richard C.; and Folk, Mary A., "Physiology of Deep Hypothermia of the Black Bear." *16th Alaskan Science Conference, American Association for the Advancement of Science,* Vol. 16, 1965.

Frazer, T.M., "Confinement and Free-Volume Requirements." *Space Life Sciences,* August, 1968.

Gage, Andrew A., and Emmings, Fred G., "Bone Freezing in Cryotherapy." Symposium on Technical Applications of Cryogenics in Medicine and Surgery, January, 1967.

———; Koepf, Sheldon; Wehrle, David; and Emmings, Fred, "Cryotherapy for Cancer of the Lip and Oral Cavity." *Cancer,* December, 1965.

Gale, W.A., and Sinclair, A.C.E., "Polar Temperature of Venus." *Science,* September 26, 1969.

———, Liwshitz, M., and Sinclair, A.C.E., "Venus: An Isothermal Atmosphere." *Science,* May 30, 1969.

Geikie, James, *The Great Ice Age.* New York, D. Appleton & Co., 1902.

General Dynamics, "Cryotransfer, A New Nitrogen Flash Freezing Process for the Baking Industry." Paper presented at the American Institute of Baking, Conference on Freezing and Baking, 1965.

Gibbon, John H., Jr., "Development of the Artificial Heart and Lung Extracorporeal Blood Circuit." *Journal of the American Medical Association,* November 25, 1968.

Gissen, Aaron J.; Matteo, Richard S.; Housepian, Edgar M.; and bowman, Frederick O., "Elective Circulatory Arrest During Neurosurgery for Basilar Artery Aneurisms." *Journal of the American Medical Association*, February 17, 1969.

Goodman, J.M., "Liquid Nitrogen Therapy of Warts and Other Skin Lesions." *Canadian Medical Association Journal*, March 19, 1960.

Grant, Norman H., and Alburn, Harvey E., "Fast Reactions of Ascorbic Acid and Hydrogen Peroxide in Ice, a Presumptive Early Environment." *Science*, December 17, 1965.

Hall, Jacquelyn H., and Swenson, David D., *Psychological and Social Aspects of Human Tissue Transplantation, an Annotated Bibliography*. Chevy Chase, Md., National Clearinghouse for Mental Health Information, 1968.

Harrison, R.E., *What Is Congelation?* or the Benumbing Influence of Cold in Producing Insensibility to Pain in Dental Operations, popularly explained with remarks on the introduction of a "Painless System" in Dental Surgery. London, John Churchill, 1858.

Henderson, Alfred R.; Cox, Joseph A.; Islami, Abdol H.; Block, Harvey C.; and Meyer, Robert, "Forgotten Pioneers of Clinical Hypothermia." *Journal of St. Barnabas Medical Center*, September, 1962.

———, and Fay, Temple, "Emulating the Hibernators." *Journal of St. Barnabas Medical Center*, February, 1963.

Hock, Raymond J., "The Potential Application of Hibernation to Space Travel." *Aerospace Medicine*, June, 1960.

Horvath, Steven, M., ed., *Transactions of the Conference on Cold Injury* (1958). Sponsored by Josiah Macy, Jr., Foundation, New York, 1960.

Howard, Gene S., and Brown, G.B., "Hardy, Productive Tree Fruits for the High Altitude Section of the Central Great Plains." Agricultural Research Service, U.S. Department of Agriculture, October, 1962.

———, and ———, "Twenty-eight Years of Testing Tree-Fruit Varieties at the Cheyenne Horticultural Field Station, Cheyenne, Wyoming." Agricultural Research Service, U.S. Department of Agriculture, October, 1962.

Ingraham, Francis D., and Bering, Edgar A., "Safe Limits of Hypothermia and Hypotension." Progress report, May 1, 1960.

International Institute of Refrigeration, *Refrigeration Techniques in Developing Countries*. Paris, April, 1965.

Irving, Laurence, "Adaptations to Cold." *Scientific American*, January, 1966.

Johnson, F. S., "Atmosphere of Mars." *Science*, December 10, 1965.

Karow, Armond M., and Webb, Watts R., "Principles and Problems of Hypothermic Organ Preservation." *Surgery, Gynecology, and Obstetrics,* September, 1964.

Keatings, W.R., et al., "Sudden Failure of Swimming in Cold Water." *British Medical Journal,* February 22, 1969.

Kelman, Charles D., "Complications of Cryosurgical Cataract Extraction." *International Ophthalmology Clinics,* March, 1965.

———, "Cryosurgery for Cataract Extraction and the Treatment of Other Eye Diseases." *Boyd's Highlights of Ophthalmology,* Vol. 7, No. 3, 1964 Series.

———, "A New Cryosurgical Instrument for Ophthalmic Surgery." *Transactions, American Academy of Ophthalmology and Otolaryngology,* March-April, 1965.

———, and Cooper, Irving S., "Cryogenic Ophthalmic Surgery." *American Journal of Ophthalmology,* November, 1963.

———, and ———, "Cryosurgery of Retinal Detachment and Other Ocular Conditions." *The Eye, Ear, Nose, and Throat Monthly,* January, 1963.

Kirwan, L.P., *A History of Polar Exploration.* New York, W.W. Norton, 1960.

Kline, Ira, and Trapani, Robert-John, "Freezing and Preservation of Intact Transplantable Mouse Tumors." *Cryobiology, a Conference, Federation Proceedings,* March-April, 1965.

Knize, David M.; Weatherley-White, R.C.A.; Paton, Bruce C.; and Owens, J. Cuthbert, "Prognostic Factors in the Management of Frostbite." Sent by author.

Kolb, Charles R., and Holmstrom, Fritz M.G., "Review of Research on Military Problems in Cold Regions." *Technical Documentary Report* AAL-TDR 64-28, Arctic Aeromedical Laboratory and Arctic Test Center, December, 1964.

Kondo, Yoshio; Grädel, Franz; and Kantrowitz, Adrian, "Heart Homotransplantation in Puppies." *Circulation,* Supplement 1, April, 1965.

Krick, Irving P., and Fleming, Roscoe, *Sun, Sea, and Sky.* Philadelphia, J.B. Lippincott, 1954.

Langway, Chester C., "Some Physical and Chemical Investigations of a 411 Meter Deep Greenland Ice Core and Their Relationship to Accumulation." Publication #58, IASH Commission of Snow and Ice, 1962.

Lazarus, L.; Bleasel, K.F.; Connelley, J.J.; and Young, J.D., "Serum-Growth-Hormone in Acromegaly Effect of Cryogenic Pituitary Destruction." *Lancet,* July 9, 1966.

Lear, John, "The Water that Won't Freeze." *Saturday Review,* September 6, 1969.

Leovy, C., "Mars Ice Caps." *Science,* December 2, 1966.

Levin, Alexander, "An Experiment in QMC Systems Research." 8th

Annual Army Human Factors Engineering Conference Report, October, 1962.

Levitt, J., "Bound Water and Frost Hardiness." *Plant Physiology,* November, 1959.

——, "Cryobiology as Viewed by the Botanist." *Cryobiology,* September-October, 1964.

——, "Frost Resistance in Plants and Animals, Some Similarities and Differences." *Scientia,* March, 1959.

Lewis, Richard S., *A Continent for Science.* New York, Viking, 1965.

Libby, Willard F., "Ice Caps on Venus?" *Science,* March 8, 1968.

——, "Ice on Venus: Can It Exist: Rebuttal." *Science,* August 30, 1968.

——, "Life in Space." *Space Life Sciences,* March, 1968.

——, "Water on Venus?" Sent by author.

Lindberg, Robert G., "Hibernation in the Space Age." Paper presented 3rd International Hibernation Symposium, September, 1966.

Loebsack, Theodore, *Our Atmosphere.* New York, Pantheon Books, 1959.

Lovelock, J.E., and Smith, Audrey U., "Heat Transfer from and to Animals in Experimental Hypothermia and Freezing." *Annals, New York Academy of Sciences,* April 13, 1960.

Lower, Richard R., and Cleveland, Richard J., "The Current Status of Heart Transplantation." Sent by author.

——, Stofer, Raymond C., and Shumway, Norman E., "Homovital Transplantation of the Heart." *Journal of Thoracic and Cardiovascular Surgery,* February, 1961.

Luyet, B.J., "Human Encounters with Cold." *Cryobiology,* September-October, 1964.

——, "Some Panoramic Vistas in the Realm of Cold." *Cryobiology,* January-February, 1966.

MacDonald, D.K.C., *Near Zero.* New York, Doubleday (Anchor), 1961.

Masters, Thomas, *The Ice Book.* London, Simpkin, Marshall & Co., 1844.

Mazur, Peter, "Physical Factors Implicated in the Death of Microorganisms at Subzero Temperatures." *Annals, New York Academy of Sciences,* April 13, 1960.

McLachlan, Thomas, "Some Historical Notes on Food Technology." *Chemistry and Industry,* August 19, 1961.

Melnick, Joseph L., "Preservation of Viruses by Freezing." *Cryobiology, a Conference, Federation Proceedings,* March-April, 1965.

Meryman, Harold T., ed., *Cryobiology.* New York, Academic Press, 1966.

Meryman, Harold T., "Freezing and Drying of Biological Materials."

Annals, New York Academy of Sciences, April 13, 1960.

Meyer, George H.; Morrow, Marie B.; and Wyss, Orville, "Viable Micro-organisms in a 50-Year-Old Yeast Preparation in Antarctica." *Nature*, November 10, 1962.

Meyers, H. Russell, "Surgical Experiments in the Therapy of Certain Extrapyramidal Diseases: A Current Evaluation." *Acta Psychiatrica et Neurologica*, Copenhagen, 1951.

――――, "Surgical Procedure for Postencephaletic Tremor with Notes on the Physiology of Premotor Fibers." *Archives of Neurology and Psychiatry*, 1940.

Miller, James A., "Hypothermia in the Treatment of Asphyxia." *New York State Journal of Medicine*, September 1, 1961.

――――, and Miller, Faith S., "Factors in Neonatal Resistance to Anoxia." *American Journal of Obstetrics and Gynecology*, July 1, 1962.

Miller, L. Keith, "Freezing Tolerance in an Adult Insect." *Science*, October 3, 1969.

Milne, Lorus J., and Milne, Margery J., "Temperature and Life." *Scientific American*, February, 1949.

Mullen, David A., "Disease as a Factor in Population Declines of the Brown Lemming, *Lemmus trimucronatus*." 19th Annual International Northwest Conference on Diseases in Nature Communicable to Man.

――――, "Physiologic Correlations with Population Density and Other Environmental Factors in the Brown Lemming, *Lemmus trimucronatus*." *Dissertation Abstracts*, Vol. 26, No. 2, 1965.

――――, "Reproduction in Brown Lemmings (*Lemmus trimucronatus*) and Its Relevance to Their Cycle of Abundance." Berkeley and Los Angeles, University of California Press, 1968.

National Aeronautics and Space Administration, "Apollo 11 Lunar Landing Mission." July 6, 1969.

――――, "Space Food General Collation." Houston, Manned Spacecraft Center.

National Conference of Commissioners on Uniform State Laws, "Uniform Anatomical Gift Act." July 30, 1968.

National Frozen Food Association, *1969 Frozen Food Fact Book & Directory*, New York.

Negrin, Juan, Jr., "Regional Cooling of Central Nervous System by Extravascular Perfusion Hypothermia." *New York State Journal of Medicine*, December 1, 1965.

――――, "Relief of Muscle Spasticity and Rigidity by Local Hypothermia of the Spinal Cord." *Proceedings, 8th International Congress of Neurology*, Vienna, September 10, 1965.

Niazi, Suad A., and Lewis, F. John, "Profound Hypothermia in Man." *Annals of Surgery*, February, 1958.

Orkin, P.A. "Modern Views on Fish Migration," in *Science Survey*, A.W. Haslett and John St. John, eds. New York, Macmillan, 1960.

Otterman, Joseph, and Bronner, Finn E., "Martian Wave of Darkening: A Frost Phenomenon?" *Science*, July 1, 1966.

Owens, Tobias, and Mason, Harold P., "Mars: Water Vapor in Its Atmosphere." *Science*, August 29, 1969.

Parkes, A.S., "Biological Effects of Low Temperature." *The New Scientist*, April 29, 1960.

Pedersen, Alwin, *Polar Animals*. London, George G. Harrap, 1962.

Pennsylvania State University, *Commercial Ice Cream and Other Frozen Desserts*. College of Agriculture, Circular 525.

Pogrund, Robert S., "Human Engineering or Engineering of the Human Being—Which?" *Aerospace Medicine*, April, 1961.

Ponnamperuma, Cyril, and Gabel, Norman W., "Current Status of Chemical Studies on the Origin of Life." *Space Life Sciences*, March, 1968.

Popovic, Vojin P., and Masironi, Robert, "Disappearance of Euthermic Tumors after 10-hour Generalized Hypothermia." *Life Sciences*, January, 1965.

Porsild, A.E.; Harington, C.R.; and Mulligan, G.A., *"Lupus Arcticus Wats* Grows from Seeds of Pleistocene Age." *Science*, October 6, 1967.

Proceedings of the International Symposium on Cold Acclimatization, Buenos Aires, August 5-7, 1959, Federation of American Societies for Experimental Biology: Edholm, O.G., "Polar Physiology"; Edholm, O.G., Scholander, P.F., Hart, J.S., Carlson, L., Irving, L., "Discussion"; Hart, J.S., "Energy Metabolism during Exposure to Cold"; Irving, Laurence, "Man in a Cold Environment"; Scholander, P.F., "Discussion"; Siple, Paul, "Comment."

Quay, W. B., "Comparative Occurrence of Brain Colloid Deposits in Microtine Rodents from Churchill, Manitoba." *Journal of Mammalogy*, February, 1969.

Ray, Carleton, "The Application of Bergmann's and Allen's Rules to the Poikilotherms." *Journal of Morphology*, January-May, 1960.

———, and Lavallee, David, "Self-contained Diving Operations in McMurdo Sound Antarctica: Observations of the Sub-ice Environment of the Weddell Seal." *Zoologica*, Fall, 1964.

Renwick, G.M.; Giumarro, C.; and Siegel, S.M., "Hydrogen Metabolism in Higher Plants." *Plant Physiology*, May, 1964.

Riklan, Manuel, and Levita, Eric, "Psychological Effects of Lateralized Basal Ganglia Lesions: A Factorial Study." *The Journal of Nervous and Mental Disease*, March, 1964.

———, and ———, "Relationships between Cognitive Neurologic and Electroencephalographic Changes following Thalamic Surgery." *Journal of Clinical Psychology*, July, 1965.

Ritchie, Wallace P., Jr.; Edlich, Richard F.; Breen, John J.; Molina, Jose Ernesto; and Wangensteen, Owen H., "Experimental and Clinical Experience with Gastric Freezing." *Journal of the American Medical Association*, October 17, 1966.

Roberts, Melville, and Chadduck, William M., "Cryoleucotomy: A New Procedure for the Control of Intractable Pain." *Virginia Medical Monthly*, May, 1966.

Rosomoff, Hubert L., "Protective Effects of Hypothermia against Pathological Processes of the Nervous System." *Annals, New York Academy of Sciences*, April 13, 1960.

St. Whitelock, Otto v., and Adolph E.F., eds., *Hypothermia, Annals, New York Academy of Sciences*, 1959: Brauer, R.W., Holloway, R.J., Krebs, J.S., Leong, G.F., and Carroll, H.W., "The Liver in Hypothermia"; Hegnauer, Albert H., "Lethal Hypothermic Temperatures for Dog and Man"; Hume, D.M., and Egdahl, R.H., "Effect of Hypothermia and of Cold Exposure on Adrenal Cortical and Medullary Secretion"; Keller, A.D., "Neurologically Induced Physiological Resistance to Hypothermia"; Meyer, John H., "The Effect of Hypothermia on Renal Function and Renal Damage from Ischemia"; Smith, Audrey, "Viability of Supercooled and Frozen Mammals."

Sanchez, R.; Ferris, J.; and Orgel, L., "Conditions for Purine Synthesis: Did Prebiotic Synthesis Occur at Low Temperatures?" *Science*, July 1, 1966.

Saslaw, William C., and Wildey, Robert L., "On the Chemistry of Jupiter's Upper Atmosphere." *Icarus*, July, 1967.

Schneour, Elie A., and Otteson, Eric A., compiled by, *Extraterrestrial Life, an Anthology and Bibliography*. National Academy of Sciences, 1966.

Scholander, Per F., "The Wonderful Net." *Scientific American*, April, 1957.

———, Flagg, Walter; Hock, R.J.; Irving, Laurence, "Studies on the Physiology of Frozen Plants and Animals in the Arctic." *Journal of Cellular and Comparative Physiology*, September, 1953.

Schreiber, K., and LaCroix, L.J., "Manufacture of Coated Seed with Delayed Germination." *Canadian Journal of Plant Science*, July, 1967.

Schwab, Robert S., and Prichard, John S., "An Assessment of Therapy in Parkinson's Disease." *American Medical Association Archives of Neurology and Psychiatry*, April, 1951.

Shapley, Harlow, ed., *Climatic Change*. Cambridge, Massachusetts, Harvard University Press, 1953.

Sherman, J.K., "Banks for Frozen Stored Human Spermatozoa." Proceedings of the 11th International Conference of Genetics, The Hague, 1963.

————, "Low Temperature Research on Spermatozoa and Eggs." *Cryobiology*, Vol. 1, No. 2, 1964.

————, "Practical Applications and Technical Problems of Preserving Spermatozoa by Freezing." *Cryobiology, a Conference, Federation Proceedings*, March-April, 1965.

————, "Research on Frozen Human Semen." *Fertility and Sterility*, September-October, 1964.

Sieburth, John McNeill, "Biochemical Warfare Among the Microbes of the Sea." 1962 Honors Lecture, University of Rhode Island.

————, "Microbiology of Antarctica." *Biogeography and Ecology in Antarctica*, The Hague, Dr. W. Junk, 1965.

Siegel, Sanford M.; Daly, O.; Halpern, L.; Giumarro, C.; and Davis, G., "The General and Comparative Biology of Experimental Atmospheres and Other Stress Conditions: Some Notes on the Behavior of Insects and Other Invertebrates." *Aerospace Medicine*, September, 1963.

————, and Giumarro, C., "Survival and Growth of Terrestrial Micro-organisms in Ammonia-Rich Atmospheres." *Icarus*, February, 1965.

————, ————, and Latterel, R., "Behavior of Plants under Extraterrestrial Conditions: Seed Germination in Atmospheres Containing Nitrogen Oxides." *Proceedings, National Academy of Sciences*, July, 1964.

————, Halpern, L.; Davis, G.; and Giumarro, C., "The General and Comparative Biology of Experimental Atmospheres and Other Stress Conditions." *Aerospace Medicine*, November, 1963.

————, ————, and Giumarro, C., "Germination and Seedling Growth of Winter Rye in Deuterium Oxide." *Nature*, March 21, 1964.

————, ————, ————, Renwick, G., and Davis, G., "Martian Biology: the Experimentalist's Approach." *Nature*, January 26, 1963.

————, and Roberts, Karen, "The Activity of Heme Enzymes in Non-Aqueous Media." *Space Life Sciences*, March, 1968.

————, Rosen, L.A., and Giumarro, C., "Plants at Sub-atmospheric Oxygen Levels." *Nature*, June 29, 1963.

Sittig, Marshall, *Cryogenics*. Princeton, N.J., D. Van Nostrand, 1963.

Smith, Audrey U., "Life at Low Temperatures." *Nature*, October 4, 1958.

————, "Problems in Freezing Organs and Their Component Cells and Tissues." *Cryobiology, a Conference, Federation Proceedings*, March-April, 1965.

Smith, Ian MacLean, "Mechanisms of Death." *Hospital Practice*, October, 1966.

————, "Metabolic Response of the Host to Staphylococcal Infection." *Annals, New York Academy of Sciences*, July 23, 1965.

Steere, William C., "A Botanist at McMurdo Sound." *The Garden Journal*, July-August, 1965.

Stellar, Stanley, and Cooper, Irving S., "Basal Ganglia Surgery for Abnormal Movement Disorders." *South Dakota Journal of Medicine and Pharmacy*, May, 1963.

Stephen, C. Ronald, "Current Status of Hypothermia." *Anesthesia and Analgesia*, January-February, 1964.

———; Dent, Sara J.; Hall, K.D.; and Smith, W.W., "Physiological Reactions during Profound Hypothermia with Cardioplegia." *Anesthesiology*, November-December, 1961.

———, ———, Sealy, W.C., and Brown, Ivan W., "Hypothermia in Open Heart Surgery." *New York State Journal of Medicine*, September 1, 1961.

Stern, Lawrence W., and Fay, Temple, "Observations on Human Beings with Cancer, Maintained at Reduced Temperatures of 75°-90°F." *American Journal of Clinical Pathology*, January, 1940.

Sullivan, Walter, *Assault on the Unknown*. New York, McGraw-Hill, 1961.

———, *Quest for a Continent*. New York, McGraw-Hill, 1957.

Transplantation, Conference on, Santa Barbara, January 11-13, 1967: Angell, William, "Discussion"; Blumenstock, David A., "Transplantation of the Lung"; Cleveland, Richard J. and Lower, Richard R., "Transplantation of Canine Cadaver Hearts after Short-term Preservation"; Humphries, Arthur L., Jr., "Organ Preservation: A Review"; Murray, Joseph E., and Barnes, Benjamin A., "Introductory Remarks on Kidney Transplantation with Observations on Kidney Transplant Registry"; Paton, Bruce C., Kwong, K.H., Clark, D., Halseth, W.L., and Hull, R.B., "Immunosuppressive Therapy in the Management of Homo and Heterografted Cardiac Valves"; Rudolf, Leslie E., and Mandel, Stanley, "Supercooling, Intermittent Perfusion and High Pressure Oxygen in Whole Organ Preservation"; Shumway, Norman E., Angell, William W., and Wuerflein, Robert D., "Progress in Transplantation of the Heart."

Turnbow, Grover Dean; Tracy, Paul Hubert; and Rafetto, Lloyd Andrew, *The Ice Cream Industry*, 2nd ed. New York, John Wiley & Sons, 1956.

Valeri, C. Robert; Runck, Alan H.; Brodine, Charles E., "Recent Advances in Freeze-Preservation of Red Blood Cells." *Journal of the American Medical Association*, April 21, 1969.

Vance, Robert W., ed., *Cryogenic Technology*. New York, John Wiley & Sons, 1963.

Webb, R. Watts; Harrison, Norman; Dodds, Ross; Wax, Stennis D.; and Sugg, Winfred L., "Protective Effect of Ethyl Alcohol in Profound Hypothermia." *Cryobiology*, May-June, 1968.

392

Weinberger, John H., "Temperatures and Fruits and Seeds." *Yearbook of Agriculture*, U.S. Department of Agriculture, 1961.

Whitaker, J. Russell, and Ackerman, Edward A., *American Resources*. New York, Harcourt, Brace & Co., 1951.

White, Robert J., "Isolating the Brain." Sent by author.

———, Albin, Maurice S.; Locke, George E.; and Davidson, Eugene, "Brain Transplantation: Prolonged Survival of Brain after Carotid-Jugular Interposition." *Science*, November 5, 1965.

———, ———, and Verdura, Javier, "Preservation of Viability in the Isolated Monkey Brain Utilizing a Mechanical Extracorporeal Circulation." *Nature*, June 13, 1964.

———, ———, ———, and Locke, George E., "Differential Extracorporeal Hypothermic Perfusion of and Circulatory Arrest to the Human Brain." *Medical Research Engineering*, 2nd quarter, 1967.

———, ———, ———, ———, "The Isolated Monkey Brain: Operative Preparation and Design of Support Systems." *Journal of Neurosurgery*, Vol. 27, No. 3, 1967.

———, ———, ———, ———, "Prolonged Whole-Brain Refrigeration with Electrical and Metabolic Recovery." *Nature*, March 26, 1966.

Wildey, Robert L., "Hot Shadows of Jupiter." *Science*, February 26, 1965.

———, "Temperature Measurements in the Solar System." Astronomical Society of the Pacific, November, 1964.

———, "Thermal Contrast of Eclipse Shadows and Band Structure during the 1965 Apparition of Jupiter." *Astrophysical Journal*, June, 1966.

———, and Plummer, William T., "Hot Shadows on Jupiter—Discussion." *Science*, September 16, 1966.

Wilton, A.C.; Hodgson, H.J.; Klebesadel, L.J.; and Taylor, R.L., *Polar Bromegrass, New Winterhardy Forage*. University of Alaska, Agricultural Experiment Station, May, 1966.

Wolfson, Robert J.; Cutt, Roger A.; Ishiyama, Eiichi; and Myers, David, "Cryosurgery of the Labyrinth—Preliminary Report of a New Surgical Procedure." *Laryngoscope*, April, 1966.

Woodbury, David O., *The Great White Mantle*. New York, Viking Press, 1962.

World Health Organization, "Medicine and Public Health in the Arctic and Antarctic." Technical Report Series #253, Geneva, 1963.

Wright, R. C.; Rose, Dean H.; and Whiteman, T.M., *The Commercial Storage of Fruits, Vegetables, and Florist and Nursery Stocks*. U.S. Department of Agriculture, September, 1964.

Young, Richard S., "Exobiology." Presented NASA University Conference, November 1-3, 1962.

————; Deal, P.H.; Bell, J.; and Allen, J.L., "Bacteria under Simulated Martian Conditions." *Life Sciences and Space Research II*, 1964.

————, ————, and Whitfield, O., "Response of Soil Bacteria to High Temperatures and Diurnal Freezing and Thawing." *Nature*, October 28, 1967.

————, ————, ————, "The Response of Spore-Forming vs. Non-Spore-Forming Bacteria to Diurnal Freezing and Thawing." *Space Life Sciences*, I, 113-117, 1968.

Zacarian, Setrag A., and Adham, Mustafa I., "Cryotherapy of Cutaneous Malignancy." *Cryobiology*, January-February, 1966.

Index

395

54, 180, 318
Byrd Station, 163-64, 171, 184

Cacao beans, 301-02
Cactus, 362
Cahan, Dr. William G., 277, 290
Calories consumed in cold regions, 56-57
Calories in frozen desserts, 307
Cambridge University, 38
Camouflage, 80, 94
Camp Century, 98
Cancer, 150-52, 219, 226-27, 229, 237, 239, 256, 269, 276-84
Cancer, cryosurgery, 277-82
Cancer, cryosurgery, experimental findings, 281
Cannon, W. B., 28
Canada, 34, 38, 56, 87, 99
Carbon dioxide, gas, 235, 324, 350, 352-53, 360, 364, 369
Carbon dioxide, solid, *see* Dry ice
Carbon 14 dating, *see* Dating, carbon 14
"Cardiac psychosis," 131
Caribou, 85-86, 110, 318
"Carnivorean lethargy," 373
Carrel, Dr. Alexis, 127
Cataracts, 16, 285-88
Catherine de Medici, 294
Cattle, 16, 206-07, 209-10, 212-14, 233
Cell banks, 219, 220-29, 232, 243
Cells, frozen, 205-29, 241. *Also see* Cryosurgery
Cells, frozen, preservation limits, 212-13
Celosia, 349
Celsus, Aulus Cornelius, 140
Central Institute for Trauma and Orthopedics, 230
Cerebral palsy, 155

Cervicitis, 284
Ceti, 346-47
Chaenichthyidae, 62
Chang Chung-ching, 140
Chapman, Sydney, 181
Chadduck, Dr. William M., 277
Charcot, Jean Martin, 264
Charles I of England, 294
Charpentier, Jean de, 171
Cheese, 221, 313, 333
Cheyenne Horticultural Field Station, 101, 106
Ch-hua t'o, 140
Children, Laboratory-produced, 205-06
Children's Hospital, Philadelphia, 227
Chimpanzee, 128, 223
Chippaux, Lieutenant Colonel C., 152
Chocolate, 301-02
Chocolate ice cream, 299, 302, 334
"Chocólatl," 301-02
Cholesterol, 307
Chondrus crispus, 305
Cicero, 172, 238
Cirrhosis of liver, 148
Civil War, 332
Clark, Col. Elmer F., 23, 40, 41, 55-56
Climate, ancient, 70, 111, 166-68, 170
Clo, 51-52
Clothing, 19, 25-26, 49-54, 309-10
Clothing, battery-heated, 53
Coal in Antarctica, 167, 168, 186-87
Cockett, Capt. Abraham T. K., 364
Cocioba, Dr. I. D., 196
Coe, Dr. John, 269, 270
Coffee, freeze-dried, 220, 332, 334-36

"Martian" air, 352
Masters Thomas, 148, 295-96, 299
Matanuka Farm, 105
Materials, affected by cold, 182-83
Mealworm, 354-55
Meat, dried, 331-32
Meat export shipments, 315-16
Meat, freeze-dried, 333-38, 340
Meat, frozen, 320-22, 327, 330
Mechanics Magazine, 295
Medawar, Sir Peter B., 137
Medical College of Virginia, 128, 234
Medical Estate of St. Helena, East India Company, 275
Mellorine, 307-08
Mellorine production, 308
Ménière's disease, 290
Mercator, Gerald, 173
Mercury, 347
Meryman, Dr. Harold T., 210, 212
Metabolism, 17, 72-73, 90-91, 112, 120, 123, 139, 142, 151, 156, 374, 376
Methane, 360-61
Methyl anthranilate, 303
Meyers, Dr. H. Russell, 265
Microorganisms, 16, 69, 142, 191-202, 213, 218-21, 349-50, 361, 371, 373 *Also see* Algae; Bacteria; Fungi; Viruses
Microorganisms, freezing, 324-25, 359 *Also see* Algae; Bacteria; Fungi; Viruses
Microorganisms in simulated extraterrestrial conditions, 349-51, 359-61, 362
Migration, 16, 84-90, 93-95
Migration, distances traveled, 85-86, 88
Migration, navigation, 88
Migration, role of day length, 87-88, 91
Migration, role of food supply, 86-87, 93-94
Migration, role of sex organs, 87
Migration, role of temperature, 86-88
Milk solids, 307-08
Mill Hill laboratories, 236
Millard Fillmore Hospital, 280-81
Miller, Dr. James A., 143
Mineral resources of Antarctic, 186-87
Mirage, 184-86
Mites, 60, 68-69, 198
Molluscs, 64-65
Monkey, 128, 138-39, 217, 223, 237, 290
Monkey brain experiment, 138-39
Montezuma, 301
Moon, 18, 200, 223, 251, 340, 349, 375
Moon shot, 331
Morgagni, Jeannes Baptista, 153
Morov, V. A., 54
Moss, 109, 112-15, 353-54, 358
Moss' reproduction, 114
Mother's milk, freeze-dried, 222, 332
Mount Sidley, 184
Mouse, 205, 209-10, 229, 370-71
Mouth, cryosurgery in, 279, 282
Mucor, 362
Mullen, Dr. David A., 89, 90
Muller, Dr. Herman J., 207-08
Multiple sclerosis, 155, 272-73
Murray, Dr. Joseph E., 124-25

Napier, Capt. William, 111
Napoleon, 15, 41, 242, 275
National Aeronautics & Space Administration, 94, 200, 338, 363-64

412

414